D1378287

Principles of Healthcare Reimbursement

Second Edition

Anne B. Casto,
RHIA, CCS

Elizabeth Layman,
PhD, RHIA, CCS, FAHIMA

AHIMA
American Health Information
Management Association®

ISBN 1-58426-192-7 or 978-1-58426-192-6
AHIMA Product No. AB202008

June Bronnert, RHIA, CCS, CCS-P, Technical Reviewer
Katie Greenock, Assistant Editor
Kimberly L. Hines, MS, Project Editor
Melissa Ulbricht, Editorial/Production Coordinator
Ken Zielske, Director of Publications

All information contained within this book, including Web sites and regulatory information, was current and valid as of the date of publication. However, Web page addresses and the information on them may change or disappear at any time and for any number of reasons. The user is encouraged to perform his or her own general Web searches to locate any site addresses listed here that are no longer valid.

AHIMA strives to recognize the value of people from every racial and ethnic background as well as all genders, age groups, and sexual orientations by building its membership and leadership resources to reflect the rich diversity of the American population. AHIMA encourages the celebration and promotion of human diversity through education, mentoring, recognition, leadership, and other programs.

American Health Information Management Association
233 North Michigan Avenue, 21st floor
Chicago, Illinois 60601-5800

http://www.ahima.org

Contents

About the Authors

The Foundation of Research and Education (FORE) Triumph Awards are national awards designed to recognize those special individuals who have made a difference in the health information management (HIM) field. Specifically, the Legacy Award honors significant contribution to the knowledge base of the HIM field through an insightful recent publication, building on the enduring tradition of the Edna K. Huffman Literary Award.

The 2007 recipients of the Legacy Award are Anne B. Casto, RHIA, CCS, and Elizabeth Layman, PhD, RHIA, CCS, FAHIMA, who authored this publication, *Principles of Healthcare Reimbursement,* Second Edition. This publication makes a complex topic understandable for students and practitioners and helps to clarify the United States (U.S.) healthcare reimbursement maze.

More About the Authors

Anne B. Casto, RHIA, CCS, is the President of Casto Consulting, LLC. Prior to founding the firm Anne was the Program Manager of the HIMS Division at The Ohio State University School of Allied Medical Professions. Ms. Casto taught healthcare reimbursement, ICD-9-CM coding and CPT coding courses for several years. Additionally, Ms. Casto was responsible for curriculum revisions in the areas of chargemaster management, clinical data management and healthcare reimbursement.

Additionally, Ms. Casto was the Vice President of Clinical Information for Cleverley & Associates where she worked very closely with APC regulations and guidelines, preparing hospitals for the implementation of the new Medicare PPS. Ms. Casto was also the Clinical Information Product Manager for CHIPS/Ingenix. She joined CHIPS/Ingenix in 1998 and spent the majority of her time developing coding compliance products for the inpatient and outpatient settings.

Ms. Casto has been responsible for inpatient and outpatient coding activities in several large hospitals including Mt. Sinai Medical Center (NYC), Beth Israel Medical Center (NYC), and The Ohio State University. She has worked extensively with CMI, quality measures, physician documentation, and coding accuracy efforts at these facilities.

Ms. Casto received her degree in Health Information Management at The Ohio State University in 1995. She received her Certified Coding Specialist credential in 1998 from the American Health Information Management Association. Ms. Casto received the 2008 OHIMA Distinguished Member Award honoring her commitment, creativity, and leadership to the HIM profession.

Elizabeth Layman, PhD, RHIA, CCS, FAHIMA, is professor and chair in the Department of Health Services and Information Management at East Carolina University, Greenville, North Carolina.

She previously worked at Hennepin County Medical Center and the University of Minnesota Hospitals, both in Minneapolis, Minnesota, from 1974 through 1990. Dr. Layman worked in several departments, such as third-party reimbursement, credit and collections, account auditing, outpatient registration, inpatient admissions, research studies, and quality management.

In 1990, Dr. Layman joined the faculty of the Medical College of Georgia in Augusta, Georgia. While on the faculty, she also consulted for the Physicians' Practice Group.

Dr. Layman successfully sat for the first CCS examination in 1992. In 2001, she was awarded the designation of Fellow of the American Health Information Management Association, one of the first two individuals in the country to receive this award. She was the first editor of *Perspectives in Health Information Management* and has delivered presentations at numerous AHIMA events

She earned her baccalaureate degree from the University of Minnesota. While working, she returned to school to earn her associate's degree in medical record technology. She completed St. Scholastica's progression program to earn her post-baccalaureate certificate in health information administration. She earned her master's degree in organizational leadership from the College of St. Catherine's and her doctorate in higher education from Georgia State University,

Acknowledgments

The authors wish to thank
Eleanor Ann Joseph, MPA, RHIA, CHP, CPHQ, CCS, CCS-P, CPC,
and Leona Thomas, MHS, RHIA,
who served as external reviewers for the first editon.

In addition, they wish to thank Bonnie Hemp, MBA, RHIA, CPHQ,
for her review of the current edition.

Foreword

by William O. Cleverley, Ph.D.
Professor Emeritus, Ohio State University

I have taught healthcare financial management to graduate students for thirty years and have always believed that the critical area of understanding was reimbursement. When I first started teaching, the primary—perhaps exclusive—focus was on hospitals, but that has changed. Financing and organizational patterns have shifted over time to create large healthcare firms in other sectors, such as medical groups, nursing facilities, imaging centers, surgery centers, home health firms, and many others. The primary focal point of difference between healthcare firms and businesses in other industries is still, however, payment. Healthcare firms are very unique in the manner in which they receive compensation for the services that they provide. I could not find any other industry that had as complex a revenue function as healthcare firms when I started teaching thirty years ago, and that statement is still true today. In fact, the level of complexity for healthcare firms has increased exponentially over the last thirty years.

Noting that the revenue function, or reimbursement, is complex for a healthcare firm does not explain why this is critical. Let's examine the very basis of management in any business. Simply stated, management must control the difference between revenue and cost, which we define as profit. It makes little difference whether the firm is a taxable or tax-exempt entity. Viable businesses must manage that profit function. Although there are clearly differences in cost functions between healthcare firms and firms in other industrial sectors, the dif-

ferences are not all that significant. Generic principles for cost management might apply equally in a software firm or a hospital. The revenue function is, however, a completely different manner.

Why is the revenue function so different for healthcare firms compared to other industries? I believe there are at least four reasons. First, the vast majority of payment is not actually paid by the client (patient), but rather by a third party on behalf of the patient. Second, the level of payment for a set of identical services may vary dramatically based upon the actual third party payer. Third, the actual determination of payment for a specific third party payer is often complex, based upon preestablished or negotiated rules of payment that are frequently related to the codes entered upon a patient's bill or claim. Fourth, the government is often the largest single payer and does not negotiate payment but simply defines the rules for payment upon which it will render compensation for services provided to its beneficiaries.

To get a partial view of the complexity of reimbursement in the healthcare industry, let's describe a typical managed care contract with a hospital. Let's assume this payer pays for inpatient services on a per-diem basis, with separate rates for medical and surgical cases. In addition, carve-outs are present for cardiology DRGs. Finally, obstetrics and nursery care services are paid on case rates. To provide some additional risk protection to the hospital, a stop loss provision is also inserted after total charges exceed a certain limit. Outpatient services are paid on a mix of fee schedules and discounted billed charges. Outpatient surgical cases are paid on a fee schedule based upon designated ambulatory surgical groups. Emergency visits are also on a fee schedule, based upon level of service. Other fee schedules exist for specific imaging procedures, and everything else is paid on a discounted, billed-charge basis. Multiply this one payer by 100 to recognize other payers and throw in Medicare and Medicaid payment rules, and you have a nightmare in administration. It may be a nightmare, but it is very real to most healthcare firms; their very financial viability is contingent upon successful management of this complex revenue function.

Coding and billing issues are central to most of the present reimbursement plans. In fact, many healthcare firms can lose substantial sums of money because they are not coding their patients' claims in an accurate and complete manner. For example, failing to code an additional diagnosis can result in assignment of a lower DRG, and therefore lost revenue. While some healthcare executives may fail to understand the importance of the coding function, it would behoove them to acquire an appreciation of coding because so much of their revenue function is related to what is done by coders. Conversely, many people in health information management may understand the technical side of what they do, but they don't appreciate their role in the overall financial success of the health firm in which they work.

This background explains why I am so excited about the publication of this book. Anne Casto and Elizabeth Layman have put together a much-needed text on reimbursement that fills a void. I believe that this text is a first. It provides a comprehensive review of the reimbursement world for healthcare firms of multiple types. It also provides very specific material on the actual completion of claims and the rules for final payment determination. Medicare payment

provisions are covered in great detail, but the text also includes other payers. It covers payment provisions for hospitals, but it also covers payment for other payers including managed care plans.

I believe this book is a must-read reference for healthcare executives who need a comprehensive reference on payment in the healthcare industry. It will be a fine supplement for healthcare management students who need to know how the firms they will manage will be paid and how coding and billing functions can impact results. It is also a critical text for health information managers and students. It is often easy to lose sight of the forest when you are engaged in tree cutting. This text provides a clear, concise description of the payment landscape for healthcare firms, which will enable health information managers to better integrate their functions into the overall organizational strategic position of the healthcare firms where they work. A large number of specific examples are also provided to help cement conceptual frameworks with operational reality. Another great feature of this text is its explanation of the myriad acronyms and jargon used in the healthcare industry. Short, concise definitions are given for everything from APCs to RBRVS.

This text met and exceeded the three R's that I use in evaluation. First, the text is very readable and easy to understand. Second, the text is especially relevant to all healthcare managers as they seek to improve financial performance. Third, the text is rich in detail and practical illustrations. This book will occupy a prominent position on my bookshelf and will be a great reference.

William O. Cleverley, Ph.D.
Professor Emeritus
Ohio State University

Preface

Health information management (HIM) professionals play a critical role in the delivery of healthcare services in the U.S. To be fully effective in their roles, however, HIM professionals need an in-depth understanding of healthcare reimbursement systems, reimbursement methodologies, and payment processes throughout the healthcare industry.

Principles of Healthcare Reimbursement integrates information about all U.S. healthcare payment systems into one authoritative source. It examines the complex financial systems within today's healthcare environment and provides an understanding of the basics of health insurance and public funding programs, managed care contracting, and how services are paid. Not only does the text provide step-by-step detail about how each payment system functions, but the history behind each is provided. This gives the reader an appreciation for the complexity of reimbursement systems and an understanding of the profound impact they have had on providers and payers, consumers, public policy makers, and the development of classification and information technology systems over the years.

Healthcare leaders and administrators often have to learn about healthcare payment systems on-the-job and on-the-fly. Other texts feature healthcare finance and healthcare economics, but not the bottom line and nitty-gritty of the healthcare payment systems themselves. This book fills that gap.

Chapter 1, Healthcare Reimbursement Methodologies, introduces and explains the basic concepts and principles of healthcare reimbursement in step-by-step, simple terms. This introduction provides the reader with the solid foundation needed to understand the more detailed and complex discussions that follow in later sections of the book.

Chapter 2, Clinical Coding and Coding Compliance, presents baseline information about today's approved code sets and their functionality and explains the complex interrelationships between reimbursement, coded data, and compliance with the rules and regulations of public and private third party payers.

Chapter 3, Voluntary Healthcare Insurance Plans, explains private or commercial healthcare insurance plans and Blue Cross/Blue Shield plans, and provides the reader with a detailed understanding of the sections of a healthcare insurance policy.

Chapter 4, Government-Sponsored Healthcare Programs, differentiates among the various government-sponsored healthcare programs in effect today, explains the impact that these programs have had on the American healthcare system, and presents the history of Medicare and Medicaid programs in America.

Chapter 5, Managed Care Plans, describes the origins, evolution, and principles of managed care and discusses the numerous types of plans that have emerged through the integration of administrative, financial, and clinical systems to both deliver and finance healthcare services.

Chapter 6, Medicare-Medicaid Prospective Payment Systems (PPSs) for Inpatients, explains common models and policies of payment for inpatient Medicare and Medicaid prospective payment systems and defines basic language associated with reimbursement under PPSs in acute care hospitals and inpatient skilled nursing, long-term care, rehabilitation, and psychiatric facilities.

Chapter 7, Ambulatory and Other Medicare-Medicaid Reimbursement Systems, explains common models and policies of payment for Medicare and Medicaid healthcare payment systems for physicians and outpatient settings, which include physician offices, ambulance services, ambulatory surgery centers, hospital outpatient services, and home health agencies.

Chapter 8, Revenue Cycle Management, explains the components of the revenue cycle, defines revenue cycle management, and describes the connection between effective revenue cycle management and providers' fiscal stability.

Chapter 9, Quality Issues, provides a history of pay for performance in the American healthcare system. Additionally, CMS quality initiatives for the hospital inpatient and outpatient settings that have been recently implemented are discussed in detail.

A complete glossary of reimbursement terminology is included at the end of the book. Throughout the text chapters, boldface type is used to indicate the first substantial reference to key terms included in the glossary. A detailed content index is also included at the conclusion of the text.

Notes to educators:

Each chapter contains "Check Your Understanding" questions for discussion and/or to help the reader in focusing on important points within the text. The answers to these questions are included at the end of the book.

Review quizzes also follow each chapter. The answer key for the review quizzes is included in the Instructor Guide, which contains other materials, such as Power Point slides for classroom lectures and an exercise test bank. The Instructor Guide is available to instructors in online format from the individual book pages in the AHIMA Bookstore or through the Assembly on Education (AOE) Community of Practice (CoP). Instructors who are AHIMA members can sign up for this private community by clicking on the help icon with the CoP home page and requesting additional information on becoming an AOE CoP member. An instructor who is not an AHIMA member or a member who is not an instructor may contact the publisher at publications@ahima.org to request instructor resources. The instructor materials are not available to students enrolled in college or university programs.

Chapter 1
Healthcare Reimbursement Methodologies

Objectives

- To use basic language associated with healthcare reimbursement methodologies

- To differentiate payment methods on unit of payment, time frame, and risk

- To distinguish major payment methods in the United States

Key Terms

Allowable fee
Block grant
Capitated payment method
Capitation
Case
Case-based payment
Charge
Claim
Clinical risk group (CRG)
Copayment
Customary, prevailing, and reasonable (CPR)
Deductible
Episode-of-care reimbursement
Fee
Fee schedule
Fee-for-service reimbursement
Global payment method

Guarantor
Insurance
Payer
Per-diem payment
Premium
Prospective payment method
Provider
Reimbursement
Resource-based relative value scale (RBRVS)
Retrospective payment method
Risk pool
Self-insured plan
Sliding scale
Third-party payer
Third-party payment
Usual, customary, and reasonable (UCR)

Introduction to Healthcare Reimbursement

The healthcare system of the U.S. is complex. Many varied payment methods and rules contribute to the complexity. In 1999, this complexity was listed as one of five trends threatening the very future of medicine (Washburn 1999, 34). For example, a physician's office might have "at least a dozen separate contracts for providing healthcare services" (Washburn 1999, 35). The complexity has not lessened. For example, in January 2006, a Medicare pharmacy benefit plan was implemented. Surely, if insiders find the system confusing, outsiders, the patients, confront a veritable maze (Wilson 1990, 51).

Health Insurance

Generally, **reimbursement** for healthcare services is dependent upon patients having health **insurance.** Insurance is a system of reducing a person's exposure to risk of loss by having another party (insurance company or insurer) assume the risk. In healthcare, the risk the healthcare insurance company assumes is the unknown cost of healthcare for a person or group of persons.

However, the insurance company that assumes the risk reduces its own risk by distributing the risk among a larger group of persons (insureds). This group of persons has similar risks of loss and is known as a **risk pool.** In healthcare, the variability of health statuses across many people allows the healthcare insurance company to make a better estimate of the average costs of healthcare.

The insurance company, however, receives a **premium** payment in return for assuming the insureds' exposure to risk of loss. The premium payments for all the insureds in the group are combined in a pool of money. Insurers use actuarial data to calculate the premiums so that the pool of money is sufficiently large to pay losses of the entire group. Thus, specific to healthcare, the risk is the potential that a person will get sick or require health services and will incur bills (costs) associated with his or her treatment or services. The premium payments for health insurance are calculated to pay for all the potential covered healthcare costs for an entire group of patients.

Historical Perspectives

Health insurance in the U.S. has been made available to help offset the expenses of the treatment of illness and injury. The first "sickness" clause was inserted in an insurance document in 1847. However, health insurance did not become established until 1929, when Blue Cross first covered school teachers in Texas. In 1932, a city-wide plan was begun in Sacramento, California. As an industry, health insurance became widespread after World War II (Longest, Rakich, and Darr 2000, 89–90).

Health Insurance and Employment

In the U.S., health insurance is usually tied to employment. Many larger employers as part of a package of employment benefits pay a portion of the health insurance premium. Employees may be required to pay extra for health insurance for their spouse or children (dependent coverage). Medicare is also considered insurance because payroll taxes, through both employers' and employees' contributions, finance one portion of Medicare coverage. Premiums paid by eligible individuals and matched by the federal government also finance Medicare's supplemental medical insurance program.

When people lose their jobs, they often lose their health insurance. Although people can continue their health insurance by paying for the insurance entirely by themselves, the payments are expensive. In certain circumstances, under the Consolidated Omnibus Budget Reconciliation Act (COBRA) of 1985, people can extend their health insurance for a limited period (Department of Labor n.d.). Therefore, people without jobs are unlikely to have adequate health insurance.

Example: Effect of Loss of Health Insurance on Public Healthcare Spending

People's loss of health insurance affects us all, not just the unemployed person. For example, Medicaid is a joint federal and state program that provides medical and health services to the poor. During an economic downturn between 2000 and 2003, more people were eligible for Medicaid. Their enrollment in Medicaid resulted in an increase of Medicaid spending by one-third, from $205.7 billion to $275.5 billion. Therefore, people's loss of health insurance results in greater public spending on healthcare.

Source of content: Holahan, J. and A. Ghosh. 2005, January–June. Understanding the recent growth in Medicaid spending, 2000–2003. *Health Affairs Web Exclusives:* W5-52–W5-62.

For some employed people, the adequacy of the health insurance is an issue. Some health insurance plans require patients or their families to pay 20 percent or more of the costs of their healthcare. Healthcare costs can easily be in the thousands of dollars; 20 percent of $10,000 is $2,000, which is a sizable sum for many people. Other employees work for employers that do not offer health benefits. These persons must purchase their own insurance at an extremely high rate, or go without health insurance. Obtaining and retaining adequate health insurance are problems for many U.S. workers.

Compensation for Healthcare

Reimbursement is the healthcare term that refers to the compensation or repayment for healthcare services. Reimbursement is being repaid or compensated for expenses already incurred or, as in the case of healthcare, for services that have already been provided. In healthcare, services are often provided before payment is made. Unlike the car dealership, in which customers pay for a car or arrange a loan before driving the car off the lot, patients walk out of the hospital treated. Therefore, the physicians and clinics must seek to be paid back for services that they have already provided and for

expenses, such as supplies, that they have already incurred. These physicians, clinics, hospitals, and other healthcare organizations and practitioners are requesting reimbursement for health services.

Third Party Payment

Experts in healthcare finance refer to **third party payment** or **third party payers.** Who or what are these parties? The first party is the patient himself or herself or the person, such as a parent, responsible for the patient's health bill. The second party is the physician, clinic, hospital, nursing home, or other healthcare entity rendering the care. These second parties are often called **providers** because they provide healthcare. The third party is the uninvolved insurance company or health agency that pays the physician, clinic, or other second party provider for the care or services to the first party (patient).

Characteristics of Reimbursement Methodologies

Three characteristics describe various methods of healthcare reimbursement. These characteristics are the unit of payment, the time orientation, and the degree of financial risk for the parties (Wouters, Bennett, and Leighton 1998, 3) (See table 1.1). The unit of payment can range from a payment for

Table 1.1.   Characteristics of reimbursement methodologies

Characteristic	Description
Unit of Payment	Element that is the basis of payment; ranges in aggregation from single service such as a laboratory test, to entire clinic visit, to episode of care, to hospitalization, and, finally, to entire population
Time Orientation	Retrospective (learned after care or services provided) or Prospective (determined in advance of care or services)
Degree of Financial Risk	Level of uncertainty related to the cost of healthcare or to a potential financial loss or harm

each service, such as a payment for each laboratory test, to a block payment for an entire population for a period of time, such as a governmental budget transfer to the state health department. The time orientation is retrospective versus prospective. In **retrospective payment methods,** the payer learns of the costs of the health services after the patient has already received the services. The provider also receives payment after the services have been provided. In a **prospective payment method,** the payments are preset before care is delivered. Financial risk refers back to the definition of health insurance. When the costs of health services are learned after the care is provided, the third party payer (health insurance entity) is at risk. When providers must project the costs of treating patients into the future and contract to provide all care for those estimated costs, the provider is at risk. Patients assume risk as they must pay higher and higher percentages of the costs as their share.

Types of Healthcare Reimbursement Methodologies

This chapter discusses the fundamental concepts in healthcare reimbursement methodologies. The chapter is organized by the two major types of unit of payment: **fee-for-service reimbursement** or **episode-of-care reimbursement** (See table 1.2). Also briefly addressed are the other characteristics of healthcare payment methods—time frame and risk. The chapter concludes with a peek into the future of healthcare reimbursement.

Table 1.2.   Major types of reimbursement methodologies

Fee-for-Service	Episode-of-Care
Self-Pay	Capitated Payment
Traditional Retrospective Payment	Global Payment
Managed Care*	Prospective Payment

*Some forms.

Fee-for-Service Reimbursement

Fee-for-service reimbursement is a healthcare payment method in which providers receive payment for each service rendered. Fee-for-service is a common method of calculating healthcare reimbursement.

A **fee** is a set amount or a set price. Fee-for-service means a specific payment is made for each specific service provided or rendered. In the fee-for-service method, the provider of the healthcare service (the second party) charges a fee for each type of service, and the health insurance company pays each fee for a covered service. These fees or prices are known as **charges** in healthcare. Sometimes, there is little relationship between the actual costs to provide a service and its charge.

Typically, the physician, healthcare organization, or other practitioner bills for each service provided on a **claim** that lists the fees or charges for each service. The claim is sent to the third party payer (health insurance company or health agency). In healthcare, sending the claim to the third party payer is known as submitting a claim. Within the stipulations of the health insurance policy (contract) or the governmental regulations, the third party pays the claim. The majority of U.S. physicians, healthcare organizations, and other practitioners use this method of billing.

People who have health insurance that reimburses on the basis of fee-for-service have the advantage of great independence. Their health insurance plans allow them to make almost all health decisions about which physician to see and about which conditions to have treated. The patient or the provider submits a claim to the health insurance company, and, if the service is covered in the health insurance policy, the patient or provider receives reimbursement. For the patient, the disadvantage of fee-for service is that fee-for-service plans often have higher **deductibles** or **copayments** than other types of health insurance, such as managed care plans.

For health insurance plans, fee-for-service has the disadvantage of uncertainty. The costs of reimbursing the providers are unknown because the services that patients will receive are unknown. Moreover, costs will increase if the providers increase the fees for each service, if patients receive more services than expected, and if more expensive services are substituted for less expensive services. Examples of fee-for-service reimbursement are self-pay, traditional retrospective payment, and managed care.

Self-Pay
Self-pay is a type of fee-for-service because the patients or their **guarantors** (responsible persons, such as parents for children) pay a specific amount for each service received. The patients or guarantors make such payments themselves to the providers, such as physicians, clinics, or hospitals that rendered each service. There are two situations in which self-pay occurs.

In the first situation, the patients or guarantors have health insurance. However, the patients or guarantors choose to pay the healthcare provider themselves and to subsequently seek reimbursement directly from their private health insurance or from the governmental agency that covers their health benefits.

In the second situation, the patients or guarantors do not have health insurance (as previously discussed). These patients or guarantors have not made advance payments via an insurance premium. For these individuals, self-pay results because they lack health insurance or benefits under governmental health programs.

The outcome, though, in both situations is self-pay. Some patients and guarantors may seek recompense from a third party payer and others may bear the burden of the costs of their healthcare themselves. Thus, in self-pay, the patients or guarantors directly pay their healthcare providers for the costs of their healthcare.

A related concept is the **self-insured plan.** A self-insured plan is one in which the employer eliminates the "middle-man." The employer administers its own health insurance benefits. Rather than shift the risk to a health insurance entity, the employer (or other entity, such as a professional association) assumes the costs of healthcare for its employees or members and their dependents.

Traditional Retrospective Payment
The traditional retrospective payment method of reimbursement pays providers after the services have been rendered. Retrospective reimbursement is a type of fee-for-service because the providers are reimbursed for each service rendered. Third party payers reimburse providers for charges previously incurred. The reimbursement payments are based on the charges for the services provided. This method has historically been the traditional method of reimbursement.

Fee Schedules
In a fee-for-service environment, third party payers establish a **fee schedule.** A fee schedule is a predetermined list of fees that the third party payer allows for payment for all healthcare services. The **allowable fee** represents the average or maximum amount the third party payer will reimburse providers for the service.

Discounted Fee-for-Service Payments
To begin to control costs, the third party payers negotiated reduced fees for their members or insureds. The payment method using these reduced fees is known as discounted fee-for-service. Versions of the discounted fee-for-service payment method are the **UCR,** the **CPR,** and the **resource-based relative value scale (RBRVS)** (Blount and Waters 2001, 6).

UCR stands for **usual, customary, and reasonable.** This is defined as usual in the provider's practice; customary in the community; and reasonable for the situation. **CPR** stands for **customary, prevailing, and reasonable.** The UCR and the CPR are methods of payment within the type of traditional retrospective payment. Both methods are based on data from past claims. Private insurance companies use the UCR method. Medicare prior to the implementation of its current payment methods employed CPR. Both UCR and CPR are becoming rare.

Established in 1992, the RBRVS is a discounted fee schedule that Medicare uses to reimburse physicians. The RBRVS is a payment method that classifies health services based on the cost of providing physician services in terms of effort, practice expenses (overhead), and malpractice insurance.

Uncertainty for Third Party Payers

For third party payers, the retrospective fee-for-service payment method has the disadvantage of great uncertainty. The payers have no way of knowing the total charges that will be incurred and for which they must reimburse the providers.

Managed Care Methods

In managed care reimbursement methods (discussed fully in Chapter 5), third party payers "manage" both the costs of healthcare and the outcomes of care. In managed care plans, the third party payer has implemented some provisions to control the costs of healthcare while maintaining quality care.

Features of Managed Care

Common features of managed care include:

- Comprehensiveness
- Coordination and planning
- Education of patients and providers
- Assessment of quality
- Control of costs

Purposes of Managed Care

The two purposes of the management or control are to reduce the costs of healthcare for which the third party payer must reimburse the providers and to ensure continuing quality of care.

Managed care payers have instituted many means to control the costs and quality of health-care. One example of a provision is the requirement that patients obtain prior approvals for surgeries. Another example is a hybrid of the discounted fee-based system in which the payer reimburses the provider up to a percentage of the allowable fee and the insured must pay the remaining percentage (Koch 2002, 109). Finally, having one primary care provider to coordinate all aspects of healthcare supports the quality of healthcare by reducing fragmentation and enhancing integration.

Forms of Managed Care

There are numerous forms of managed care. These forms include health maintenance organizations (HMOs), exclusive provider organizations (EPOs), point-of-service plans (POSs), and preferred provider organizations (PPOs). One can imagine these forms as a continuum of control with the HMOs representing the most controlled and the PPOs representing the least controlled.

Criticisms of Managed Care

Some critics of managed care argue that managed care too severely limits the following capabilities:

- Patients' access to care and their freedom to choose healthcare providers
- Providers' ability to order diagnostic tests and therapeutic procedures

These critics contend that administrators rather than medical and health personnel are making decisions about patients' health futures.

In general, in a fee-for-service environment, providers are reimbursed for each service they provide. In a fee-for-service environment, the more services a provider renders, the more reimbursement the provider receives. Some experts contend that fee-for-service reimbursement inappropriately inflates the costs of health care because the payment method rewards providers for more services, whether or not these services are warranted.

Episode-of-Care Reimbursement

Episode-of-care reimbursement is a healthcare payment method in which providers receive one lump sum for all the services they provide related to a condition or disease. In the episode-of-care payment method, the unit of payment is the episode, not each individual health service. Therefore, the episode-of-care payment method eliminates individual fees or charges. The episode-of-care payment method is an attempt to correct perceived faults in the fee-for-service reimbursement method. Thus, the episode-of-care reimbursement method controls costs on a grand or systematic scale.

An episode of care is the health services that a patient receives:

- For a particular health condition or illness

- During a period of relatively continuous care from a provider

In the episode of care, one amount is set for all the care associated with the condition or illness. Forms of episode-of-care reimbursement are the **capitated payment method,** the **global payment method,** and the prospective payment method.

Occasionally, an episode of care is defined as a specific number of days. The federal government's payment method for home care services is an example. The per-episode home health payment covers all home care services and nonroutine medical supplies delivered to the patient during a 60-day period.

Capitated Payment Method

The capitated payment method, or **capitation,** is a method of payment for health services in which the third party payer reimburses providers a fixed, per capita amount for a period. "Per capita" means "per head" or "per person." A common phrase in capitated contracts is "per member per month" (PMPM). The PMPM is the amount of money paid each month for each individual enrolled in the health insurance plan. Capitation is characteristic of HMOs.

In capitation, the actual volume or intensity of services provided to each patient has no effect on the payment. More services do not increase the payment, nor do fewer services decrease the payment. If the provider contracts with a third party payer to provide services to a group of workers for a capitated rate, the provider receives the payments for each member of the group regardless of whether all the members receive the provider's services. There are no adjustments for the complexity or extent of the health services.

Example:

Z Company has a health insurance plan for its workers and their families through Wellness HMO. Wellness HMO has contracted with Dr. T to provide health services (care) to members of the Z Company group for the capitated rate of $15 per month ($15 PMPM).

Dr. T is under contract to receive $15 per month for every member of the Z group. The members of the Z group total 100. Each month Dr. T receives $1,500 ($15 × 100 members) from Wellness HMO for the Z group. Dr. T receives $1,500 whether no members of the group see him in clinic or all the members of the group see him in clinic. Dr. T receives $1,500 whether all the members receive complex care for cancer or all the members receive simple care for preventive flu shots.

The advantages of capitated payment are that the third party payer has no uncertainty and that the provider has a guaranteed customer base. The third party payer knows exactly what the costs of healthcare for the group will be and the providers know that they will have a certain group of customers. However, for the provider, there is also great uncertainty because the patients' usage of provider services is unknown and the complexity and cost of the services are unknowns.

Global Payment Method

In the **global payment method,** the third party payer makes one combined payment to cover the services of multiple providers who are treating a single episode of care. Thus, this payment method consolidates payments. A **block grant** is a fixed amount of money given or allocated for a specific purpose. For example, in a block grant there is a transfer of governmental funds to cover health services. In the global payment method, there is no additional payment for higher volumes of services or more expensive or complex services.

Medicare's payment system for home health services is an example of a global payment method. Various types of home health services are consolidated into the single payment. These services include all speech therapy, physical therapy, and occupational therapy; skilled nursing visits; home health aide visits; medical social services, and nonroutine medical supplies.

The most comprehensive version of the global payment system is the total-episode-of-care. For an episode of care, the total-episode-of-care payment rate is a single price that covers costs across the continuum of care, which could include all of the following:

- Facility costs across the continuum of care, such as hospital, nursing home, clinic, and outpatient rehabilitation

- Technical and professional components of procedures in radiology, pathology, and the laboratory

- Physician professional fees for anesthesia, surgery, and consultation

- Home care costs

Less comprehensive versions of the global payment method exist. For example, some global payment methods include only ambulatory costs or only inpatient costs. These methods are termed ambulatory-episode-of-care and inpatient-episode-of-care, respectively. Another less comprehensive version is a global surgical package. The global surgical package encompasses the operation, local or topical anesthesia, a preoperative clinic visit, immediate postoperative care, and usual postopera-

tive follow-up. In the special-procedure package, all the costs associated with a diagnostic or therapeutic procedure are included in the payment. Examples include extracorporeal shock wave lithotripsy and vasectomy. Another common package is for obstetrical services. An ambulatory-visit package includes all ambulatory services, including the physicians' charges, laboratory tests, x-rays, and other ambulatory services associated with one clinic visit. The per-episode home health payment is also a less comprehensive global payment rate. The single payment covers all home care services and nonroutine medical supplies that a patient receives during a 60-day period.

As can be seen, third party payers and providers have created multiple variations of the global payment method. The multiple variations, however, have added to the complexity of healthcare reimbursement.

Prospective Payment Methods

In the **prospective payment method,** payment rates for healthcare services are established in advance for a specific time period. The predetermined rates are based on average levels of resource use for certain types of healthcare. It is important to note that prospective payment methods are based upon averages. On individual patients, providers can lose money or make money, but, over time, providers should come out even. Payment is determined by the resource needs of the average patient for a set period of time or given set of conditions or diseases. Prospective payment methods representing these two situations are **per-diem payment** and **case-based payment,** respectively.

Providers are paid the pre-established rates regardless of the costs they actually incur. Therefore, prospective payment is another method in which the actual number or intensity of the services does not affect a pre-established compensation. The intent of prospective payment methods is to reduce the likelihood that charges will increase because limits on payments are pre-set for the future time period.

Per-Diem Payment

Per diem or per day (daily rate) is a limited type of prospective payment method. The third party payer reimburses the provider a fixed rate for each day a covered member is hospitalized. The Indian Health Service and some supplemental health insurance plans use per-diem methods. Traditionally, the per-diem payment method has been used to reimburse providers for inpatient hospital services.

Third party payers set the per-diem rates using historical data. For example, to establish an inpatient per diem, the total costs for all inpatient services for a population during a period are divided by the sum of the lengths of stay in the period. To determine the payment, the per-diem rate is multiplied by the number of days of hospitalization. In the absence of historical data, third party payers and providers must consider several factors to establish per-diem rates. These factors include costs, lengths of stay, volumes of service, and patients' severity of illness.

Critics of the per-diem payment method contend that the method encourages providers to increase the number of inpatient admissions, to extend the lengths of stay, or both. These strategies would result in increased reimbursements. Another prospective payment method, case-based reimbursement, corrects the flaws perceived in the per-diem payment method.

Case-Based Payment

In the case-based payment method, providers receive a fixed, preestablished payment for each case. **Cases** are patients, residents, or clients who receive health services for a condition or disease. Third party payers reimburse providers for each case rather than for each service (fee-for-service) or per diem.

Example:

Two patients were hospitalized with pneumonia. One patient was hospitalized for three days and the other patient was hospitalized for thirty days. Each patient is a case.

The third party payer has established a payment rate for cases with pneumonia. The hospital would receive two payments, exactly the same, for the two cases.

The payment is determined by the historical resource needs of the average patient for a given set of conditions or diseases. Case-based payment can be one flat rate per case or can be multiple rates that represent categories of cases (sets of conditions or diseases).

An example of the case-based payment system built on categories of cases is Medicare's method of payment for inpatient hospital services (prospective payment system or PPS). This method of payment is based on categories of payment called diagnosis related groups (DRGs). Each DRG categorizes patients who are homogeneous in terms of clinical profiles and requisite resources. Thus, patients classified to the same group have similar diagnoses and treatments, consumption of resources, and lengths of stay. Each DRG has a payment rate called a "weight." Weights are relative to one another. Higher weights are associated with groups in which patients require more resources for care and treatment. Higher resource consumption is related to higher intensity of services due to the severity of illness or the types of services needed for care and treatment, such as expensive equipment or medications. Higher weights translate into higher payments.

In 2007, Medicare's analysts enhanced DRGs by making them more sensitive to the resource complexity and severity of illness (Bowman 2007, 16). These enhanced DRGs are known as **Medicare Severity DRGs** or MS-DRGs (Bowman 2007, 16). In this enhancement, diagnosis codes were classified into three hierarchical levels in terms of their severity. The extent to which these diagnoses increased consumption of hospital resources was then evaluated. Next, the MS-DRGs' weights were aligned to their consumption of resources due to their resource complexity or severity of illness. Higher weights were assigned to MS-DRGs that required higher resource consumption with lower weights being assigned to MS-DRGs that required fewer resources.

Several U.S. federal payment methods are case-based prospective payment methods. (See table 1.3 for a comparison of federal prospective payment systems.)

In summary, the relatively weighted group is the basic unit of payment. Higher relative weights link to higher payment rates.

Criticisms of Episode-of-Care Reimbursement

The impact of the case-based payment method is that it rewards effective and efficient delivery of health services and penalizes ineffective and inefficient delivery. The case-based payment rates are based on averages of costs for patients within the group. Generally, costs for providers that treat patients efficiently and effectively are beneath the average costs. The providers make money in this situation. On the other hand, providers that typically exceed average costs lose money. Inefficiencies include duplicate laboratory work, scheduling delays, and lost reports. Many healthcare organizations have implemented procedures to streamline the delivery of health services to offset inefficiencies. Poor clinical diagnostic skills are an example of ineffectiveness. Thus, the more efficiently and effectively a provider delivers care, the greater its operating margin will be.

Some consumer advocates have voiced concerns about episode-of-care reimbursement. These advocates have noted that the payment method creates incentives to substitute less expensive diagnostic and therapeutic procedures and laboratory and radiologic tests and to delay or deny procedures and treatments.

Table 1.3.   Federal prospective payment systems

Site	System	Relative Weighted Group	Abbreviation	Effective Date
Ambulatory Surgery Center	Ambulatory surgery center (ASC) payment method	Ambulatory surgery center group Ambulatory payment classification group *(integrated into outpatient prospective payment system)*	ASC group	1980 January 1, 2008
Inpatient Acute Care Hospital	Prospective payment system (PPS)	Diagnosis related group Medicare-severity diagnosis related group *(enhancement)*	DRG	October 1, 1983 October 1, 2007
Skilled Nursing Facility	Skilled nursing facility prospective payment system (SNF PPS)	Resource utilization group, version III	RUG III	July 1, 1998
Home Health Agency	Home health prospective payment system (HHPPS)	Home health resource group	HHRG	October 1, 2000
Outpatient Hospital Service	Outpatient prospective payment system (OPPS)	Ambulatory payment classification group	APC group	August 1, 2000
Inpatient Rehabilitation Facility	Inpatient rehabilitation facility prospective payment system (IRF PPS)	Case mix group	CMG	January 1, 2002
Long Term Care Hospital	Long term care hospital prospective payment system (LTCH PPS)	Diagnosis related group Medicare-severity diagnosis related group *(enhancement)*	DRG	October 1, 2002 October 1, 2007

Healthcare analysts, on the other hand, point out the savings associated with eliminating wasteful or unnecessary procedures and tests and that volume and expense do not necessarily define quality.

Check Your Understanding 1.1

1. Insurers pool premium payments for all the insureds in a group, then use actuarial data to calculate the group's premiums so that:
   a. Premium payments are lowered for insurance plan payers
   b. The pool is large enough to pay losses of the entire group
   c. Accounting for the group's plan is simplified
   d. All of the above are reasons for using the data
2. Where and when did health insurance become established in the U.S.?
3. All of the following are types of episode-of-care reimbursement except:
   a. Global payment
   b. Prospective payment
   c. Capitation
   d. Self-insured plan
4. What discounted fee schedule does Medicare use to reimburse physicians?
5. Name and describe some versions of the global payment method.

Future of Healthcare Reimbursement Methodologies

The prospective payment system (PPS) for inpatient hospital services that Medicare implemented in 1983 proved to be successful. Based on that success, many current and future healthcare reimbursement methodologies are refinements and derivations of the PPS. However, despite the success of Medicare's PPS, spending on healthcare continues to increase.

During the period, 2002 through 2005, the rate of increase slowed. This slightly slowed rate of increase is demonstrated in the slightly decreased percentage of increase per year (See table 1.4.). How-

Table 1.4. Percentage increase in total national healthcare spending over time

2002	2003	2004	2005
9.3%[a]	7.7%[b]	8.2%[c]	6.9%[d]

[a] Smith, C., et al. 2005, January-February. Health spending slows in 2003. *Health Affairs* 24(1):185–194.

[b] Ibid.

[c] Strunk, B.C., P.B. Ginsburg, and J.P. Cookson. 2005, January-June. Tracking health care costs: Declining growth trend pauses in 2004. *Health Affairs Suppl Web Exclusives:* W5-286–W5-295.

[d] Catlin, A., et al. 2007, January-February. National health spending in 2005: The slowdown continues. *Health Affairs* 26(1):142–153.

ever, despite this deceleration, the trend of increasing healthcare expenditures continues. This increase represents billions of dollars. For example, in 2003, $1.7 trillion was spent on healthcare which equaled $5,670 per person in the United States (Smith et al. 2005, 185). Despite the slowing rate of increase, in 2005, almost $2.0 trillion was spent on healthcare which equaled $6,697 per person (Catlin et al., 2007, 142). At this rate of increase, healthcare spending is projected to reach 19.6 percent of the gross domestic product (GDP) by 2016, up from 13.7 percent in 1993 (Poisal et al. 2007, W242–W243).

This continued increased spending spurs the development of various methods of reimbursement for healthcare services. This section addresses four methods: universal healthcare, physician care groups, refinements in case-based payment methods, and case-mix adjusted payment methods.

Universal Healthcare Coverage

Some argue that as healthcare continues to consume a larger and larger share of the gross domestic product, universal healthcare coverage becomes a moral imperative (Luft 2007, 1115). Universal health care is a system of healthcare that has a single **payer** and that provides a basic level of healthcare for everyone (Luft 2007, 1115; Rashford 2007, 4). A payer is an entity that pays for health services, such as an insurance company, Workers'

Compensation, Medicare, or an individual. A basic level of healthcare includes family physician or general practitioner services; preventive, specialty, and surgical care; hospitalization; rehabilitative services; long-term care; and prescription drug coverage (Rashford 2007, 4). Massachusetts' universal healthcare plan became effective in July 2007 (Anonymous 2007, 103). This reform effort extended healthcare coverage and contained costs without fundamentally changing the existing system (Anonymous 2007, 103). Under this plan, all adults must obtain health insurance (Anonymous 2007, 103). The goal of this reform effort is 99 percent coverage of the state's citizens (See table 1.5.). Analysts believe that the success or failure of this reform effort is dependent upon its ability to control costs (Anonymous 2007, 103). This experiment bears careful watching as a potential model for other states and the nation or an indicator that more radical reform is required.

Physician Care Groups

Physician care groups (PCGs) is a prospective payment method for physician services in ambulatory settings. This method classifies patients into similar, homogenous categories (groups). PCGs

Table 1.5. Provisions of universal health care in Massachusetts, July 2007

Poorest individuals with incomes less than 150% of the federal poverty level (approximately $15,300 annually) enroll in government-funded plans for free
Low-income individuals and families with incomes between 151% and 300% of the federal poverty level ($30,630 for an individual and $61,950 for a family of four) purchase health insurance with government subsidies based on a **sliding scale** (varying to match income and ability to pay)
Companies with eleven or more employees must provide insurance or establish accounts allowing employees to purchase health insurance with pre-tax dollars (noncompliance results in a penalty of $295 per worker per year)
Individuals who fail to obtain insurance lose a tax exemption that began at $219 in December 2007 and rises over time

are visit-based and classify services according to clinical similarity and setting (Averill et al. 1999). Proponents of the PCG payment method emphasize that the basis of payment is the purpose of the visit, necessitating clear definition of the patient's problem (Averill et al. 1999). The various ambulatory settings included in this payment method are "physician offices, hospital outpatient departments, hospital emergency rooms, ambulatory surgical centers, community mental health centers, comprehensive outpatient rehabilitation facilities, state or local public health facilities, and rural health clinics" (Averill et al. 1999, 4).

The payment method accounts for resource use in terms of physician's (professional) services, technical services (equipment and technicians), interpretation (by the same physician or another physician), facility overhead, and ancillary services (laboratory tests) (Averill et al. 1999, 4–5). It is important to note the payment method also accounts for differences in resource use across ambulatory settings. Averill and colleagues explain that settings vary in terms of consuming the five components (1999, 4–5).

Example:

Patient A is seen in a hospital outpatient department for pneumonia. The hospital bills the third party payer for the facility overhead, technical services, interpretation, and ancillary services. The PCG for the physician's services include only the physician's professional services. However, if the same physician sees Patient A in her clinic instead of the hospital outpatient department, the PCG needs to account for resources for all five components (physician's services, technical services, interpretation, facility overhead, and ancillary services; Averill et al. 1999, 4–5).

The PCGs simplify payments to physicians for ambulatory services because there are about 400 PCGs compared to the more than 4,000 types of health services in the RBRVS payment method (Averill et al. 1999, 12). Each PCG has a predetermined relative weight. For ambulatory services, it is envisioned that PCG payment method could replace the federal government's RBRVS payment method.

Refined Case-Based Payment

Refined case-based payment methods enhance case-based payment methods to include patients from all age groups and from regions of the world with varying mixes of diseases and differing patterns of healthcare delivery. In the U.S., projects investigated means to enhance the inpatient PPS, the diagnosis related groups (DRGs). In its enhanced versions, the payment system is applicable to all types of patients, not the mostly elderly patients as covered by the DRGs. For international use, researchers created a classification method that, independent of coding system, measured patients' severity of illness and consumption of resources (Mullin et al. 2002).

Pediatric Modified Diagnosis Related Groups

In the mid-1980s, the National Association of Children's Hospitals and Related Institutions developed pediatric modified diagnosis related groups (PM-DRGs). This classification had classifications for neonates and pediatric patients (Averill et al. 2002, 46).

All-Patient Diagnosis Related Groups

In the late 1980s, the New York State Health Department contracted with researchers at 3M Health Information Systems (3M HIS) to develop a DRG payment method for nonMedicare patients. Including the PM-DRGs, the researchers developed the all-patient DRGs (AP-DRGs) (Averill et al. 2002). AP-DRGs included classifications for neonatal patients, pediatric patients, high-risk obstetrical patients, multiple trauma patients, organ transplant patients, and ventilator-dependent patients. In addition, groups were created for patients with the following conditions or diseases: human immunodeficiency virus (HIV), cystic fibrosis, nutritional disorders, acute leukemia, hemophilia, and sickle cell anemia. Some Medicaid programs and Blue Cross plans adopted AP-DRGs. The Centers for Medicare and Medicaid Services (CMS) also later

modified and adopted some of these refinements (Averill et al. 2002) for the inpatient PPS.

All-Patient Refined Diagnosis Related Groups

In the mid-1990s, continuing research and refinement by the 3M HIS team resulted in all-patient refined DRGs (APR-DRGs). The refinement is the inclusion of adjustments for severity of illness and risk of mortality. These adjustments result in 1,422 APR-DRGs. The classification method allows accurate comparisons of patients in terms of length of stay, resource consumption, and outcomes. "Through APR-DRGs, hospitals, consumers, payers, and regulators can gain an understanding of the patients being treated, the costs incurred, and within reasonable limits, the outcomes expected" (Averill et al. 2002, 50). Developers of the classification system suggest that, through APR-DRGs, organizational leaders can increase organizational efficiency and effectiveness as well as quality of care.

International Refined Diagnosis Related Groups

At the global level, the 3M HIS researchers developed a classification system that could be used within countries to describe patients' resource use and around the world to compare patients from one country to another (Mullin et al. 2002, 1). The international refined DRGs (IR-DRGs) are an inpatient classification system designed specifically to become the basis for payment, "budgeting, outcomes analysis, benchmarking, profiling, and utilization assessment" of international healthcare (Mullin et al. 2002, 3). There are 939 IR-DRGs reflecting severity of illness and resource consumption. The classification system provides healthcare decision makers with "a means of making relative comparisons of the resources patients consume and their associated clinical courses" (Mullin et al. 2002, 2).

Case-Mix Adjustment Models

Rising healthcare costs have stimulated payers to closely examine payment methodologies. One aspect that affects the payers' overall risk is variation in populations' health. Some populations have higher costs of healthcare and prevention than other populations because they utilize more healthcare resources. For example, a population with many persons with chronic diseases, high rates of acute illnesses or rehabilitation, or frequent use of services would have greater utilization of healthcare resources and higher costs than a healthy population that rarely uses health services. Payers for the "sicker" population could face significantly higher risk than payers for the "healthier" population could face. Traditionally, payers have used the factors of age and sex to assess the level of potential risk (Sevcik et al. 2004, W-5-26). These factors, however, account for less than 5 percent of the variance in use of healthcare resources (Sevcik et al. 2004, W-5-26). Another model, case-mix adjustment has a far greater ability to explain variances in utilization of healthcare resources.

Case-mix adjustment is the modification of payment and incentives based on an individual's or population's utilization of health services and expected risk for utilization of health services (Sevcik et al. 2004, W-5-26). There are various models of case mix adjustment, including adjusted clinical groups, diagnostic cost groups, episode risk groups™, and **clinical risk groups (CRGs).** These models have a power to explain variations in utilization of health services that is ten times greater than the factors of age and sex alone (Sevcik et al. 2004, W-5-26). CRGs will be discussed in detail to illustrate the general functioning of the various case-mix adjustment models.

The methodology of CRGs is a prospective payment system that predicts future healthcare expenditures. It is a capitated payment system for healthcare services for populations (Averill et al. 2001, 8). Its developers state that the methodology is a means to administer clinical pathways, product line management, and case management (Averill et al. 2001).

The payment method adjusts for risk and supports the clinical management of patients (Averill et al. 2001). CRGs classify patients into categories that account for the severity of the patient's illness or condition and that predict the costs of future medical care, debility, or death (Averill et al. 2001). To predict future healthcare expenditures, CRGs are assigned prior to health services being rendered. Moreover, CRGs predict costs for "an extended period of time" (Averill et al. 2001, 2).

CRGs include all age groups and cover the continuum of care. There are 1,075 CRGs (Averill et al. 2001, 8). These 1,075 CRGs are organized into the following nine statuses:

- Catastrophic conditions
- Dominant and metastatic malignancies
- Dominant chronic disease in three or more organ systems
- Significant chronic disease in multiple organ systems
- Single dominant or moderate chronic disease
- Minor chronic disease in multiple organ systems
- Single minor chronic disease
- History of significant acute disease
- Healthy

The 1,075 CRGs are not distributed evenly across the nine statuses. The status with the fewest CRGs is "Healthy" with one; the status with the most CRGs is "Single dominant or moderate chronic disease" with 398. Within these statuses, the severity-of illness level can range from none (healthy) to 6 (catastrophically ill) (Averill et al. 2001, table 1.1). According to Averill, "The severity level describes the extent and progression of the disease. A high level of severity is indicative of a high degree of treatment difficulty and a need for substantial future medical care" (Averill et al. 2001, 6).

Research has supported the ability of CRGs to identify patients who will require interaction with the health care system (Neff et al., 2002; 2004). Neff et al. found that CRGs were a useful tool to identify, classify, and stratify children with chronic health conditions. Thus, CRGs were found to support patient tracking, case management, utilization, and cost prediction (Neff et al., 2002; 2004).

To facilitate decision making, the CRGs can be collapsed into three hierarchical tiers of aggregate groups. Each tier of aggregate clinical risk groups (ACRGs) has fewer groups and less clinical precision. Thus, ACRG1 has the greatest number of CRGs, with 413, and ACRG3 the fewest, with 37 (Averill et al. 2001, 8). However, each tier of aggregation maintains clinical meaningfulness and severity levels. Thus, the classification system supports the various levels of detail needed by payers and providers (Averill et al. 2001).

The payment weights are calculated based on two years of historical data. The first year's data serves to classify the patient into a CRG. Averages of the second year's data are computed to set the weights of the CRGs. The second year's data predicts healthcare expenditures for patients in the CRG (Averill et al. 2001, 9). Higher weights correspond to higher severity levels. As a payment method, CRGs predict future consumption of healthcare resources. Their clinical precision and meaningfulness enable them to be used to manage care and their categorical nature serves as a means of reporting and communication. Finally, research has demonstrated that CRGs are able to predict payments comparable to other risk adjustment systems (Hughes et al. 2004).

Summary

The U.S. healthcare system is complex, partially because health insurance and employment are closely linked. Multiple methods exist to reimburse hospitals, physicians, and other health providers for the healthcare they render patients. Because recompense occurs after the healthcare has been provided,
the term used is reimbursement. Two major types of payment methodologies—fee-for-service reimbursement and episode-of-care reimbursement—are based upon the unit of payment. Other descriptive characteristics of healthcare payment methods are time frame and bearer of risk. Important contemporary reimbursement methods are retrospective fee-for-service, managed care, capitation, global payments, and prospective payment systems. Researchers and government health agencies continue to develop and advance payment methods, both in the U.S. and internationally. Healthcare professionals need to monitor the continuing evolution of healthcare reimbursement methodologies.

Chapter 1 Review Quiz

1. Who are the first, second, and third parties in healthcare situations?

2. Compare the UCR and CPR payment systems.

3. Describe the two purposes of managed care.

4. Why have many insurers replaced retrospective health insurance plans with group plans such as HMOs and PPOs?

5. What are advantages of capitated payments for providers and payers?

6. How do third party payers set per-diem payment rates?

7. Describe the major benefits of episode-of-care reimbursement according to its advocates and the major concerns about episode-of-care reimbursement expressed by its critics.

8. How does the payment method used by physician care groups (PCGs) account for resources used in patient care?

9. In the episode-of-care reimbursement approach, providers are reimbursed a lump sum for all provided services related to a patient's condition or disease. True or false?

10. How do clinical risk groups (CRGs) manage healthcare costs?

References and Bibliography

Anonymous. 2007, July 14. Universal health care in Massachusetts. *Lancet* 370(9582):103.

Averill, R. F., J. Eisenhandler, N. I. Goldfield, J. S. Hughes, D. E. Gannon, B. V. Shafir, and L. W. Gregg. 1999. The development of a prospective payment system for ambulatory professional services. 3M HIS Research Report 3–99. Available online from www.3m.com/us/healthcare/his/pdf/reports/pcg-article399.pdf .

Averill, R. F., N. I. Goldfield, J. Eisenhandler, J. S. Hughes, and J. Muldoon. 2001. Clinical risk groups and the future of healthcare reimbursement. In *Reimbursement Methodologies for Healthcare Services* [CD-ROM], edited by L. M. Jones. Chicago: American Health Information Management Association.

Averill, R. F., N. I. Goldfield, J. Muldoon, B. A. Steinbeck, and T. M. Grant. 2002. A closer look at all-patient refined DRGs. *Journal of American Health Information Management Association* 73(1):46–50.

Blount, L. L., and J. M. Waters. 2001. *Managing the Reimbursement Process.* 3rd ed. Chicago: American Medical Association Press.

Bowman, S. 2007, July-August. Severity-adjusted DRGs for FY08?: CMS proposes DRG refinements based on severity of illness. *Journal of the American Health Information Management Association* 78(7):16–20.

Catlin, A., C. Cowan, S. Heffler, and B. Washington. 2007, January-February. National health spending in 2005: The slowdown continues. *Health Affairs* 26(1):142–153.

Department of Labor. n.d. Health Plans & Benefits: Continuation of Health Coverage – COBRA. Accessed at http://www.dol.gov/dol/topic/health-plans/cobra.htm. Accessed 11 December 2007.

Holahan, J. and A. Ghosh. 2005, January–June. Understanding the recent growth in Medicaid spending, 2000–2003. *Health Affairs Suppl Web Exclusives:* W5-52–W5-62.

Hughes, J. S., R. F. Averill, J. Eisenhandler, N. I. Goldfield, J. Muldoon, J. M. Neff, and J. C. Gay. 2004. Clinical risk groups (CRGs): A classification system for risk-adjusted capitation-based payment and health care management. *Medical Care* 42 (1):81–90.

Koch, A. L. 2002. Financing health services. In *Introduction to Health Services.* 6th ed., edited by S. J. Williams and P. R. Torrens. Albany, N.Y.: Delmar.

Longest, B. B., J. S. Rakich, and K. Darr. 2000. *Managing Health Services Organizations and Systems.* 4th ed. Baltimore: Health Professions Press.

Luft, H.S. 2007, March 14. Universal health care coverage: A potential hybrid solution. *Journal of the American Medical Association* 297(10):1115–1118.

Mullin, R., J. Vertrees, R. Freedman, R. Castioni, and A. Tinker. 2002. Case-mix analysis across patient populations and boundaries: A refined classification system defined specifically for international use. 3M HIS Research Report 5–98. Available online from www.3m.com/us/healthcare/his/pdf/reports/ir_drg_whitepaper_09_02.pdf.

Neff, J. M., V. L. Sharp, J. Muldoon, J. Graham, J. Popalisky, and J. C. Gay. 2002. Identifying and classifying children with chronic conditions using administrative data with the clinical risk group classification system. *Ambulatory Pediatrics* 2 (1):71–79.

Neff, J. M., V. L. Sharp, J. Muldoon, J. Graham, and K. Myers. 2004. Profile of medical charges for children by health status group and severity level in a Washington state health plan. *Health Services Research* 39 (1):73–89.

Poisal, J.A., C. Truffer, S. Smith, A. Sisko, C. Cowan, S. Keehan, and B. Dickensheets. 2007, March-April. Health spending projections through 2016: Modest changes obscure Part D's impact. *Health Affairs* 26(2):W242–W253.

Rashford, M. 2007, January-March. A universal healthcare system: Is it right for the United States? *Nursing Forum* 42(1):3–11.

Sevcik, A.E., T. Abu-Jaber, and L. Marek. 2004, September-October. Understanding approaches to case-mix assessment and case-mix adjustment. *Journal for Healthcare Quality Web Exclusive* 26(5):W5-24–W5-34.

Smith, C., et al. 2005, January-February. Health spending slows in 2003. *Health Affairs* 24(1):185–194.

Washburn, E. R. 1999. The coming medical apocalypse. *Physician Executive* 25(1):34–39.

Wilson, J.S. 1990, January-February. In search of a $5-deductible mammogram: How to negotiate the insurance maze. *Home Healthcare Nurse* 8(1):51–52.

Wouters, A., S. Bennett, and C. Leighton. 1998. Alternative Payment Methods: Incentives for Improving Health Care Delivery. *PHR Primer for Policymakers.* Available online from www.phrplus.org/Pubs/pps1.pdf.

Chapter 2
Clinical Coding
and Coding Compliance

Objectives

- To differentiate the different code sets approved by the Health Insurance Portability and Accountability Act of 1996

- To describe the structure of approved code sets

- To examine coding compliance issues that influence reimbursement

Key Terms

Abuse
AHA Coding Clinic for HCPCS
AHIMA Standards of Ethical Coding
Ambulatory payment classification (APC)
Average length of stay (ALOS)
Balanced Budget Act (BBA) of 1997
Benchmarking
Case mix index
Centers for Medicare and Medicaid Services (CMS)
Classification system
Coding Clinic for ICD-9-CM
Coding compliance plan
Comorbidity
Compliance
Compliance officer
Compliance program guidance
Complication
CPT Assistant
Current Procedural Terminology (CPT)
Current Procedural Terminology Category I Code
Current Procedural Terminology Category II Code
Current Procedural Terminology Category III Code

Diagnosis related group (DRG)
False Claims Act
Fraud
Health Care Procedure Coding System (HCPCS)
Health Insurance Portability and Accountability Act of 1996 (HIPAA)
Health information technology (HIT)
Hospital Outpatient Prospective Payment System (HOPPS)
Hospital Payment Monitoring Program (HPMP)
International Classification of Diseases, 9th Revision, Clinical Modification (ICD-9-CM)
ICD-9-CM Coordination and Maintenance Committee
Length of stay (LOS)
Local Coverage Determination (LCD)
Local Medical Review Policy (LMRP)
Major diagnostic category (MDC)
Medicare administrative contractor (MAC)
Modifier
Mortality
National Center for Health Statistics (NCHS)
National Correct Coding Initiative (NCCI)

National Coverage Determination (NCD)
Office of Inspector General (OIG)
Office of Inspector General Workplan
Operation Restore Trust
Outpatient Service Mix Index (SMI)
Payment Error Prevention Program (PEPP)
Program for Evaluation Payment Patterns
   Electronic Report (PEPPER)

Quality Improvement Organization (QIO)
Recovery Audit Contractor (RAC)
Scope of Work/Statement of Work
Third party payer
Utilization Review Committee
World Health Organization (WHO)

The Clinical Coding–
Reimbursement Connection

Simply put, reimbursement is payment to health-care providers and facilities for services rendered to patients. Communication of the services provided is transmitted from the provider to the **third party payer,** public or private, via coded information. Using standardized coding systems allows for a stable and efficient payment process. Payment methodologies and systems used to determine coverage of services and supplies vary, but the code sets used remain constant across all the different healthcare settings.

One need not be a coding expert per se to be able to understand healthcare reimbursement. However, just using the designated code set is not enough. Physicians and healthcare facilities will receive accurate reimbursement for the services they render to patients only if claims submitted comply with the guidelines and conventions published for the various clinical coding sets. In order to fully understand the intricate workings of the various Medicare prospective payment systems (PPSs) and private payer systems, baseline knowledge of the approved code sets and their functionality is essential. The **Health Insurance Portability and Accountability Act of 1996 (HIPAA)** designated the code sets for healthcare services reporting to public and private insurers. The HIPAA compliant code sets are listed in table 2.1.

Table 2.1.   HIPAA designated code sets

Provider	Inpatient		Outpatient	
	Diagnosis	**Procedure**	**Diagnosis**	**Procedure**
Physician	ICD-9-CM	CPT	ICD-9-CM	CPT
Facility	ICD-9-CM	ICD-9-CM	ICD-9-CM	HCPCS (CPT and HCPCS Level II)

The International Classification of Diseases

HIPAA designates the International Classification of Diseases, 9th Revision, Clinical Modification, to report diagnoses in all healthcare settings and procedures for inpatient encounters. (See table 2.1.) The International Classification of Diseases (ICD) coding and **classification system** is used throughout the world for **mortality** reporting. ICD is maintained by the **World Health Organization (WHO)** and is updated approximately every 10 years.

ICD-10

The current international version of ICD is in the 10th revision and is referred to as ICD-10. The United States, however, adopted the 9th revision of ICD (ICD-9), modified it clinically, and continues to use it as the method for communicating diagnoses and inpatient procedures for public and private reimbursement systems.

ICD-9-CM

This clinical modification (CM) of ICD-9 was developed by the **National Center for Health Statistics (NCHS)** and has been in use since 1979. Although the international version of ICD focuses on acute illnesses and mortality, **ICD-9-CM** was expanded to include morbidity or chronic conditions and procedure reporting.

ICD-9-CM has several uses (AHA Central Office 2004):

- Classifying morbidity and mortality information for statistical purposes

- Classifying diagnosis and procedure information for epidemiological and clinical research

- Indexing of hospital records by disease and surgical procedure

- Reporting information to various healthcare reimbursement systems

- Analyzing resource consumption patterns
- Analyzing adequacy of reimbursement for health services

Providers use ICD-9-CM coding to determine payment categories for various PPSs, including the following:

- Hospital inpatient: Medicare severity diagnosis related groups (MS-DRGs)
- Hospital rehabilitation: Case mix groups (CMGs)
- Long-term care: Long-term care Medicare severity diagnosis related Groups (LTC-MS-DRGs)
- Home health: Home health resource groups (HHRGs).

Structure of ICD-9-CM
ICD-9-CM contains three volumes:

- The Tabular List of Diseases and Injuries
- The Alphabetic Index to Diseases
- The Classification for Procedures

Table 2.2 lists the contents of each volume.
ICD-9-CM diagnosis codes vary in character length from three to five digits, with a decimal point placed after the third digit. The first three characters are a category code. The fourth and fifth digits are subcategory and subclassification codes that provide the specificity necessary to accurately describe a patient's clinical condition. (See figure 2.1.)

Procedure codes also vary in length from two to four digits, with the decimal point placed after the second digit. The first two digits for procedures compose the category code and the third and fourth digits are the subcategory and subclassification codes indicating specific details about diagnostic and surgical procedures. (See figure 2.2.) Table 2.3. lists the top ten diagnosis codes and top ten procedure codes reported to Medicare for inpatient services in federal fiscal year 2006.

Maintenance of ICD-9-CM
The **ICD-9-CM Coordination and Maintenance Committee,** composed of NCHS and the **Centers for Medicare and Medicaid Services (CMS),** is responsible for maintaining the U.S. clinical modification version of the code set. NCHS makes determinations regarding diagnosis issues, whereas CMS maintains the procedures. Advisory in nature, the committee was created in 1985 to discuss possible updates and revisions to ICD-9-CM. Final determinations are made by the director of the NCHS and the administrator of the CMS.

Table 2.2.   ICD-9-CM codebook structure

Volume One—Tabular List of Diseases and Injuries	Volume Two—Alphabetic Index to Diseases	Volume 3—Classification for Procedures
Classification of Diseases and Injuries	Index to Diseases and Injuries	Alphabetic Index to Procedures
Supplementary Classifications	Table of Drugs and Chemicals	Tabular List for Procedures
Appendices	Alphabetic Index to External Causes of Injury and Poisoning	

Figure 2.1.   ICD-9-CM diagnosis code structure

250.41

250	Diabetes mellitus
250.4	Diabetes with renal manifestations
250.41	Diabetes with renal manifestations, type 1, not stated as uncontrolled

Figure 2.2.   ICD-9-CM procedure code structure

36.03

36	Operations on vessels of heart
36.0	Removal of coronary artery obstruction and insertion of stent(s)
36.03	Open chest coronary artery angioplasty

Table 2.3. ICD-9-CM codes

Medicare Top 10 Diagnoses by Volume FY 2006		Medicare Top 10 Procedures by Volume FY 2006	
Code	Description	Code	Description
401.9	Hypertension	99.04	Transfusion of packed cells
428.0	Congestive heart failure	38.93	Venous catheterization
250.00	Diabetes, unspecified	88.56	Coronary arteriography
427.31	Atrial fibrillation	37.22	Left heart cardiac catheterization
414.01	Coronary atherosclerosis	39.95	Hemodialysis
272.4	Hyperlipidemia, unspecified	88.53	Angiocardiography, left heart
496	Chronic airway obstruction	00.66	Percutaneous transluminal coronary angioplasty
599.0	Urinary tract infection	00.40	Procedure on single vessel
530.81	Esophageal reflux	45.16	Esophago-gastroduodenscopy
244.9	Hypothyroidism, unspecified	36.07	Stent insertion

The committee holds public meetings every year in March and September, and suggestions for new codes, modifications, and deletions are submitted by members of both public and private sectors. Proposals for code changes are submitted prior to the semiannual meetings and include a description of the diagnosis or procedure and rationale for the requested modification. Supporting references, literature, statistics, and cost information may also be submitted. Requests must follow industry-accepted ICD-9-CM coding conventions. Each year after the December meeting, the committee determines code modifications that become effective October 1 of the following year. Minutes and proposals for diagnosis issues are located on the NCHS portion of the Centers for Disease Control and Prevention Web site (www.cdc.gov). Minutes and Proposals for procedure issues are located on the CMS Web site (www.cms.hhs.gov).

ICD-9-CM Coding Guidelines

Because ICD-9-CM codes serve as the communication vehicle between providers and insurers, it is vital to follow ICD-9-CM guidelines at all times. Accurate reimbursement is dependent upon timely, accurate, and complete coding of the services and procedures provided to beneficiaries. The Cooperating Parties—NCHS, CMS, American Hospital Association (AHA), and American Health Information Management Association (AHIMA)—and the Editorial Advisory Board—are responsible for publishing coding guidelines for ICD-9-CM. The coding guidelines are published by the AHA in *Coding Clinic for ICD-9-CM,* the only official publication for ICD-9-CM coding guidelines and advice. *Coding Clinic* is published quarterly and includes the following information (AHA Central Office 2004):

- Official coding advice and official coding guidelines
- Correct code assignments for new technologies and newly identified diseases
- Articles and topics which offer practical information and improve data quality
- Coding changes and/or corrections
- Ask the Editor questions with practical examples

Coding Clinic should be a component of all coding education and **compliance** programs for healthcare provider and facility coding units.

Healthcare Common Procedural Coding System

The **Healthcare Current Procedural Coding System (HCPCS)** is a two-tiered system of procedural codes used primarily for ambulatory care and physician services. A third tier, pertaining to codes developed by local payers, was eliminated as of December 31, 2003, in compliance with HIPAA standard procedure code requirements. HCPCS codes are frequently attached to inpatient and outpatient charge description masters (CDMs) for convenience and to facilitate communication between providers and payers about services and supplies included in the CPT or HCPCS Level II system.

CPT (HCPCS Level I)

Current Procedural Terminology (CPT®) is used throughout the United States to report diagnostic and surgical services and procedures. Created and first published by the American Medical Association (AMA) in 1966, CPT was designed to be a means of effective and dependable communication among physicians, patients, and third party payers (LaTour/Eichenwald 2002, 264). The terminology provides a uniform coding scheme that accurately describes medical, surgical, and diagnostic services. The CPT coding system is used by physicians to report services and procedures performed in the hospital inpatient and outpatient setting and by facilities for outpatient services and procedures (See table 2.1). CPT has several uses:

- Communication vehicle for public and private reimbursement systems
- Development of guidelines for medical care review
- Basis for local, regional, and national utilization comparisons
- Medical education and research

The code set was adopted into the Healthcare Common Procedure Coding System in 1985 and became the HCPCS Level I code set for Medicare reporting. Therefore, CPT is referred to as HCPCS Level I as well as CPT in the coding and reimbursement communities.

Structure of CPT

The terminology is divided into six main sections, known as **Category I codes,** plus two types of supplementary codes (**Category II** and **Category III codes),** and **modifiers.**

Category I CPT codes comprise the following six sections:

- Evaluation and Management
- Anesthesia
- Surgery
- Radiology
- Pathology and Laboratory
- Medicine

The Surgery Section is further divided as follows:

Integumentary System	10021 to 19499
Musculoskeletal System	20000 to 29999
Respiratory System	30000 to 32999
Cardiovascular System	33010 to 39599
Digestive System	40490 to 49999
Urinary System	50010 to 53899
Male Genital System	54000 to 55980
Female Genital System	56405 to 58999
Maternity Care and Delivery	59000 to 59899
Endocrine System	60001 to 60699
Nervous System	61000 to 64999
Eye and Ocular Adnexa	65091 to 68899
Auditory System	69000 to 69979
Operating Microscope	69990

Table 2.4 contains a listing of the top 10 CPT codes reported to Medicare in 2006.

Each of the three code categories in the CPT coding system serves a different and unique purpose.

Category I codes describe a procedure or service that is consistent with contemporary medical practice and is performed by many physicians in clinical practice in multiple locations (Beebe 2003, 84). The specific use of devices and drugs for all services in this category must be approved by the Food and

Table 2.4.   CPT codes

Medicare Top 10 Procedures by Unit of Service—CY 2006	
Code	Description
35415	Venipuncture
85025	Automated hemogram
93005	Electrocardiogram, tracing
80053	Comprehensive metabolic panel
80048	Basic metabolic panel
71020	Chest x-ray
85610	Prothrombin time
99213	Office/outpatient visit, established
84484	Troponin, quantitative
88305	Tissue exam by pathologist

Drug Administration (FDA). Category I codes are represented by a five-digit numeric code.

Within Category I codes there are unlisted codes. Unlisted codes are used to report services and procedures that are not represented by an existing code. Typically unlisted codes are used for new or innovative procedures that have not been added to the CPT coding system. When an unlisted code is reported, supporting documentation should be submitted to the third party payer to establish correct coding and medical necessity for that service.

Category II codes were created to facilitate data collection for certain services and/or test results that contribute to positive health outcomes and quality patient care (Beebe 2003, 84). This category of codes is a set of optional tracking codes for performance measurement. The services included in this category are often part of the Evaluation and Management service or other component part of a service. Category II codes have been implemented to help medical practices and facilities reduce operational costs by replacing time-consuming medical record documentation reviews and surveys

with this streamlined code tracking system (Beebe 2003, 84). Use of Category II codes is optional, and they may not be used as substitutes for Category I codes. Category II codes are represented by a five digit alphanumeric code with the alpha character F in the last position: (1234F).

Category III codes represent emerging technologies. This category of codes was created to help facilitate data collection and assessment of new services and procedures (Beebe, 2003, 85). In order to qualify for inclusion in this category, a service or procedure must have relevance for research, either ongoing or planned. Like Category II codes, Category III codes are represented by an alphanumeric five-digit code with the alpha character T in the last field: (1234T).

In addition to the three categories of codes, CPT contains modifiers for use by physicians and other healthcare providers. A modifier is a two-digit numeric or alphanumeric character designed to give Medicare and other third party payers additional information needed to process a claim. A physician or facility uses a modifier to flag a service provided to a patient that has been altered by some special circumstance(s) but for which the basic code description itself has not changed. Following are common reasons to use a modifier (AMA 2005, xiv):

- A service or procedure has been increased or reduced.
- Only part of a service was performed.
- A bilateral procedure was performed.
- A service or procedure was performed more than once.
- Unusual events occurred during a procedure or service.

Medical record documentation must support the use of a modifier because the modifier may change the reimbursement for the service or procedure. For example, modifier 91 is used to indicate that a clinical laboratory test was repeated. Rules governing the usage of this modifier specify that it may not be used when an equipment or testing failure has occurred, but only when the test has been reordered to determine whether a change in the result has occurred. Therefore, using modifier 91 relays to the third party payer that the duplicate code reported was not accidental or fraudulent but instead was correct and that the physician ordered the test twice based on medically necessary foundations. However, failure to have supporting documentation in the medical record that establishes medical necessity can result in claim denials and **fraud** or **abuse** penalties.

Maintenance of CPT
The CPT Editorial Research and Development Department supports the modification process for the code set. A sixteen-member CPT Editorial Panel meets four times per year to consider proposals for changes to CPT. The Editorial Panel is supported by the CPT Advisory Committee, which is composed of representatives of more than 90 medical specialty societies and other healthcare professional organizations. To stay current with new technologies and pioneering procedures, CPT is revised each year with changes effective the following January 1.

Requesting a Code Modification for CPT
CPT coding modifications are submitted to the CPT Editorial Research and Development Department at the AMA. The Coding Change Request Form found on the AMA Web site (www.ama-assn.org) must be used and submitted along with supporting documentation and clinical vignettes. A coding modification may be requested for all three categories of codes. Once the Coding Change Request Form is received, it is reviewed for completeness by the AMA staff. If the form is complete, Coding Charge Request Forms for Category I and Category III codes are forwarded to the CPT Advisory Committee for a detailed review.

Coding Change Request Forms for Category II CPT Codes are sent to the Performance Measure-

ment Advisory Group for review. These requests must receive a two-thirds majority opinion from the advisory group before they are passed on to the CPT Advisory Committee. The AMA established the Performance Measurement Advisory Group to help create and maintain the performance measurement codes (Beebe 2003, 84). The group comprises representatives from various organizations, AMA's CPT and clinical quality improvement staffs, the CPT Editorial Panel, health services researchers, and other knowledgeable experts.

After review by the CPT Advisory Committee, those requests that warrant final review are submitted to the CPT Editorial Panel responsible for final decisions on all coding modifications (AMA 2004). A calendar of regular meetings for the CPT Advisory Committee and the CPT Editorial Panel is posted in the AMA Web site.

CPT Coding Guidelines
The AMA provides several resources regarding the appropriate use of CPT. The official publication for CPT coding issues and guidance is ***CPT Assistant*** (AMA 1989–2007). *CPT Assistant* contains the following helpful features:

- Coding communication that provides up-to-date information on codes and trends
- Clinical vignettes that offer insight into confusing coding and modifier usage scenarios
- Coding consultation that covers the most frequently asked questions

All coding education and compliance programs should include the use of *CPT Assistant.*

HCPCS Level II
The Healthcare Common Procedure Coding System (HCPCS) was developed by CMS in the 1980s to report services, supplies, and procedures that are not represented in the CPT (HCPCS Level I) code set but are submitted for reimbursement (CMS 2004a).

The descriptions identify items or services rather than specific brand names and do not endorse any manufacturer. This alphanumeric code set is a standardized coding system that provides an established environment for claims submission and processing. The system is managed by both private and public health insurers. The existence of a particular code does not guarantee or indicate coverage/reimbursement by Medicare, Medicaid, or other third party payers. There are two types of codes within the HCPCS Level II system: permanent and temporary.

HCPCS Level II Permanent Codes
HCPCS Level II permanent codes may be used by all public and private health insurers. Permanent codes are alphanumeric with five digits with an alpha character in the first position (A2345). The alpha character designates the category to which the code is classified. Table 2.5 lists the categories of permanent HCPCS codes.

Within the permanent codes are "miscellaneous/not otherwise classified" codes. These codes enable suppliers and healthcare providers to report items/

services that have not been incorporated into the coding system but nonetheless have been approved for marketing by the Food and Drug Administration (FDA) (CMS 2004a). Miscellaneous codes are manually reviewed and must be submitted with accompanying pricing and medical necessity documentation.

Current Dental Terminology (CDT4) commonly known as "dental codes," comprises a separate category of national permanent codes. The codes are copyrighted and maintained by the American Dental Association (ADA). Dental codes are easily identified because they begin with the letter D.

HCPCS Level II Temporary Codes
HCPCS Level II temporary codes are used to meet the immediate and short-term operational needs of individual insurers, public and private (CMS 2004a). Temporary codes are also alphanumeric, with five digits and an alpha character in the first position. Like permanent codes, the alpha character designates the category to which the code is classified. Table 2.6 lists the categories of temporary HCPCS codes. Temporary codes may remain as

Table 2.5.   Permanent HCPCS codes

Permanent Code Categories	Covers	Insurers
A codes	Ambulance and transportation services, medical and surgical supplies, administrative, and miscellaneous and investigational services and supplies	All payers
B codes	Enteral and parenteral therapy	All payers
D codes	Dental	All payers
E codes	Durable medical equipment	All payers
J codes	Drugs that cannot ordinarily be self-administered, chemotherapy, immunosuppressive drugs, inhalation solutions	All payers
L codes	Orthotic and prosthetic procedures and devices	All payers
M codes	Office services and cardiovascular and other medical services	All payers
P codes	Pathology and laboratory services	All payers
R codes	Diagnostic radiology	All payers
V codes	Vision hearing and speech-language pathology services	All payers

Table 2.6.   Temporary HCPCS codes

Temporary Code Categories	Covers	Insurers
C codes	Items that may qualify for pass-through payment under HOPPS	Medicare hospital outpatient claims
G codes	Professional health care procedures and services	Medicare hospital outpatient claims
Q codes	Drugs, biologicals, medical equipment	Medicare hospital outpatient claims
K codes	Durable medical equipment	DMERCs—durable medical equipment regional carriers
S codes	Drugs, services and supplies	BCBSA and AHIP and Medicaid
H codes	Mental health services	State Medicaid agencies
T codes	Items for which there are no permanent national codes	State Medicaid agencies and private insurers

such for an indefinite period of time. However, if deemed necessary, a permanent code will be created to replace the temporary code and the temporary code will be deleted. The top 10 HCPCS codes reported to Medicare in 2006 are found in table 2.7.

HCPCS Level II Modifiers
Like CPT, HCPCS Level II allows for modifiers. HCPCS Level II modifiers are two-digit alpha or alphanumeric codes. A modifier is designed to give Medicare and other third party payers additional information needed to process a claim. Many HCPCS Level II modifiers indicate body areas that allow for specific information to be provided to third party payers. Table 2.8 provides examples of HCPCS Level II modifiers.

Maintenance of HCPCS Level II Coding System
Permanent codes are maintained jointly by America's Health Insurance Plans (AHIP), the Blue Cross and Blue Shield Association (BCBSA), and the Centers for Medicare and Medicaid Services (CMS). Together these organizations compose the National Panel (CMS 2004a). Permanent National Codes are updated annually every January 1. Temporary codes, which compose 35 percent of

HCPCS Level II codes, are maintained by the individual members of the National Panel rather than the group (CMS 2004a). For example, the HCPCS workgroup, a part of the CMS workgroup, makes the decisions about temporary codes for Medicare. Temporary codes can be added, changed, or deleted on a quarterly basis.

Requesting a Code Modification for HCPCS Level II
There are three types of coding modifications to HCPCS Level II codes that users can request: a code may be added to the code set, the language used to describe an existing code may be changed, and an existing code may be deleted. The HCPCS Level II coding review process is a continuous process. The review cycle runs from April 2 through the following April 1.

Requests for code changes may be submitted at any time throughout the year. The proper request format can be found on the CMS Web site (www.cms.hhs.gov). Requests for coding modifications are submitted to the Alpha-Numeric HCPCS Coordinator at the CMS. Once a request is submitted, it is reviewed by the CMS HCPCS Workgroup at one of its regular monthly meetings. After considering the request, the HCPCS Workgroup will make a recommendation to the HCPCS National Panel.

Table 2.7. HCPCS Level II codes

Medicare Top 10 Service, Procedures, or Supplies by Unit of Service—CY 2006	
Code	**Description**
Q9949	Low osmolar contrast material
J0881	Injection, darbepoetin alfa, 1 mcg
Q9950	Low osmolar contrast material
G0378	Hospital observation service, per hour
J0885	Injection, epoetin alfa, 1000 units
J0878	Injection, daptomycin, 1 mg
J1756	Injection, iron sucrose, 1 mg
J2250	Injection, midazolam HCl, per 1 mg
Q9952	Injection, gadolinium-based magnetic resonance contrast agent
C8952*	Therapeutic injection IV push

* Code has been deleted; see CPT codes 90774–90775

Table 2.8. HCPCS Level II modifier examples

LT	Left side
RT	Right side
E1	Upper left, eyelid
F1	Left hand, second digit

The HCPCS Workgroup may also create a temporary Medicare national code pending the National Panel action. The HCPCS Workgroup's recommendations usually fall into one of the following categories:

- Add a Code
- Use an Existing Code that Describes the Item or Service
- Use an Existing Code for Miscellaneous Items or Services
- Revise an Existing Code
- Delete an Existing Code

The National Panel is responsible for approving all coding modifications. All three members of the National Panel must agree on all requests before a change may be made. Once the decision is made regarding a request, the Panel will send a decision letter to the requester. If the requestor is unsatisfied with the decision, a new request with new supporting information may be submitted for reconsideration and evaluation (CMS 2004a).

HCPCS Level II Coding Guidelines
AHA Coding Clinic for HCPCS is a resource newsletter that provides coding advice for the users of HCPCS Level II. This quarterly newsletter was first introduced in March of 2001 and is published by the Central Office of ICD-9-CM. The newsletter includes an Ask the Editor section with actual examples, correct code assignment for new technologies, articles, and a bulletin of coding changes and/or corrections (AHA 2004). Although this is not official coding guidance, it is expert. There is no official coding resource for HCPCS Level II other than coverage determinations issued by CMS and its **Medicare administrative contractors (MDCs).** It is important to keep in mind that coding does not dictate coverage of medical services or reimbursement policies.

Coding Systems as Communication Facilitators

Clinical coding systems serve as the communication vehicle between healthcare providers and public and private third party payers. This solid and reliable communication enables providers and facilities to be accurately reimbursed in a timely manner. Understanding the basics of clinical coding systems enables coding, billing and reimbursement professionals to fully grasp reimbursement principles and concepts.

Coding Compliance and Reimbursement

For coding, billing, and reimbursement professionals, being compliant means to perform one's job functions according to the laws, regulations, and guidelines set forth by Medicare and other third party payers. Today, being compliant with the rules and regulations is just one component of being proficient at a healthcare professional's job, but it is an indication that, as a professional, the person is able to perform at an acceptable skill level and ethical standard. It is the responsibility of coding, billing, and reimbursement professionals to perform their jobs with integrity at all times. The appendix to this chapter, *AHIMA Standards of Ethical Coding,* sets forth guidelines that all coding, billing, and reimbursement professionals should understand and ponder during ethical decision making.

Fraud and Abuse

Medicare defines **fraud** as "an intentional representation that an individual knows to be false or does not believe to be true and makes, knowing that the representation could result in some unauthorized benefit to himself/herself or some other person" (CMS 2004b). An example of fraud is billing for a service that was not rendered.

Abuse occurs when a healthcare provider unknowingly or unintentionally submits an inaccurate claim to for payment. Abuse generally results from unsound medical, business, or fiscal practices that directly or indirectly result in unnecessary costs to the Medicare program. An example of abuse involves inadvertently reporting a procedure code that describes a service that was more extensive that the procedure performed. In Medicare, the most common forms of fraud and abuse include (CMS 2004b):

-   Billing for services not furnished

-   Misrepresenting the diagnosis to justify payment

-   Soliciting, offering, or receiving a kickback

-   Unbundling or "exploding" charges

-   Falsifying certificates of medical necessity, plans of treatment, and medical records to justify payment

-   Billing for a service not furnished as billed, known as upcoding

The mid-1980s through late 1990s brought about a wave of legislation targeted at fighting Medicare and Medicaid fraud and abuse.

Legislative Background

It is important to explore and understand the legislative history of fraud and abuse. In an effort to eliminate erroneous healthcare spending for the Medicare and Medicaid programs, Congress passed several acts targeting fraud and abuse. Not only did the revamped and newly created legislation show a commitment to protecting the Medicare Trust Fund by Congress, but it gave CMS the resources and penalties necessary to battle fraud and abuse. Several target areas introduced in the legislation are still under review by **Quality Improvement Organizations (QIOs)** in the 8th **Statement of Work** (formerly known as **Scope of Work**).

False Claims Act

The **False Claims Act** was passed during the Civil War in order to prohibit contractors of any kind from knowingly filing a false or fraudulent claim, using a false record or statement, or conspiring to defraud the U.S. government (Schraffenberger 2005, 200). Today, the False Claims Act provides the support for the federal government to rebuke abusers of the Medicare and Medicaid systems. The Medicare and Medicaid Patient and Program Protection Act of 1987 supports the use of civil monetary penalties for acts of fraud and abuse against the Medicare and Medicaid programs. This act allows for fines up to $10,000 per violation and exclusions from Medicare participation.

Office of Inspector General (OIG) Compliance Program Guidance

In 1991, the **OIG** released seven elements which the office believed should serve as the foundation of an effective corporate compliance plan (OIG 1991). These elements are:

1. Written policies and procedures
2. Designation of a **compliance officer**
3. Education and training
4. Communication
5. Auditing and monitoring
6. Disciplinary action
7. Corrective action

In response to numerous laboratory investigations for improper coding and billing, *Compliance Program Guidance for Clinical Laboratories* was released in February 1997 and then revised in February of the following year. The guidance provides principles for compliant documentation and coding practices in laboratories. For example, laboratories were instructed that they may not use diagnostic information from earlier dates of service on current laboratory testing orders. At the time, this was common practice and is a compliance risk because a patient's condition warranting a procedure may change from visit to visit.

In February of 1998, the OIG released *Compliance Program Guidance for Hospitals.* This document highlighted several coding and billing areas that were at risk for noncompliance. Some examples are: upcoding services, unbundling services, and reporting incorrect discharge destination.

Since 1998, numerous other *Compliance Program Guidance* documents have been released for various healthcare settings, including: hospice, home health, physician practices, and skilled nursing facilities.

Several years have passed since the *Compliance Program Guidance for Hospitals* was released. In January 2005, CMS released the *Supplemental Compliance Program Guidance for Hospitals* in the *Federal Register.* Because hospitals' operations and reimbursement systems have changed since 1998, the OIG decided to revise the Program Guidance. Though expanded, the original seven elements continue to be the basis for an effective hospital compliance plan (DHHS 2005, 4874–4876):

1. Designation of a Compliance Officer and compliance committee
2. Development of compliance policies and procedures, including standard of conduct
3. Developing open lines of communication
4. Appropriate training and education
5. Internal monitoring and auditing
6. Response to detected deficiencies
7. Enforcement of disciplinary standards

The *Supplemental Compliance Program Guidance for Hospitals* provides further detail about compliance risk areas for outpatient procedure coding, admissions and discharge criteria, supplemental payment considerations and use of information technology (DHHS 2005, 4860–4862). A copy of the *Supplemental Compliance Program Guidance for Hospitals* can be found on the OIG Web site (www.oig.hhs.gov).

Operation Restore Trust

A joint effort of the Department Health and Human Services (DHHS), OIG, Centers for Medicare and Medicaid Services (CMS) and Administration on Aging (AOA), **Operation Restore Trust** was released in 1995 to target fraud and abuse among healthcare providers. The program originally focused on five states (California, Illinois, Florida, New York, and Texas) where one-third of the Medicare and Medicaid population resided. Within the first two years, Operation Restore Trust spent 7.9 million dollars and recovered 188 million dollars—a 24 to 1 return on investment. This major push for accurate coding and billing eventually spread to be a nationwide effort. In addition to fraud and abuse investigations, Operation Restore Trust paved the way for implementation of a national toll-free fraud and abuse hotline, the Voluntary Disclosure Program, and Special Fraud Alert documents.

Health Insurance Portability and Accountability Act of 1996

Although the Health Insurance Portability and Accountability Act (HIPAA) is widely known for its security and privacy provisions, a large portion of the Act focused on fraud and abuse prevention. The key fraud and abuse areas targeted by HIPAA are:

- Medical necessity
- Upcoding
- Unbundling
- Billing for services not provided

In addition to highlighting these key areas, HIPAA created the Medicare Integrity Program. Not only did Medicare continue to review provider claims for fraud and abuse, but the focus expanded to cost reports, payment determinations, and the need for ongoing compliance education (Schraffenberger 2005, 201).

Balanced Budget Act of 1997

One objective of the **Balanced Budget Act (BBA) of 1997** was to improve program integrity for Medicare. The provisions within the BBA attempted to educate Medicare beneficiaries on their role in preventing and reporting fraudulent acts. Beneficiaries were advised to review Medicare Summary Notices (formerly Explanations of Medicare Benefits or EOMBs) for errors and to report errors to the secretary of DHHS. Additionally, they were notified of their right to request copies of detailed bills for healthcare services and informed of the implementation of a toll-free fraud and abuse hotline. The BBA also initiated a data collection program to collect fraud and abuse information in the healthcare sector as mandated by HIPAA.

As legislation regarding healthcare fraud and abuse became more prevalent, the need for a stronger workforce behind the laws was inevitable. Personnel were added to the Department of Justice (DOJ) and Federal Bureau of Investigation (FBI) in order to keep up with the warranted reviews. Likewise, the focus of the quality improvement organizations, or QIOs (formerly peer review organizations, or PROs) shifted from the quality focus of the early 1990s to a payment error prevention role.

Quality Improvement Organizations

Quality improvement organizations (QIOs) have worked with Medicare for more than twenty years to improve the quality of care provided to its beneficiaries. Individual QIOs contract every three years with Medicare to monitor hospital performance on a state or regional basis. The QIOs are guided by Medicare's Scope of Work (currently labeled Statement of Work). In 1999, the 6th Scope of Work (SOW) introduced CMS' **Payment Error Prevention Program (PEPP).** Working under the assumption that most payment errors were caused by simple mistakes, not fraudulent or abusive acts (KePRO 2004), PEPP instructed the QIOs to reduce the number of payment errors in their states or regions through awareness, education, and training. PEPP focused on several coding and billing areas that have historically contributed to payment errors:

- Medically unnecessary admissions and/or procedures

- Incorrect DRG assignment

- Readmission to facility

- Inappropriate transfers

QIOs used public data from CMS to identify abnormal payment patterns at hospitals in their contracted region or state. Those facilities were targeted for review and if payment errors were identified, education and training was provided. If the deviation from normal reporting rates were due to fraud or abuse, those cases would be passed on to the OIG for further investigation.

7th Scope of Work

During the 7th Scope of Work, QIOs continued to focus on payment errors at Medicare participating facilities. The 7th Scope of Work had three goals (Estrella 2003, 47):

- Improve the quality of care for beneficiaries by ensuring that beneficiary care meets professionally recognized standards of healthcare

- Protect the integrity of the Medicare Trust Fund by ensuring Medicare pays only for services and items that are reasonable, medically necessary, and provided in the most appropriate setting

- Protect beneficiaries by expeditiously addressing individual cases such as beneficiary complaints, hospital-issued notices of noncoverage (HINNs), Emergency Medical Treatment and Active Labor Act (EMTALA) violations, and other statutory responsibilities

Several tasks were created to assist QIOs with achieving the 7th SOW goals. Task 3, improving the Medicare beneficiary protection program, includes the **Hospital Payment Monitoring Program (HPMP),** which expanded and replaced the PEPP.

Clinical Data Abstraction Centers (CDACs) have contracted with Medicare to provide encounter screening and validation services for QIOs across the nation. CDACs use random selection to review cases for Medicare-participating hospitals in the various states and regions. Encounters that cannot be validated by the CDACs are passed on to the QIOs for further review. When a coding error is identified, it is corrected. If an overpayment has been made to the hospital, it is recouped by the fiscal intermediary. Underpayment resulting from coding errors is made to the hospital. All coding errors are entered into a QIO database for further analysis (KePRO 2004).

First-Look Analysis Tool for Hospital Outlier Monitoring Software

QIOs use Medicare's First-look Analysis Tool for Hospital Outlier Monitoring (FATHOM) software to identify hospitals with outliers. Target areas include (Estrella 2003, 44):

- One-day stays

- Same-day readmissions

- Against medical advice discharges

- Historically problem DRGs

- Case mix index creep

- DRG relationship groups

QIOs analyze data from FATHOM to identify hospitals that perform outside of the state norm. QIOs look not only at current data but at data trends over a period of time to identify sudden shifts in reporting patterns. Sudden shifts can be caused by various issues, including:

- Coder turnover

- Increase or decrease of education and training

- Implementation of new information systems

- Implementation of a documentation improvement program

- Expansion or establishment of a service area

- Inaccurate advice received from healthcare consultants

Program for Evaluation Payment Patterns Electronic Report (PEPPER)

QIOs are also provided with hospital-specific data from the Hospital Payment Monitoring Program (HPMP) Quality Improvement Organization Support Center (QIOSC), which is the Texas Medical Foundation (TMF).

TMF provides hospital data for fourteen target areas on a quarterly basis to the QIOs via the **Program for Evaluation Payment Patterns Electronic Report (PEPPER)** v. 5.0. (KePRO 2004, 1) For a listing of the PEPPER target areas, see table 2.9. QIOs determine which of these fourteen reports to share with the hospitals in their contracted state or region. If a facility is at or above the 75th percentile or at or below the 10th percentile the facility may be targeted for an intensive medical record review. If fraud or abuse is suspected, the case is forwarded on to the OIG for further investigation.

8th Statement of Work

The 8th Statement of Work (in effect from August 1, 2005 through July 31, 2008) emphasizes qual-

ity care with particular attention at nursing homes, home health agencies, hospitals, and physician offices. The SOW includes a plan that addresses five major areas (CMS 2005):

- Promote dramatic improvements in the quality of healthcare so that every beneficiary receives the right care every time

- Promote the adoption and effective use of **healthcare information technology (HIT)**

- Work with prescription drug plans and providers to ensure quality care by creating improvement projects to monitor issues such as inappropriately prescribed drugs and harmful drug interactions

- Improve healthcare access for disadvantaged populations

- Work to improve provider-patient communication during beneficiary complaints regarding quality of care issues

Even though heavy emphasis is being placed on quality and HIT in the 8th SOW, the Hospital Payment Monitoring Program is still in effect. Groundwork laid during the 7th SOW for the HPMP will continue during the 8th SOW. In order to lessen the chance of a payment error investigation, coding and billing units should include preventative measures in their coding compliance plans.

Recovery Audit Contractors (RACs)

Section 306 of the Medicare Modernization Act of 2003 (MMA) called for CMS to launch a Medicare payment recovery demonstration project. The project's purpose is to determine if the use of **recovery audit contractors** is a cost-effective means of ensuring correct payments are provided under Medicare. The demonstration project is based on the Improper Medicare FFS Payments Report provided by the Comprehensive Error Rate Testing Program in November 2006. This report identified

Table 2.9. PEPPER target areas

Short-Term Hospitals	
Target Area	**Focus**
One-day stays excluding transfers	Site of service—was an inpatient admission warranted or could the patient have been treated more efficiently as an outpatient?
DRG 127 one-day stays (Maps to MS-DRGs 291, 292, and 293)	Site of service—was an inpatient admission warranted or could the patient have been treated more efficiently as an outpatient?
DRG 143 one-day stays (Maps to MS-DRG 313)	Site of service—was an inpatient admission warranted or could the patient have been treated more efficiently as an outpatient?
DRGs 182 and 183 one-day stays (Maps to MS-DRGs 391, and 392)	Site of service—was an inpatient admission warranted or could the patient have been treated more efficiently as an outpatient?
DRGs 296 and 297 one-day stays (Maps to MS-DRGs 650, and 641)	Site of service—was an inpatient admission warranted or could the patient have been treated more efficiently as an outpatient?
DRG 014 (Maps to MS-DRGs 064, 065, and 066)	Correct assignment of principal diagnosis
DRG 079 (Maps to MS-DRG 177, 178, and 179)	Correct assignment of principal diagnosis—under close review are ICD-9-CM codes: 507.x, 482.83, and 482.89
DRG 089 (Maps to MS-DRGs 193, 194, and 195)	Correct assignment of principal diagnosis
DRGs 243 (Maps to MS-DRGs 551 and 552)	Site of service—was an inpatient admission warranted or could the patient have been treated more efficiently as an outpatient?
DRG 416 (Maps to MS-DRGs 870, 871, and 872)	Correct assignment of principal diagnosis—under close review is ICD-9-CM code 038.9
Seven-day readmit to same facility or elsewhere	Inappropriate admission or discharge, quality of care issues, or coding and/or billing errors. Under close review for billing errors are discharge destination codes
Complication/comorbidity (CC) pairs	Correct assignment of secondary diagnosis codes, adequate documentation to support secondary diagnosis codes
Three-day skilled nursing facility (SNF)-qualifying admissions	Inappropriate admission or discharge, quality of care issues, or coding and/or billing errors. Under close review for billing errors are discharge destination codes
Long-Term Hospitals	
Target Area	**Focus**
DRG 012 (Maps to MS-DRGs 056 and 057)	Correct assignment of principal diagnosis
DRG 087 (Maps to MS-DRG 189)	Correct assignment of principal diagnosis
DRG 088 (Maps to MS-DRGs 190, 191, and 192)	Correct assignment of principal diagnosis
DRG 249 (Maps to MS-DRGs 559, 560, and 561)	Correct assignment of principal diagnosis

that 4.4% of Medicare dollars paid did not comply with Medicare coverage, coding, billing, or payment rules. These improper payments totaled 10.8 billion dollars (CMS RAC Status Document, page 6).

Recovery Audit Contractors are charged with identifying underpayments and overpayments for claims filed under Medicare Part A and Part B. This includes claims where Medicare is the primary payer and those where Medicare is the secondary payer (MSP). Additionally, the Recovery Audit Contractors recoup overpayments from providers. For the first time, the MMA gave CMS the authority to pay RACs on a contingency basis. Therefore, RACs keep a percentage of the overpayments that they identify and collect as reimbursement for their contracted services. This allows CMS to add resources to the compliance section of the Medicare Program without adding additional cost.

The demonstration project began on March 28, 2005, and is scheduled to be in effect through March 27, 2008. The full project timeline is provided in figure 2.3. The targeted states are California, Florida, and New York—states with a large Medicare population. During the first year of the project, RACs were able to recoup 54.1 million dollars in overpayments, which was returned to the Medicare Trust Funds (CMS RAC Status Document, page 2). For example, one area of large overpayments was found to be DRG 217 – Wound Debridement and Skin Graft excluding Hand for Musculosketal and Connective Tissue Disease (DRG 217 crosswalks to MS-DRGs 463, 464, and 465 in FY 2008). RACs collected 13.9 million dollars in overpayments because the reported procedure code indicated that excisional debridement was performed, but the medical record documentation did not support the definition of code for that procedure (CMS RAC Status Document, page 16).

Even though RACs have only reported on their first year's experience, CMS is already indicating that RACs are a successful and cost-effective way to uncover improper payments and to assist CMS with creating corrective action plans aimed

Figure 2.3   Recovery Audit Contractor Demonstration Project Timeline (CMS RAC Status Document, page 11)

2005	January	CMS announces RAC Demonstration
		CMS releases Requests for Proposal for CA, FL, NY
	March 28	CMS signs contracts for Claim RACs in CA, FL, NY
		CMS signs contracts for MSP RACs in CA, FL
		3-year clock begins
	April	RACs start receiving claims from CMS
2006	January	RACs begin releasing significant overpayment notifications
	February 23	CMS signs contract for MSP RAC in NY
	September 30	CLOSE OF FY 2006
	November	CMS releases *FY 2006 RAC Status Document*
2007	September 30	CLOSE OF FY 2007
	November	CMS plans to release *FY 2007 RAC Status Document*
2008	March 27	**3-year demonstration ends**
	September	CMS plans to release *RAC Demonstration Report To Congress*
	September 30	CLOSE OF FY 2008
	November	CMS plans to release *FY 2008 RAC Status Document*

at preventing future improper payments. Healthcare professionals can monitor the progress of this demonstration project by reviewing reports found on the CMS Web site at: www.cms.hhs.gov/Demo ProjectsEvalRpts.

Coding Compliance Plan

Every coding unit should have a **coding compliance plan,** which is a component of the HIM department compliance plan and the overall corporate compliance plan at its facility. The plan should focus on the unique regulations and guidelines with which coding professionals must comply. As discussed previously, the Department of Health and Human Services has released several versions of the *Compliance Program Guidance* for various healthcare settings. The model provided by the OIG guidance is also applicable to individual coding units. Building a complete compliance plan is essential for establishing a solid coding team. The core areas of the coding compliance plan are policies and procedures, education and training, and auditing and monitoring.

Policies and Procedures

Well-designed and complete policies and procedures provide employees with consistent guidance to perform their assigned tasks. Without such guidance, employees may complete their tasks in different ways causing major confusion, inefficiencies, and possibly noncompliance. Managers should perform a job analysis to assure that every task has an established policy or procedure to govern it. Because coding has so many rules and official guidelines, it is critical that this section of the coding compliance plan be methodically compiled. Following is a far from exhaustive list of issues that should be included in a coding compliance plan:

- Physician query process

- Coding diagnoses not supported by medical documentation

- Upcoding (reporting services at a higher level than warranted)

- Unbundling (reporting multiple codes when only one is necessary)

- Coding medical records without complete documentation

- Assignment of discharge destination codes

- Correct use of encoding software

- Complete process for using scrubber software

Education and Training

A good education plan is essential to succeeding as a coding team. In order to be compliant, coding, billing, and reimbursement professionals must continuously participate in their education. Rules and regulations for public and private payers are released almost daily. Recognized means of communication of this vital information must be established in the coding compliance plan. A sample of issues that should be placed on the continuous education schedule includes:

- Public and private payer guidelines

- **Local Coverage Determinations (LCDs)** (LCDs replaced **Local Medical Review Policies [LMRPs]**)

- **National Coverage Determinations (NCDs)**

- Official Coding Guidelines for ICD-9-CM, CPT, and HCPCS Level II codes

- Quarterly and yearly code changes

- Quarterly and yearly prospective payment system changes

- **OIG Workplan** issues

- **National Correct Coding Initiative (NCCI)**

Special attention should be paid to the work of new coders. Every coding manager must assess a new employee's compliance level and degree of understanding. Education must be provided to bring deficient coders up to speed with expected guidelines. Completion of required educational sessions should be built into annual evaluations/reviews for all coding, billing, and reimbursement employees.

Auditing and Monitoring

Managers must be diligent at auditing and monitoring compliance in the coding unit. During the auditing phase, the coding manager gathers information on the department's compliance with policies and procedures. Incorporating internal and external auditing into the coding compliance plan has proven to be the best strategy. Internal auditing enables managers to see first-hand where their unit's strengths and weaknesses lie. External auditing provides an unbiased view of the department's performance. Together, internal and external audits help coding managers build effective education plans for their units.

Two forms of **benchmarking** can help a manager determine the staff's level of compliance: internal and external benchmarking. Internal benchmarking or trending allows the manager to examine reporting rates over a period of time. This exercise enables the manager to pinpoint the specific time period within which a compliance issue arose. External benchmarking or peer comparison helps a manager to know how his or her team has performed compared to their peers. Issues revealed, for example, include whether its **case mix index (CMI)** level puts the facility at risk. Benchmarking will help establish reasonable parameters to follow. Target areas for internal and external benchmarking should correlate with those highlighted in the policies and procedures and education and training sections of the coding compliance plan along with problem areas identified during routine internal and external audits.

Focus Areas

Establishing good focus areas takes a considerable amount of research by the coding manager. Managers must stay up-to-date on compliance issues that are published and discussed in various government and other third party payer documents. For example, the OIG Workplan should be reviewed each year. This document provides insight into the directions the OIG is taking as well as highlighting hot areas of compliance. Below are four case studies that show how a manager can use auditing results along with internal and external benchmarking to monitor compliance.

Case Mix Index Analysis

Analyzing the growth or decline of a facility's case mix index (CMI) is the beginning phase for assessing the quality of its coding and billing practices. Managers begin by comparing the CMI of the facility to that of its peers and the state or nation for the last three years. Questions posed include:

- Is the CMI steady?
- Does it increase steadily or drastically?
- Is there a sharp or sudden decline?

To explore the analysis issues, consider data for a medium size (250–400 beds), not-for-profit facility (Hospital A), its peer facilities, and the nation. Peer facilities included in this example are local hospitals with which this facility competes for market share. Figure 2.4 displays CMI trend over a three year study period.

Clearly, this facility's CMI has increased at a much greater rate than the national average or that of its peers. Additionally, figure 2.5 shows that hospital A's CMI is greater than that of the nation and its peers. So not only has its CMI increased at a fast pace but it is also the highest in this data set.

Figure 2.4.   CMI—Three year study period

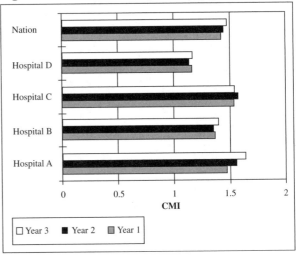

Figure 2.5.   CMI percent change—From year 1 to year 3

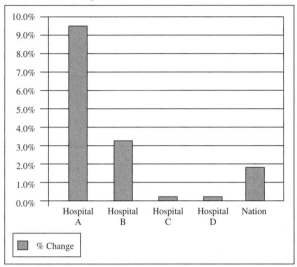

Figure 2.6.   MDC 05 CMI trend—Three year study period

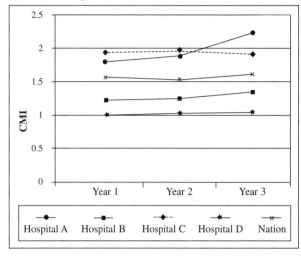

What has caused this major shift? The facility can now drill down to the **major diagnostic category (MDC)** level in order to pinpoint noteworthy changes at the service area level.

Figure 2.6 shows that the CMI for MDC 05, Diseases of the Circulatory System, increased greatly during the three-year study period (15.7 percent). What has caused this increase? One cannot tell from the data alone. However, by performing a thorough investigation, the issue(s) can be identified. Several areas to consider include:

- Coding and billing errors
- Changes in DRG assignments
- Equipment purchases
- New or expanded service areas
- Acquisition of new facilities
- Changes in physician personnel

Regardless of the root cause of the data deviations, compliance with established rules and regulations must be verified. If coding practices are questionable, a medical record review should be completed to identify whether a compliance infraction has occurred. Managers should follow established procedures for correcting and reporting a compliance lapse. This exercise can also be completed for the facility's outpatient **service mix index (SMI).**

DRG Relationships Reporting
Within the MS-DRG system, there are MS-DRGs that have a relationship or similar grouping methodology to other MS-DRGs. For example, MS-DRG sets exist where the listings of diagnoses used to drive the grouping are the same, but the presence or absence of a **complication** or **comorbidity (CC)** diagnosis or major complication or comorbidity (MCC) diagnosis assigns the case to a higher or lower MS-DRG. MS-DRG sets may contain two MS-DRGs or three MS-DRGs. These MS-DRG relationships and sets pose a compliance concern because the medical record documentation used to support the coding of principal diagnosis, complications, and comorbidities may not always be clear or used appropriately by the coder. Therefore, inaccurate coding can lead to incorrect MS-DRG assignment and thus inappropriate reimbursement.

Example:

Included in many Medicare and third payer audits is the comparison of the the reporting rates of simple pneumonia with complication(s) or comorbidity(ies) versus simple pneumonia without complication(s) or comorbidity(ies). MS-DRG 193, Simple Pneumonia & Pleurisy with MCC, has a higher relative weight than the other DRGs in this relationship and should be closely monitored. (See table 2.10.) MS-DRGs became effective on October 1, 2007. Hospital reporting of MCCs will be closely monitored to ensure that all coding rules and regulations have been followed. Further the medical record documentation will be scrutinized to ensure that it is adequate for coding purposes. Reporting MS-DRG 193 at a higher rate than warranted will cause the facility to receive reimbursement of which it is not entitled, creating non-compliance.

Again, hospital A is a medium size, not-for-profit facility and the peer facilities are local hospitals. Figure 2.7 compares hospital A's reporting rate for the MS-DRG 193 relationship group to its peers and state for the study period. Hospital A's reporting rate, 31 percent, is much higher than the state average and that of all of its peers. It is clear that a medical record review is warranted to determine if inaccurate coding practices are the root cause of the reporting differences. Medical records assigned to MS-DRG 193 should be reviewed to determine whether the assignment of this MS-DRG is supported through documentation in the medical record. Again, established procedures for compliance issues should be followed.

Table 2.10.   DRG 193 relationship set

MS-DRG Number	DRG Title	FY 2005 Relative Weight
193	Simple Pneumonia & Pleurisy with MCC	1.2505
194	Simple Pneumonia & Pleurisy with CC	1.0235
195	Simple Pneumonia & Pleurisy without MCC/CC	0.8398

Figure 2.7.   Percent assigned to MS-DRG 193

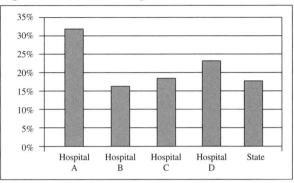

Poor documentation identified during the intensive medical record review should be addressed with the medical staff and incorrect code assignments should be immediately discussed with the coding staff.

Site of Service: Inpatient versus Outpatient
The following example illustrates the concept of a site-of-service review focused on MS-DRGs prone to compliance problems.

Example:

Several DRGs are under a site-of-service review by QIOs. Documentation and admission criteria are reviewed to determine whether the inpatient setting is the most efficient and effective treatment area for patients. One focus area is DRG 243, Medical Back Problems (Maps to MS-DRGs 551 and 552).

Compliance investigators examine the reporting rates for DRG 243 at one facility. Hospital A is a medium size, not-for-profit facility. Analysis of figure 2.8 shows the reporting rate for DRG 243 or the percent of DRG 243 cases to total discharges for the facility in the study period. Hospital A reported DRG 243 at a much higher rate than its peers and the nation.

Compliance investigators next examine whether this is a trend or a new risk area. Figure 2.9 displays the reporting rate for DRG 243 for a three-year period for hospital A. The data shows that DRG 243 has been reported at a significantly high level for the past three years, peaking in year 2 of the study period.

Figure 2.8.   DRG 243 reporting rate

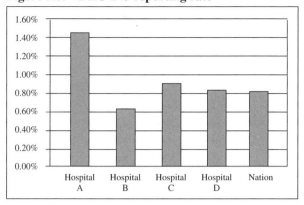

**Figure 2.10.   Hospital A LOS distribution
for DRG 243**

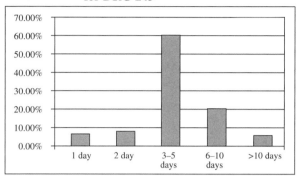

Figure 2.9.   Hospital A reporting trend DRG 243

Because this DRG is under close review due to site-of-service questions, the coding manager should also review the **length of stay (LOS)** for this DRG. Do the majority of cases follow the **average length of stay (ALOS)** for this DRG or is there a much lower LOS? A lower LOS could indicate that the patients could have been treated as outpatients rather than inpatients. The average length of stay for DRG 243 at hospital A in year three of the study period was 4.73. The national ALOS for DRG 243 is 4.5. The data shows the hospital A's LOS is consistent with what is expected for patients grouping to this DRG.

However, examiners look more deeply and examine the frequency of LOS values for DRG 243. Figure 2.10 displays the LOS distribution for DRG 243 in the study period. Again, the data shows that the LOS reporting for this DRG is consistent with the national expected ALOS. Investigators review encounters in the one-day stay category to verify that admission criteria and medical necessity were met. After drill-down analysis, it appears that this DRG is being appropriately reported at this facility. However, if other DRGs show deviation, they should be investigated by a **Utilization Review Committee** consisting of representatives from HIM, Quality, Utilization, and Medical Staff. Together this interdisciplinary team can determine whether the site or service was appropriate for the encounters under review.

*Evaluation and Management Facility Coding
in the Emergency Department*

The implementation of the **Hospital Outpatient Prospective Payment System (HOPPS)** has brought about new compliance challenges for hospitals. One area under review is Evaluation and Management (E/M) coding. Since the CPT code reported on a Medicare outpatient claim drives the **ambulatory payment classification (APC)** assignment and hence the level of reimbursement, the code assignment should be closely monitored. Currently each facility determines its hospital-specific criteria for level of service determination. Therefore, auditing is necessary to validate that the levels are correctly assigned based on the established criteria and that the criteria are reflective of resource consumption experienced at that facility for the services rendered. (See table 2.11.)

Table 2.11.   E/M Emergency department CPT codes and APC groupings (CY 2008)

	99281	99282	99283	99284	99285
APC Group	0609—Level 1 Emergency Visit	0613—Level 2 Emergency Visit	0614—Level 3 Emergency Visit	0615—Level 4 Emergency Visit	0616—Level 5 Emergency Visit
APC Relative Weight	0.7970	1.3137	2.0750	3.3377	4.9535
APC Payment (unadjusted)	$50.76	$83.67	$132.17	$212.59	$315.51

Example:

Code distribution may be compared among a medium size not-for-profit hospital, two peer facilities, and the nation. Figure 2.11 shows the E/M code distribution during the study period. The data shows that hospital A reported codes 99284 and 99285 (high-level emergency department visits) at a much higher percentage than hospital C and the nation. CMS has suggested that Emergency Department APC distribution should follow somewhat of a bell-curved shape. Clearly, hospital A deviates far from this configuration.

Again, it is important to examine the trend for hospital A. Figure 2.12 displays a trending graph for the past four years. The data show that hospital A's reporting of higher level E/M codes has increased from 25 percent of the total cases in year one to 80% of total cases in year four. This drastic increase in the reporting of levels 4 and 5 EM codes should be addressed by this facility. A medical record audit should be performed to verify that medical record documentation supports the assignment of these higher level CPT codes.

Check Your Understanding 2.2

1. The new coding assistant at the Glen Ellyn Medical Group office coded and submitted a claim to Blue Cross for an initial evaluation and management office visit when in fact the patient was established with the practice and was seen strictly for a follow-up medical check. The resulting error was an example of _____.

Figure 2.11.   E/M code distribution

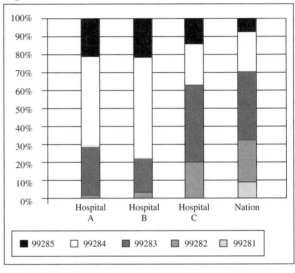

Figure 2.12.   Hospital A E/M distribution trend—Four year study period

2. All of the following are efforts to fight healthcare fraud and abuse **except:**
   a. Operation Restore Trust
   b. Medicare Integrity Program
   c. Tax Equity and Fiscal Responsibility Act of 1982 (TEFRA)
   d. Medicare and Medicaid Patient and Program Protection Act of 1987

3. What are the core areas of the coding compliance plan?

4. Audit data has demonstrated that when coding managers conduct internal audits of coding quality, they do not require external audits to build effective coding compliance plans. True or false?

5. In MS-DRG relationships reporting, MS-DRG sets are examined for _____.

Summary

Compliance is directly related to hospital reimbursement. The rules and regulations of public and private third party payers must be strictly followed to ensure that facilities receive reimbursement for which they are entitled. Good compliance practices not only reduce payment errors but also establish coding and billing diligence that leads to more focused employees. Compliance awareness is heightened through education and fostering higher-skilled employees who perform their job functions accurately and efficiently.

Chapter 2 Review Quiz

For questions 1, 2, and 3, match each coding system on the left with its description of uses on the right.

1. ICD-9-CM   ____ a. Medical and surgical supplies

2. HCPCS Level II ____ b. Physician inpatient or outpatient procedures

3. CPT   ____ c. Diagnoses and inpatient procedures

4. Common forms of fraud and abuse include all of the following **except:**
   a. Upcoding
   b. Unbundling
   c. Refiling claims after denials
   d. Billing for services not furnished to patients

5. Name and describe three of the seven OIG elements of an effective compliance plan.

6. Name the legislation that created Medicare Summary Notices and describe their use.

7. What is the focus of quality improvement organizations (QIOs), and how do they help to improve quality?

8. What are three target areas of the First-look Analysis Tool for Hospital Outlier Monitoring (FATHOM) software?

9. What version of the OIG Statement of Work/Scope of Work is being used, and when will it expire?

10. What HHS tool is available for healthcare providers to use in developing coding, HIM, and corporate compliance plans?

11. For what can a manager use internal benchmarking (trending)?

12. What resource can managers use to discover current hot areas of compliance?

13. What is the primary use of a case mix index analysis?

14. How do QIOs use site-of-service reviews?

15. What payment approach has created new compliance challenges related to E/M coding of emergency department services?

16. The International Classification of Diseases (ICD) is maintained by the American Medical Association. True or false?

17. CPT Category I codes include sections for Radiology and Medicine. True or false?

18. HCPCS Level II temporary codes may be replaced with permanent codes. True or false?

19. When the 8th SOW was implemented in August 2005, the Hospital Payment Monitoring Program ended. True or false?

References and Bibliography

American Hospital Association. 2004. AHA Central Office. www.hospitalconnect.com.

American Medical Association. 2005. *Current Procedural Terminology.* Chicago: American Medical Association.

American Medical Association. 2004. AMA Web page. www.ama-assn.org.

American Medical Association. 1989 to 2005. *CPT Assistant.* Chicago: American Medical Association.

Beebe, M., 2003. CPT Category III codes cover new, emerging technologies: New codes developed to address issues in light of HIPAA. *Journal of American Health Information Management Association* 74(9): 84–85.

Centers for Medicare and Medicaid Services. 2004a. Healthcare Common Procedure Coding System (HCPCS). www.cms.hhs.gov/medicare/hcpcs.

Centers for Medicare and Medicaid Services. 2004b. Fighting fraud and abuse. www.cms.hhs.gov/providers/fraud.

Centers for Medicare and Medicaid Services. 2005 (April 7). Medicare takes major step toward improving quality of care. www.cms.hhs.gov/media/press/release.asp.

Centers for Medicare and Medicaid Service. 2006 (November 22). Status on the Use of Recovery Audit Contractors (RACs) in the Medicare Program. www.cms.hhs.gov/DemoProjectsEvalRpts.

Centers for Medicare and Medicaid Services. 2006. CMS RAC status document: Status report on the use of RACs in the Medicare Program. www.cms.hhs.gov/RAC/.

Centers for Medicare and Medicaid Service. 2007. Crosswalk from CMS DRGs to MS-DRGs. http://www.cms.hhs.gov/AcuteInpatientPPS/FFD/.

Centers for Medicare and Medicaid Services. 2007. Comprehensive error rate testing. www.cms.hhs.gov/cert.

Department of Health and Human Services. 2005 (January 31). OIG supplemental compliance program guidance for hospitals. *Federal Register* 70 (19): 4858–4876.

Estrella, Rento. 2003, What happened to PEPP? QIOs plan for hospital payment monitoring program. *Journal of American Health Information Management Association* 74(7):43–48.

First Coast Service Options, Inc.1999, *Medicare Fraud & Abuse: A Practical Guide of Proactive Measures to Avoid Becoming a Victim.* Health Care Financing Administration.

KePRO. 2004. www.ohiokepro.com/providers/casereview/hpmp.asp.

KePRO. 2005. *A User Guide to PEPPER.* Available online from www.ohiokepro.com/providers/hospital/telemats/PepperFINAL.pdf .

KePRO. 2005. PEPPER: The Program for Evaluating Payment Patterns Electronic Report. Available online from www.ohiokepro.com/providers/hospital/events.asp#.

LaTour, K., and S. Eichenwald, eds. 2002. *Health Information Management: Concepts, Principles, and Practice.* Chicago: American Health Information Management Association.

Office of the Inspector General. 1991. (www.oig.hhs.gov/fraud/complianceguidance.html)

Schraffenberger, L. A., ed. 2005. *Effective Management of Coding Services.* Chicago: American Health Information Management Association.

Texas Medical Foundation. 2007. PEPPER Overview. Available online from www.tmf.org/pepper/st/index.htm.

Chapter Appendix
Standards for Ethical Coding

In this era of payment based on diagnostic and procedural coding, the professional ethics of health information coding professionals continue to be challenged. A conscientious goal for coding and maintaining a quality database is accurate clinical and statistical data. The following standards of ethical coding, developed by AHIMA's Coding Policy and Strategy Committee and approved by AHIMA's Board of Directors, are offered to guide coding professionals in this process.

1. Coding professionals are expected to support the importance of accurate, complete, and consistent coding practices for the production of quality healthcare data.

2. Coding professionals in all healthcare settings should adhere to the *ICD-9-CM (International Classification of Diseases, 9th revision, Clinical Modification)* coding conventions, official coding guidelines approved by the Cooperating Parties,* the CPT *(Current Procedural Terminology)* rules established by the American Medical Association, and any other official coding rules and guidelines established for use with mandated standard code sets. Selection and sequencing of diagnoses and procedures must meet the definitions of required data sets for applicable healthcare settings.

3. Coding professionals should use their skills, their knowledge of currently mandated coding and classification systems, and official resources to select the appropriate diagnostic and procedural codes.

4. Coding professionals should only assign and report codes that are clearly and consistently supported by physician documentation in the health record.

5. Coding professionals should consult physicians for clarification and additional documentation prior to code assignment when there is conflicting or ambiguous data in the health record.

6. Coding professionals should not change codes or the narratives of codes on the billing abstract so that meanings are misrepresented. Diagnoses or procedures should not be inappropriately included or excluded because payment or insurance policy coverage requirements will be affected. When individual payer policies conflict with official coding rules and guidelines, these policies should be obtained in writing whenever possible. Reasonable efforts should be made to educate the payer on proper coding practices in order to influence a change in the payer's policy.

---

*The Cooperating Parties are the American Health Information Management Association, American Hospital Association, Health Care Financing Administration, and National Center for Health Statistics. All rights reserved. Reprint and quote only with proper reference to AHIMA's authorship.

7. Coding professionals, as members of the healthcare team, should assist and educate physicians and other clinicians by advocating proper documentation practices, further specificity, and resequencing or inclusion of diagnoses or procedures when needed to more accurately reflect the acuity, severity, and the occurrence of events.

8. Coding professionals should participate in the development of institutional coding policies and should ensure that coding policies complement, not conflict with, official coding rules and guidelines.

9. Coding professionals should maintain and continually enhance their coding skills, as they have a professional responsibility to stay abreast of changes in codes, coding guidelines, and regulations.

10. Coding professionals should strive for optimal payment to which the facility is legally entitled, remembering that it is unethical and illegal to maximize payment by means that contradict regulatory guidelines.

Revised 12/99

Article citation:

American Health Information Management Association. "Standards of Ethical Coding." *Journal of AHIMA* 71, no.3 (2000): insert after p. 8.

Chapter 3
Voluntary Healthcare Insurance Plans

Objectives

- To differentiate major types of voluntary healthcare insurance plans

- To define basic language associated with reimbursement by commercial healthcare insurance plans and by Blue Cross and Blue Shield plans

- To explain common models and policies of payment for commercial healthcare insurance plans and for Blue Cross and Blue Shield plans

Key Terms

Actual charge
Adverse selection
Allowable charge
Benefit
Benefit cap
Catastrophic expense limit
Certificate holder
Claim
Coinsurance
Coordination of benefit
Copayment
Cost-sharing
Covered condition
Covered service
Creditable coverage
Credited coverage
Deductible
Defensive medicine
Dependent
Endorsement
Evidence of insurability
Exclusion
Explanation of benefits (EOB)
Formulary
Guarantor
Indemnity health insurance

Insured
Late enrollee
Limitation
Maximum out-of-pocket cost
Medical emergency
Medical necessity
Member
Moral hazard
Out-of-pocket
Policy
Policyholder
Precertification
Pre-existing condition
Premiums
Primary insurer (payer)
Prior approval
Rider
Risk pool
Secondary insurer (payer)
Stop-loss benefit
Subscriber
Supplemental insurance
Underwriting
Usual, customary, and reasonable (UCR)
Waiting period

Voluntary Healthcare Insurance

Voluntary health insurance (VHI) is the umbrella term that includes private or commercial healthcare insurance plans and Blue Cross and Blue Shield plans. Voluntary health insurance is private and denotes employment (Koch 2002, 96). VHI is differentiated from social health insurance and public welfare. Social health insurance comprises government programs based on current or past employment. Public welfare is assistance to categories of low-income people or other defined subpopulations.

Payments from voluntary health insurance plans account for approximately 33 percent of healthcare expenditures in the United States (Koch 2002, 94). Therefore, understanding this form of healthcare insurance is integral to understanding healthcare reimbursement.

Types of Voluntary Healthcare Insurance

This chapter investigates two major categories of voluntary health insurance—private or commercial healthcare insurance plans and Blue Cross and Blue Shield plans—organized in three classifications as illustrated in figure 3.1.

Private/Commercial Healthcare Insurance Plans

The first major category is private or commercial healthcare insurance, which contains two classifications: employer-based healthcare insurance plans and private healthcare insurance plans. Employer-based healthcare insurance plans are also termed "group plans." Private healthcare insurance is also known as "individual insurance."

Figure 3.1. Three classifications of voluntary healthcare insurance

Commercial (Private*) Individual (Private*) Healthcare Insurance Plan
Commercial (Private*) Employer-Based Healthcare Insurance Plan
Blue Cross and Blue Shield Plans

*Private is used two ways in the healthcare insurance industry:
(1) as a synonym for commercial healthcare insurance and (2) meaning purchased by an individual rather than by an employer for a group.

Differentiating the two classifications of private or commercial healthcare insurance is the size of the **risk pool.** A risk pool is a group of individual entities, such as individual persons, employers, or associations, whose healthcare costs are combined for evaluating financial history and experience, determining **premiums** (periodic payment for health insurance), or both (American Academy of Actuaries 2006, 2). There are three types of pools:

- Large-employer pools—employees of one employer, typically 1,000 **members** or more. These pools are large and diverse (heterogeneous).

- Multiple-employer pools— employees from several mid-size employers or small employers or groups of associations. These pools are smaller and less diverse than the large-employer pools.

- Individual pools—these are pools of individuals, such as self-employed people or people who work for companies that do not offer healthcare insurance. The people in these pools are similar because they are all seeking health insurance. Thus, these pools tend to be the least diverse or most homogeneous of the three types. (American Academy of Actuaries 2006, 2–4).

The diversity of the large-employer pools in terms of age, sex, and health status provides stable trends in utilization and financial impact. A key point is that the larger the pool, the more able the pool is to balance a wide variety of risks (from healthy persons to persons with chronic conditions or catastrophic illnesses). The risk is distributed across more entities. Because smaller pools do not provide a sufficiently wide range of diversity, health insurance is underwritten on an individual basis (American Academy of Actuaries 2006, 3). **Underwriting** is the process of identifying and classifying individuals' or groups' risk. The impact of underwriting on an individual basis may be higher premiums because of health status or denial of coverage for a family member (American Academy of Actuaries 2006, 3–4).

Therefore, employer-based healthcare insurance plans are called "group plans" because of the types of risk pools, large-employer or multiple-employer pools. Private healthcare insurance plans are also known as "individual insurance" because the pool is at the individual level and underwritten at the individual level.

Blue Cross and Blue Shield Plans

The second major category and the third classification in itself are the Blue Cross and Blue Shield plans. Historically, for-profit status differentiated private or commercial healthcare insurance from Blue Cross and Blue Shield plans. Private or commercial healthcare insurance companies were for-profit and Blue Cross and Blue Shield plans were not-for-profit. However, although commercial healthcare insurance companies continue to be for-profit, some Blue Cross and Blue Shield plans also converted to for-profit status from not-for-profit between 1993 and 2002 (Hall and Conover 2003, 510). These conversions blurred the distinction between commercial healthcare insurance companies and Blue Cross and Blue Shield plans.

Confusing Terminology

In this discussion, there are three potential areas of confusion arising because members of the healthcare industry give the same word different meanings in different contexts:

- The word private is used two ways in the healthcare insurance industry. First, the term is sometimes used as a synonym for commercial healthcare insurance. Second, the term is sometimes used to denote healthcare insurance purchased by an individual versus healthcare insurance purchased by an employer for a group of employees.

- Commercial healthcare insurance plans and Blue Cross and Blue Shield plans often have multiple divisions that offer options both to private individuals and to employers. For example, both Aetna and Blue Cross and Blue Shield of Florida have healthcare insurance plans for individuals and families and for groups of employees. Consequently, the classifications overlap through these diversified offerings.

- The word *individual* is used to mean "non-group" and also to mean "no **dependents.**"

Healthcare insurance companies sell healthcare plans to both individuals and groups of people. Individual (nongroup) plans are usually more expensive than are group plans. Also, healthcare insurance companies allow people to purchase healthcare coverage for their spouses and other family members (known as dependent or family coverage) for additional premiums. Persons who do not purchase the family coverage have individual (single) coverage or an individual plan.

Healthcare professionals must be careful to differentiate how these words are used and in what context. Finally, and most importantly, classification of a healthcare insurance plan depends upon the provisions of the healthcare insurance plan and how the plan functions, rather than its name.

Provisions and Functioning of Healthcare Insurance Plans

Prior to the 1970s, almost all voluntary health insurance was **indemnity health insurance.** Indemnity healthcare insurance plans are also called retrospective fee-for-service, as described in Chapter 1. In indemnity health insurance plans, the health insurance company pays a predetermined percentage of the cost of healthcare services and the **guarantor** pays the remaining percentage. For example, an individual (guarantor) might pay 20 percent for services and the health insurance company pays 80 percent. The providers define the fees for services, and those fees vary from physician to physician. Indemnity health plans offer individuals the freedom to choose their healthcare professionals.

Healthcare insurance companies assume the financial risk of the costs of individual and group healthcare. Healthcare insurance companies assume this risk because individuals or groups purchase the insurance companies' healthcare plans. The purchasers of healthcare plans are **policyholders** or **insureds.** If an employer or association purchases the healthcare insurance, the entity is the *group policyholder* and the employees or association members receive certificates of insurance coverage and, thus, are **certificate holders** or **subscribers.** Spouses and other family members of the policyholders are known as dependents. Policyholders pay higher premiums for dependent coverage than for single coverage. In addition to premiums, policyholders also pay **deductibles, coinsurance,** and **copayments** as provided in the **policy.**

Contracts formalize the relationship between the healthcare insurance companies and the individuals or groups for whom the companies are assuming the risk. These contracts are healthcare insurance policies. In the policies, the healthcare insurance companies promise to pay for the healthcare expenses of the policyholders and dependents. Healthcare insurance companies issue policies to individuals or groups who purchase the healthcare plan. The policies stipulate all aspects of healthcare for which the healthcare plan will pay (**covered conditions).** Healthcare services related to covered conditions are **covered services** for which the plan will pay.

Although the term *healthcare services* is used throughout this text, some sectors of the healthcare industry are more specific in their usage of terms. Medical services (care) include diagnostic and therapeutic measures provided to persons who are sick, injured, or concerned about their health status. Healthcare services expand medical services to include preventative care (Rowell 2000, 22).

Sections of a Healthcare Insurance Policy

Healthcare insurance policies are divided into sections. Typically, these sections include definitions (commonly used terms), eligibility and enrollment, **benefits, limitations, exclusions,** procedures, and appeals processes. The sections build upon one another and one aspect of healthcare may be addressed in multiple sections. Because the sections interlock, reviewing multiple sections is often necessary to determine whether the healthcare insurance company will pay for (cover) a specific diagnostic procedure, treatment, or healthcare expense.

Definitions

Definitions are often in a separate section, but they may also be incorporated into the benefits section.

Example:

Definitions are important. The healthcare plan of the state of North Carolina defines **medical necessity** as follows:

> A service or supply provided for the diagnosis, treatment, cure, or relief of a health condition, illness, injury, or disease. The service or supply must not be experimental, investigational, or cosmetic in purpose. It must be necessary for and appropriate to the diagnosis, treatment, cure, or relief of a health condition, illness, injury, disease, or its symptoms. It must be within generally accepted standards of medical care in the community. It must not be solely for the convenience of the insured, the insured's family, or the provider (State Health Plan for North Carolina 2005, 7).

Thus, by definition, cosmetic services are not considered medically necessary and, therefore, would not be paid for by the healthcare insurance company.

Definitions sometimes are specific to the healthcare plan and may be more restrictive than ones in everyday usage or dictionaries. For example, a dictionary definition of *emergency* is "an unexpected situation or sudden occurrence of a serious and urgent nature that demands immediate attention" (Pickett et al. 2000). The healthcare insurance plan may define *emergency* as life-threatening, a concept that is more extreme and less likely than demanding immediate attention. Terms often listed in definitions include the following:

- Accidental injury
- **Medical emergency**
- Medical necessity
- **Prior approval**
- **Pre-existing condition**
- **Usual, customary, and reasonable**

Eligibility and Enrollment

Eligibility and enrollment sections specify the persons eligible for healthcare insurance and the procedures for obtaining coverage. Eligibility often involves the percentage of the appointment or position or duration of employment. A common provision is that persons must be employed at least 50 percent or half-time (0.5 full-time equivalent). Enrollment is the process of becoming a policyholder or certificate holder. A common step of the procedure is the application for healthcare insurance. There are specific times when applications are received and processed. Common requirements for enrollment include application within 30 days of hire to obtain initial coverage and during certain months, such as October or November, to change healthcare plans or coverage. During enrollment periods, new insureds specify whether the coverage will be single or family.

Benefits

Benefits are the healthcare services for which the healthcare insurance company will pay (will cover). Benefits may include the following services:

- Healthcare services provided by physicians, allied health practitioners, and visiting nurses

- Confinement in an acute care hospital, long-term care hospital, partial day center, specialty hospital, and nursing home, including necessary services, supplies, and medications
- Inpatient and outpatient surgeries and associated anesthesia services
- Emergency room, physician office visits, home healthcare, mental health and chemical dependency care, vision and dental care, laboratory tests, x-rays, and other radiologic procedures and treatments
- Rental or purchase of durable medical equipment (DME), prosthetic and orthotic appliances, prescriptions, medical supplies, and blood transfusions and administration
- Emergency transport services
- **Stop-loss benefits.**

For example, a stop-loss benefit is designed to provide coverage in the event of a catastrophic illness or injury. A stop-loss benefit is a specific amount, in a certain time frame, such as one year, beyond which all covered healthcare services for that policyholder or dependent are paid at 100 percent by the healthcare insurance plan. This benefit is also known as the **maximum out-of-pocket cost** and the **catastrophic expense limit.** The total is the maximum amount that the policyholder will pay **out-of-pocket** for covered healthcare services in the specified period. Included in the total may be deductibles, coinsurance, and copayments that the policyholder is responsible to pay out-of-pocket. Specific total amounts per year may vary, by category, such as $1,500 maximum in coinsurance and $2,500 maximum in prescription copayments per year.

Often the insureds may purchase differing levels of these benefits in policies. The levels vary widely in the range of services they cover. Premiums, deductibles, coinsurances, and copayments range accordingly, as can be seen in the following examples:

- Comprehensive policies provide coverage for most healthcare services, including hospitalization, surgery, emergency room, physician services, clinic visits, diagnostic and therapeutic x-rays, laboratory tests, preventive services, and prescriptions. The deductible must be met before the health-care insurance company will pay for any covered expenses. Coinsurance for all covered expenses must be paid until the maximum out-of-pocket cost is reached. Additional covered expenses are paid in full.

- Hospital and surgical policies cover major expenses in the hospital and expenses related to surgeries, including outpatient surgery. Healthcare insurance payments may be percentages or specific dollar amounts. Hospitalization policies typically have high deductibles and high coverage limits.

- Major medical (catastrophic) policies are designed to reduce risk associated with catastrophic illness or injury. A fixed amount is available during the lifetime of the policyholder or dependent. Major medical policies typically have high deductibles and high coverage limits.

- Hospital confinement indemnity policies pay a per diem for each day in the hospital. This policy is typically in addition to comprehensive policies, hospital and surgical policies, or major medical policies.

- Long-term (extended) care policies provide benefits for nursing home care and services.

- Disability income protection policies provide weekly or monthly payments during a lengthy illness or recovery from an injury. Disability income protection policies only begin to pay after a period established in the contract (30 days to 6 months). Contracts usually contain maximum payment limits that are based on a percentage of the policyholder's salary, such as 60 percent.

- Accidental death and dismemberment (loss) policies cover expenses due to an accident that causes a loss, such as death, amputation of a limb, or blindness. Benefits vary greatly dependent upon the specific policy.

- Specific disease or accident policies provide coverage for diseases or accidents listed in the policy. An example is a cancer policy.

- Medicare supplement (Medigap) policies are designed to coordinate payments with those by Medicare. These policies may pay Medicare deductibles and coinsurance. Benefits vary by policy.

- Other **supplemental insurance** policies fill in (supplement) gaps in comprehensive policies, hospital and surgical policies, and major medical policies. The previously listed long-term policies, disability income protection policies, accidental death or dismemberment policies, and specific disease or accident policies are common examples. Another example is a short-term health insurance policy purchased for the period of a vacation, travel, or trip. Supplemental policies provide cash benefits; cover deductibles, coinsurances, copayments; or other forms of payment. Patients and guarantors often use the additional funds to pay incidental costs associated with healthcare, such as travel, lodging, meals, and daycare.

Limitations

Limitations are qualifications or other specifications that limit the extent of the benefits. Limitations can be placed on total dollar amount, time frame, duration, and number. For example, purchases of durable medical equipment exceeding $500 require prior approval. Some healthcare insurance plans limit the number of well-visit checks to three per year for children ages one through two.

Cost-Sharing Provisions

Other common limitations are **cost-sharing** provisions of policies. Cost-sharing provisions require policyholders to bear some of the costs of healthcare that they consume. Making policyholders bear some of the financial burden of healthcare is a mechanism to control healthcare costs. Examples of cost-sharing provisions include the following:

- Coinsurance is a pre-established percentage of eligible expenses after the deductible has been met. The percentage may vary by type or site of service.

- Copayment is a fixed dollar amount (flat fee). The fixed amount may vary by type of service, such as a visit or a prescription. For example, the healthcare plan may require that the policyholder pay $15 per outpatient clinic visit and $50 per outpatient surgery visit.

Use of Formulary

The use of a **formulary** is another limitation. A formulary is a list of preferred drugs. Formularies often contain both brand-name and generic drugs approved by the Food and Drug Administration. Although a policy's prescription benefit may cover drugs not in the formulary, the policyholder's cost-sharing for nonformulary products may be higher. Policies may also require higher cost-sharing contributions for nongeneric drugs (table 3.1).

Table 3.1.   Example of limitations in prescription drug benefit

Prescription Drug	Copayment per Prescription for 34-Day Supply
Tier 1: Generic	$10
Tier 2: Formulary without Generic	$25
Tier 3: Formulary with Generic	$35
Tier 4: Non-Formulary	$40

Benefit Cap

A **benefit cap** is an overarching limitation. A benefit cap is also known as a maximum dollar plan limit. A benefit cap is the total dollar amount that a healthcare insurance company will pay for a policyholder and each covered dependent for covered healthcare services during a specified period, such as a year or lifetime. Benefit caps vary by the levels of benefits that are purchased. Inexpensive healthcare insurance policies tend to have low caps, such as $250,000 per individual. Two common lifetime benefit caps, depending upon the specific policy, are $1 million per individual or $5 million per individual.

Exclusions

Exclusions are situations, instances, conditions, injuries, or treatments that the healthcare plan states will not be covered and for which the healthcare plan will pay no benefits. A synonym for exclusion is impairment **rider.** Specific and unique definitions may serve as exclusions. Typical exclusions include:

- Experimental or investigational diagnostic and therapeutic procedures

- Medically unnecessary diagnostic or therapeutic procedures

- Procedures related to pre-existing conditions (states), self-inflicted injury, sexually transmitted diseases, war-related injuries, and cosmetic procedures.

For example, a healthcare plan may deny coverage for a prescription to remove wrinkles (tretinoin) because the purpose is cosmetic. Contraceptives are also sometimes excluded. Coverage for experimental or investigational services is also often denied. Examples of experimental or investigational procedures include face transplants, medications used to treat conditions for which the Food and Drug Administration has not approved them, and cold therapy units with mechanical pumps and portable refrigerators.

A pre-existing condition (state) is a health condition, status, or injury that has been diagnosed prior to the application for healthcare insurance. Exclusions for pre-existing conditions are prevalent and, therefore, require detailed discussion. Healthcare insurance plans deny coverage for costs related to pre-existing conditions for pre-established periods of time.

The pre-established period of time during which healthcare insurance plans may deny coverage for pre-existing conditions is known as the **waiting period.** Under the Health Insurance Portability and Accountability Act (HIPAA), an employer-based group healthcare insurance plan can impose a waiting period for a pre-existing condition only if the employee or dependent was diagnosed, received care or treatment, or had care

or treatment recommended in the six months before the enrollment date. For group healthcare insurance, the maximum duration of the waiting period cannot exceed twelve months (eighteen months for **late enrollees** who applied after the earliest date on which coverage was available). However, any pre-existing condition waiting period must be reduced by a preceding period of coverage under another group health plan or health maintenance organization (HMO), Indian Health Service, Medicare, military healthcare (TRICARE), or other governmental public healthcare plans (**creditable coverage**). This reduction is known as **credited coverage.** Moreover, a pre-existing condition will be covered without a waiting period if an employee joins a new group plan if the employee had been insured for the previous 12 months under a group plan without a lapse in coverage exceeding 63 days. No pre-existing condition clause may be imposed for pregnancy or childbirth, or a newborn or adopted child (under age 18). (See table 3.2 for examples of creditable coverage in various scenarios.)

The provisions of HIPAA regarding creditable coverage do not apply to the purchase of individual healthcare insurance. Purchasers of individual healthcare insurance are required to meet specified time requirements (up to 24 months) prior to benefits being paid for pre-existing conditions.

Table 3.2.   Examples of calculations of creditable coverage

	Scenario 1	Scenario 2	Scenario 3
Duration of Coverage under Group Healthcare Insurance	2 Years	7 Months	3 Years
Duration of No Coverage between Periods of Employment	45 Days	10 Days	6 Months
Credited Coverage	2 Years	7 Months	0
Maximum Duration of Waiting Period for Preexisting Condition	0 Days	5 Months	12 Months
Rationale	Lapse in Coverage <63 Days Duration of Previous Coverage >12 Months	Lapse in Coverage <63 Days Duration of Previous Coverage <12 Months	Lapse in Coverage >63 Days

Riders and Endorsements

Riders and **endorsements** are similar to limitations and exclusions. They provide additional details about coverage or noncoverage for special situations that are not usually included in standard policies. A rider is an additional document and an endorsement is language or statements within the policy itself (See also **carve outs** in chapter 5.).

Procedures

Procedures explain how policyholders obtain the healthcare benefit or qualify to receive the healthcare benefit. Healthcare plans may deny benefits because procedures are not followed. Moreover, the procedures can function as limitations and exclusions, even though they may be stated in the positive. For example, "all mental health and chemical dependency services must be rendered by an eligible provider." Therefore, if services were provided by an ineligible provider, they would not be covered (paid for).

Prior Approval

A common procedure is obtaining prior approval. During this approval process, the healthcare plan determines medical necessity. Types of services often requiring prior approval include:

- Outpatient surgeries

- Diagnostic, interventional, and therapeutic outpatient procedures

- Physical, occupational, and speech therapies

- Mental health and chemical dependency care

- Inpatient care including surgery, home health, private nurses, and nursing homes

- Organ transplants

If a policy requires prior approval for physical therapy services and the policyholder does not obtain the prior approval, the expenses related to the physical therapy services may be denied.

Coordination of Benefits

Another common procedure is **coordination of benefits.** Coordination of benefits becomes necessary when people have multiple healthcare insurance carriers that are providing coverage. Multiple carriers can occur in instances when both spouses or parents work and both employers provide healthcare insurance, or when an automobile insurance company is paying for the treatment of injuries incurred in an automobile accident. The **primary insurer (payer)** is the healthcare insurance responsible for the greatest proportion or majority of the healthcare expenses. The **secondary insurer (payer)** is responsible for the remainder of the healthcare expenses. For example, should a person incur healthcare expenses related to an injury suffered in an automobile accident, the healthcare insurance may deny coverage because the automobile accident insurance is responsible for these expenses. Determination of primary or secondary insurer can be complicated. Some common rules are:

- Patient's healthcare insurance is primary over the spouse's healthcare insurance.

- Dependent child's primary insurer is the insurance of the parent whose birthday comes first in the calendar year ("birthday rule").

- A legal decree, such as divorce agreement, dictates determination.

- The circumstances of the case, such as automobile accident insurance for injuries from an automobile accident, dictate determination.

In many instances, when policyholders enroll in a healthcare insurance plan, they are required to list all other healthcare insurance policies they may have. Often, clauses within the healthcare insurance policy state that the primary insurance will pay for the majority of the healthcare expenses and the secondary insurance will pay for the remaining costs. Thus, the payments from all healthcare insurance companies do not exceed 100 percent of the covered healthcare expenses. This integration of payments is known as coordination of benefits (Jones 2001, 495).

Appeals Processes

An appeal is a request for reconsideration of denial of coverage for healthcare services or rejection of a **claim.** A claim is a bill for healthcare services submitted by a hospital, physician's office, or other healthcare provider facility. Claims are submitted for reimbursement to the healthcare insurance plan by either the policy or certificate holder or the provider. The appeals section of a policy describes the steps that policyholders must take to appeal a decision about coverage or payment of a claim. Typically, the appeal must be in writing and within a specific time frame of the healthcare insurance company's decision concerning the issue.

Check Your Understanding 3.1

1. Who is included in a healthcare insurance policy offering dependent healthcare coverage?

2. Which type of policy offers the widest ranging coverage but requires the insured to pay coinsurance until the maximum out-of-pocket costs are met?

3. Which of the following is **not** a type of healthcare policy limitation?
    a. Benefit cap
    b. Cost-sharing provision
    c. Geographic plan
    d. Use of formulary

4. Under HIPAA, any pre-existing condition waiting period in a group healthcare plan must be reduced by _____.

5. Describe the types of procedures and services that typically require prior approval.

Determination of Covered Services

Healthcare insurance policies must be studied in their entirety to determine covered services. All the sections of the policy operate together to delineate covered services and noncovered services. An example from a mental health and chemical dependency benefit illustrates the linkage of policy sections (figure 3.2). The benefit is inpatient care for a mental health condition or chemical dependency. In the definitions section of a policy, both **precertification** and

Figure 3.2.   Illustration of linkage of policy sections for a mental health or chemical dependency benefit

Policy Section	Language Demonstrating Linkage
Definitions	Precertification for Mental Health and Chemical Dependency: Process of calling the mental health claim management representative prior to receiving services and obtaining approval for all continuing care. (This requirement is different from prior approval and is not a guarantee of payment.)
	Prior Approval: Review of request for coverage of services prior to services being rendered that ensures certain covered services are deemed medically necessary and appropriate in order to treat the patient's condition.
Benefits	Inpatient care
Limitations	$100 copayment in addition to deductible and coinsurance
	Inpatient mental health or psychiatric treatment must be in licensed psychiatric bed and have attending physician who is a psychiatrist
	Inpatient chemical dependency treatment must be in a licensed chemical dependency bed and have attending physician who is a psychiatrist or addictionologist
	Delivered by eligible provider listed on pages 61 through 62 of the benefits manual
Exclusions	Treatment preceding precertification
	Treatment provided by ineligible provider
	Treatment at a noncontracting facility
Procedures	Obtain prior approval
	Obtain precertification

prior approval are defined. These definitions detail how to properly complete the procedures of obtaining precertification and prior approval. The limitations section notes that there is $100 copayment in addition to applicable deductibles and coinsurance. Moreover, the limitations for mental health facilities specify that patients must be in beds licensed as psychiatric or chemical dependency and that the eligible attending physician must have specialized credentials. Finally, the exclusions section specifies that care preceding precertification, delivered by a noneligible provider, or obtained at a noncontracting facility will be denied. This illustration demonstrates how intricately the sections of the policy integrate to define coverage.

Private (Individual) Healthcare Plans

Individuals and self-employed business persons purchase healthcare insurance for themselves and their families. Private healthcare plans are sometimes termed *individual plans* because individuals purchase them. For some persons, the private healthcare plan is their only plan for themselves and their families. However, some persons purchase private healthcare plans to supplement their employer-based group insurance or their Medicare. In general, individual healthcare insurance plans provide fewer covered services at a higher cost than group healthcare insurance plans.

Purchasers of individual healthcare plans usually must provide **evidence of insurability.** This evidence includes completing a survey about current and past health status and undergoing a physical examination. Based on the evidence, the healthcare insurance company may reject the applicant or may specify exclusionary clauses in the policy. Reasons for rejection include health habits, past medical history, age, income and other factors that affect risk of illness or accident.

Typically, private healthcare plans have higher premiums and deductibles, lower maximum plan dollar limits, and more restrictions on coverage for pre-existing conditions than group healthcare insurance plans have. Policyholders of private healthcare insurance pay higher premiums to obtain and to maintain their healthcare insurance. Also higher are the deductibles that the policyholder must pay before the healthcare insurance will assume its share of liability for the remaining costs. Maximum plan dollar limits may be lower than for group healthcare plans.

Employer-Based (Group) Healthcare Plans

Employer-based healthcare plans are group plans for groups of employees or members. *Employer-based healthcare plan* is a misnomer because the type includes all plans that cover groups. Individuals may form groups through professional associations and other entities. An example of an "other entity" is the Mississippi Comprehensive Health Insurance Risk Pool Association (MCHIRPA). The MCHIRPA is a nonprofit legal entity created to make the advantages of group healthcare insurance available to Mississippi citizens who cannot secure other healthcare insurance because of their health conditions.

Employer-based healthcare plans have lower premiums and deductibles and greater benefits than private healthcare plans. Persons with pre-existing conditions and who cannot obtain private healthcare insurance can obtain coverage (after a period of time) under an employer-based healthcare plan.

Analyses showed that the number of employers offering the benefit of group insurance is declining. Between 2001 and 2004, the percentage of workers covered by their employers' health plans declined from 65 percent to 61 percent, mostly among small employers (Gabel et al. 2004, 206). This decline translates into approximately 5 million fewer jobs providing health insurance in 2004 than in 2001 (Gabel et al. 2004, 2006). Moreover, the employees' premiums rose 59 percent between 2001 and 2004 (Gabel et al. 2004, 201). Finally, between 2001 and 2004, the percentage of employers that paid 100 percent of the premium steeply declined. For single coverage, this percentage declined from 34 percent to 21 percent and for family coverage from 14 percent to 7 percent (Gabel et al. 2004, 202). These declines represent an erosion of employer-based healthcare plans in the United States.

Blue Cross and Blue Shield Plans

Blue Cross and Blue Shield plans began in Dallas, Texas, in 1929, when Justin Ford Kimball established a health insurance plan for schoolteachers. In the plan, schoolteachers prepaid $6 per year for twenty-one days of hospitalization (Blue Cross and Blue Shield of Vermont n.d.). Similar plans were also formed in Michigan and New Jersey (Koch 2002, 98). In 1934, the American Hospital Association (AHA) united the plans under its auspices (Koch 2002, 98). In 1939, the AHA adopted the symbol of the blue cross to indicate the health insurance plans that met specific criteria for covering hospital care. Also, in 1939, Blue Shield was founded in California to cover physician services (Blue Cross and Blue Shield of Vermont n.d.). In 1972, the AHA's sponsorship of Blue Cross ended. Blue Cross and Blue Shield merged in 1982 to form the Blue Cross and Blue Shield Association (Blue Cross and Blue Shield of Vermont n.d.).

Today Blue Cross and Blue Shield is a federation of forty independent, locally operated plans united through membership in the Blue Cross and Blue Shield Association (BCBSA). Plans can operate at the state level, such as Blue Cross of Alabama or at the substate level, such as Blue Cross and Blue Shield of Western New York, one of six Blue plans in the state. The plans contract with hospitals, physicians, and other health care providers to offer services to their subscribers (policyholders). BCBSA is one of the most influential groups in healthcare (Hall and Conover 2003, 509).

The Blue Companies insure nearly one in three Americans (Grossman and Strunk 2004, 1). In June 2003, 88.3 million Americans were enrolled in the Blue Companies, a 28-year high (Grossman and Strunk 2004, 1). The Blue Companies offer their subscribers a wide range of options such as health maintenance organizations, point-of-service plans, preferred provider organizations, and indemnity plans.

Profit Versus Nonprofit Status

The Blue Companies had operated traditionally as nonprofit. However, in 1994, BCBSA decided to allow local plans to convert to for-profit status (Grossman and Strunk 2004, 1). Between 1993 and 2003, Blue Cross and Blue Shield plans in 15 states, including Blue Cross of California and Empire Blue Cross, serving eastern New York, converted to for-profit status (Hall and Conover 2003, 510). The result is more than one in four Blue Cross subscribers belong to a for-profit plan (Hall and Conover 2003, 510).

Types of Blue Cross and Blue Shield Accounts

Blue Cross and Blue Shield have two types of accounts: geographic plans at the state or substate level and the federal employee program (FEP). Geographic plans cover subscribers (members) in a specific state or region. The FEP covers all enrolled federal government employees across the nation and the globe.

Geographic Plans

Geographic plans cover specific geographic areas, such as Blue Cross and Blue Shield of Missouri or Regence Blue Cross and Blue Shield of Utah. The geographic plans are locally administered and have long-standing relationships with their local hospitals and medical communities (Hall and Conover 2003, 509). The subscribers carry cards with the name of the plan, their subscribers' names, and contract and group numbers.

Federal Employee Program

The government-wide federal employee program (FEP) has 4.4 million members. The FEP is also known as the Service Benefit Plan. The following notation on the insured's cards—Government-Wide Service Benefit Plan and FEP—identify the federal program.

Explanation of Benefits

An **explanation of benefits (EOB)** is a report from Blue Cross and Blue Shield (and other third party payers) that is sent from a healthcare insurer to the policyholder and to the provider. The report lists the following data elements:

- Healthcare service with provider and date

- **Actual charge** of the healthcare service

- **Allowable charge** which is the amount the healthcare insurer will cover

- Applicable cost-sharing, such as coinsurance and copayment

- The remainder of the costs, which is the policyholder's responsibility

Figure 3.3 is a sample explanation of benefits illustrating how a Blue plan provides specific benefits for a subscriber (member).

Future Trends

One of the future trends is the continuing increase in private healthcare costs. This trend has impli-

Figure 3.3.   Explanation of benefits

Blue Cross of Some State					
Member's Name: Jane Green **ID Number:** 123-45-6789 **Date** June 15, 200*					
Patient's Name: Jane Green (Member)					
Service	**Amount of Bill**	**Amount You Do Not Owe**	**Amount Paid by Plan**	**Your Balance**	**Explanation of Your Balance**
Surgicenter of Smith County 05-10-200* Ambulatory Surge	536.01	181.34	To Provider 150.00	204.67	**Your $150 wellness benefit maximum has been met.** 50.00 Outpatient services copay. 154.67 Applied to Plan year deductible.
City Physicians Group 05-10-200* Surgery	271.00	163.46	0.00	107.54	**Your $150 wellness benefit maximum has been met.** 107.54 Applied to Plan year deductible.
Smith County Hospital 05-16-200* X-Ray Services	450.63	72.10	To Provider 232.59	145.94	**Your $150 wellness benefit maximum has been met.** 58.15 Your 20% coinsurance. 87.79 Applied to Plan year deductible.
	TOTAL		382.59	458.15	
350 of 350 Deductible met for 07-01-200* to 06-30-200*		58.15 of 1500.00 Coinsurance met for 07-01-200* to 06-30-200*			

cations both for patients and clients and for providers.

Increasing Private Healthcare Costs

Healthcare costs that patients and clients pay are rising as well as the overall healthcare costs (See chapter 1). These increasing expenditures include both out-of-pocket costs and private health insurance.

Traditionally, new technologies, including new medications, devices, and procedures, were thought to account for the majority of the increase in costs (Fuchs 1996, 3; Newhouse 1992, 11). Other factors, accounting for far less of the increase in costs, were the aging population, the specialty mix of physicians, spread of health insurance, increased income, **defensive medicine,** and rising administrative costs (Fuchs 1996, 3; Newhouse 1993, 156–158).

Using a different approach, one set of researchers proposed that another key factor in the increase in private health insurance spending is the rising prevalence of treated disease (Thorpe et al. 2005, W5-317). Treated disease prevalence is the number of existing, treated diseases during a specified period. "Changes in treated disease prevalence are caused by a rise in the population prevalence of disease, changes in clinical thresholds (and awareness) for treating and diagnosing diseases, and new technologies that allow physicians to treat additional patients with a particular medical condition" (Thorpe et al. 2005, W5-318). The researchers used the 20 medical conditions that accounted for the largest portion in the increase in private healthcare spending during the period 1987 through 2002 (Thorpe et al. 2005, W5-319). Examples of these diseases are newborn and maternity care, cancer, pulmonary conditions, arthritis, mental disorders, hyperlipidemia, hypertension, heart disease, and diabetes. The researchers found that, for the period, the rise in treated disease prevalence of these 20 conditions accounted for 67 percent of the growth in private health insurance spending (Thorpe et al. 2005, W5-320). The researchers concluded that cost

containment efforts aimed at technology or cost per case do not address the factor associated with the leading cause of increased private insurance spending, the rise in treated disease prevalence (Thorpe et al. 2005, W5-323).

Out-of-pocket costs for patients and clients are steadily increasing. For example, between 1993 and 2004, out-of-pocket costs increased from $145.3 billion to $235.7 billion (Borger et al. 2006, W67). While the rate of increase declined, from 8.0 percent in 1993 to 5.5 percent in 2004, the costs are still increasing, just more slowly (Borger et al. 2006, W67). Experts predict that by 2015, out-of-pocket costs will be $421.0 billion (Borger et al. 2006, W67). Expenditures on private health insurance, such as hospital confinement policies, disability income protection policies, and other supplemental policies also increased from $297.0 billion in 1993 to $658.5 billion in 2004 (Borger et al. 2006, W67). Tracking with the out-of-pocket costs, the rate of increase for private health insurance declined from 13.7 percent in 1993 to 8.6 percent in 2004. However, by 2015, expenditures on private health insurance are expected to be $1.397 trillion (Borger et al. 2006, W67).

These out-of-pocket costs can have catastrophic effects on individuals and families. In 2001, nearly 1.5 million couples or individuals filed bankruptcy petitions (Himmelstein et al. 2005, W5-63). Research on 1771 of these couples or individuals showed that 46.2 percent of them met the following criteria:

- Cited illness or injury as the specific cause of bankruptcy

- Reported uncovered medical bills exceeding $1000

- Lost at least two weeks of work-related income because of the illness or injury

- Mortgaged their home to pay medical bills (Himmelstein et al. 2005, W5-65–W5-66).

A broader category that also included addictions to drugs, alcohol, or gambling resulted in 54.5 percent of the bankruptcies being related to medical causes (Himmelstein et al. 2005, W5-66). The researchers noted that gaps in healthcare coverage were a common problem. Of these medical debtors, 75.7 percent had health insurance at the time of the onset of the bankrupting illness or injury (Himmelstein et al. 2005, W5-69). Out-of-pocket costs averaged $11,854 (Himmelstein et al. 2005, W5-69). The demographic profile of these medical debtors was that of the typical American who gets sick. The researchers concluded that middle-class Americans who get seriously ill face impoverishment (Himmelstein et al. 2005, W5-72).

While increased private expenditures on healthcare affect patients and clients, collecting out-of-pocket costs affects physician practice managers, reimbursement specialists, and directors of hospital **accounts receivables.** These out-of-pocket costs must be collected from patients and clients to maintain cash flow. Experts advise healthcare organizations to develop:

- Policies and procedures
- Collection systems
- Front-office and check-out desk processes (Redling 2007, 29)

Preparing business offices of healthcare organizations for the increased share of healthcare costs that patients and clients must bear is essential to the financial welfare of the organization (See table 3.3.).

Consumer-Directed Healthcare Plan

Consumer-directed (driven) healthcare plans (CDHPs) are a trend of the future. CDHPs decrease the effects of **moral hazard.** Moral hazard is "any change in behavior that occurs as a result of becoming insured" (Nyman 1998, 57). In healthcare, examples of potential moral hazards are undergoing

Table 3.3.   Preparing for increased out-of-pocket costs for patients and clients

Revamp cash collection processes	Collect deductibles, copayments, and coinsurances at front-desk or check-out desk
	Collect small deposit for other potential non-covered services (unless prohibited)
Revise policies and procedures	Institute minimum payments
	Implement discounts for full payment at time of service
	Offer extended payment plans
	Collect deductibles, copayments, and coinsurances at time of service
Equip staff	Preview appointments at least 24 hours in advance
	Obtain complete health insurance information from patients or clients prior to appointments
	Verify insurance coverage, deductibles, copayments, coinsurances, and allowable charges prior to appointments
	Create scripts for staff to use when they ask patients and clients for payments
Inform patients and clients	Educate patients and clients about organization's policies and procedures (Web site, statements, scripts for staff, and promotional and educational brochures and materials)
	Confirm with patients their covered and non-covered services, deductibles, copayments, coinsurances, and allowable charges
Communicate with payers	Obtain definitions, terms, and benefit structure
Update physicians and providers	Demonstrate effects of payments at time of service on cash flow

Source of content: Redling, B. 2007, February. Double exposure: Higher deductibles, uninsured patients add to administrators' challenges. *MGMA Connexion/Medical Group Management Association* 7(2): 29–32.

an expensive procedure when a comparable inexpensive procedure exists or becoming an inpatient when outpatient services would have the same outcome (Nyman 1998, 57).

In consumer-directed healthcare, patients and clients are more involved in the design of their packages of health benefits. CDHPs provide patients and clients with information about packages' costs and with incentives to select the more cost-efficient package. With decision-support tools and information, the patients and clients determine the level of cost-sharing appropriate for their health and their economic situation. Three models of CDHPs exist: health reimbursement accounts (HRAs), premium-tiered, and point-of-service tiered (Rosenthal and Milstein 2004, 1055).

The model of health reimbursement accounts (personal care account, personal medical fund) combines an employer-funded account with a high deductible. For example, a member may have a $500 HRA and a $1500 deductible. After the member has used the $500 HRA, the member must pay $1000 out-of-pocket before insurance becomes effective (Rosenthal and Milstein 2004, 1059).

The tiered models are focused on influencing healthcare behaviors by linking freedom of choice and either premiums or cost-sharing. Premium-tiered models link freedom of choice and premiums. Less restrictive packages have higher premiums; more restrictive packages allow greater freedom of choice. Point-of-service tiered models link freedom of choice and cost-sharing. Copayments are higher when members select providers outside the preferred network (Rosenthal and Milstein 2004, 1059).

In these plans, patients and clients (consumers) are made more aware of and responsible for the costs of their healthcare than in fee-for-service or other types of reimbursement. Experts believe that awareness and responsibility will influence patients and clients to choose the lower-priced package. For employers, CDHPs are a means to control the costs of their employees' health benefits. For consumers,

CDHPs give them flexibility in choosing how they spend their healthcare benefit dollars.

CDHPs are not without their critics. The benefits of low premiums and high deductibles are not evenly distributed. Women, because they bear children and need pap smears and mammograms, are among the least benefitted under CDHPs (Woolhandler and Himmelstein 2007, 880). Others who are least benefitted are persons with chronic illnesses, such as hypertension and diabetes (Woolhandler and Himmelstein 2007, 880). Best benefitted are young, healthy males. Finally, critics of CDHPs point out that the plans discourage low-cost primary and preventive care, known means to better health (Woolhandler and Himmelstein 2007, 880).

Value-Based Insurance Design

The next generation of consumer-directed healthcare is value-based insurance design (VBID) (Brennan and Reisman 2007, W207). In value-based insurance design, copayments are set based on the value of the clinical services (Chernow et al. 2007, W196). Unlike traditional practices that focus only on costs of clinical services, VBID calculates both benefit and cost (Chernew et al. 2007, W196). There are two models of VBID:

- Targeting valuable interventions, such as beta blockers

- Targeting valuable interventions to patients with select diseases, such as beta blockers for patients with congestive heart failure (Chernew et al. 2007, W197)

Value-based insurance design acknowledges and addresses the heterogeneity of patients and clients. VBID also addresses the concern of the critics of consumer-directed healthcare that patients and clients do not have the requisite education and information to choose needed medications and treatments when faced with high copayments (Brennan and Reisman 2007, W205). VBID has been instituted by employers in Connecticut, North Carolina, Michigan, and by Aetna insurance. Barriers exist to its growth, such as concerns about initial overutilization, implementation costs, legal challenges, insufficient research, inadequate clinical information systems, and **adverse selection** (disproportionate enrollment of sick patients) (Chernew et al. 2007, W198-W199; Brennan and Reisman 2007, W206). The advantage of VBID is that it pays attention to assuring appropriate access to consumer-directed healthcare and to providing high-quality care.

Prospective Payment Systems for NonMedicare Populations

Some commercial healthcare insurance plans have implemented or are considering the implementation of prospective payment systems for their covered members (See chapter 1). Federal prospective payment systems have effectively decelerated healthcare costs for Medicare patients. Therefore, commercial healthcare insurance are interested in replicating that success (Price and Farley 2005, 17).

Federal payment systems provide several models across the continuum of care. Commercial healthcare insurance companies have the history of the models' performance and details of their functions and algorithms. Commercial healthcare insurance companies would also realize advantages from operational simplification and standardization. Prospective payment systems shift the risk of estimating populations' healthcare costs to providers (See chapter 1). Thus, commercial healthcare insurance companies could benefit by instituting the proven risk management strategies of prospective payment systems (Price and Farley 2005, 17).

Summary

Voluntary health insurance includes private or commercial healthcare insurance plans and Blue Cross and Blue Shield plans. This sector of the healthcare industry is very important as approximately 33 percent of healthcare expenditures in the U.S. are payments from voluntary health insurance plans. Healthcare insurance policies are comprised of sections, such as definitions, eligibility and enrollment, benefits, limitations, exclusions, procedures, and appeals processes. The sections operate together to clearly delineate healthcare services for which the healthcare insurance company will pay.

Types of healthcare insurance include private or commercial healthcare insurance, which can be purchased by individuals or employers and other entities. Employer-based group plans tend to be more flexible and provide greater benefits at less cost than individual policies. Blue Cross and Blue Shield is a federation of 40 independent, locally-operated plans that collectively form one of the most influential private groups in the healthcare industry.

Trends for the future include increasing healthcare costs for consumers and the continuing evolution of payment methodologies. Consumer-directed healthcare plans shift decision making to consumers. These plans also allow consumers to determine their level of cost-sharing. Value-based insurance design is the next generation of consumer-directed healthcare. These trends will require changing behaviors and ways of thinking for both consumers and providers.

Chapter 3 Review Quiz

1. What is the relation between covered conditions and covered services in private or commercial insurance plans?

2. Name at least two of the three benefit terms that mean the amount beyond which all covered healthcare services for an insured or dependent are paid 100 percent by the insurance plan.

3. What type of insurance policy provides benefits to (a) a resident requiring nursing home care and services, (b) an insured who becomes blind, and (c) a homeowner who requires an eight-month recuperation after a fall down her basement stairs?

4. Why can use of a formulary be considered a policy limitation?

5. List at least three typical exclusions found in insurance plan riders.

6. Describe the health insurance plan that covers federal government employees.

7. How does Blue Cross and Blue Shield notify insureds about the extent of payments made on a claim? What data elements does that notification include?

8. Voluntary health insurance plan payments account for about one-fourth of U.S. healthcare expenditures. True or false?

9. Copayments are cost-sharing provisions of policies that require insureds to pay a flat fee to healthcare service providers and suppliers. True or false?

10. Individuals having pre-existing conditions are financially better off using private healthcare plans than either employer group plans or managed care alternatives. True or false?

References and Bibliography

American Academy of Actuaries. 2006, September. Issue Brief: Wading through Medical Insurance Pools: A Primer. Available online from http://www.actuary.org/pdf/health/pools_sep06.pdf. Accessed 11 December 2007.

Blue Cross and Blue Shield of Vermont. n.d. Accessed at http://www.bcbsvt.com/pages/corporate/BCBSVTHistory.htm08February2008.

Borger, C., S. Smith, C. Truffer, S. Keehan, A. Sisko, J. Poisal, and M.K. Clemens. 2006, January-June. Health spending projections through 2015: Changes on the horizon. *Health Affairs Suppl Web Exclusives* 25(2):W61–W73.

Brennan, T., and L. Reisman. 2007, January 30. Value-based insurance design and the next generation of consumer-driven health care. *Health Affairs Suppl Web Exclusives* 26(2): W204–W207.

Chernew, M.E., A.B. Rosen, and A.M. Fendrick. 2007, January 30. Value-based insurance design. *Health Affairs Suppl Web Exclusives* 26(2):W195–W203.

Fuchs, V.R. 1996, March. Economics, values, and health care reform. *American Economic Review* 86(1):1–24.

Gabel, J., G. Claxton, I. Gil, J. Pickreign, H. Whitmore, E. Holve, B. Finder, S. Hawkins, and D. Rowland. 2004, September-October. Health benefits in 2004: Four years of double-digit premium increases take their toll on coverage. *Health Affairs* 23(5):200–209.

Grossman, J. M., and B. C. Strunk. 2004. For profit conversions and merger trends among Blue Cross Blue Shield health plans. *Issue Brief/Center for Studying Health System Change* 76 (January): 1–6.

Hall, M. A., and C. J. Conover. 2003. The impact of Blue Cross conversions on accessibility, affordability, and the public interest. *The Milbank Quarterly* 81 (December) (4): 509–542.

Himmelstein, D.U., E. Warren, D. Thorne, and S. Woolhandler. 2005, January-June. Illness and injury as contributors to bankruptcy. *Health Affairs Suppl Web Exclusives* 24:W5-63–W5-73.

Jones, L. M., ed. 2001. Glossary. In *Reimbursement Methodologies for Healthcare Services* [CD-ROM]. Chicago: American Health Information Management Association.

Koch, A. L. 2002. Financing health services. In *Introduction to Health Services*. 6th ed., edited by S. J. Williams and P. R. Torrens. Albany, N.Y.: Delmar.

Newhouse, J.P. 1992, Summer. Medical care costs: How much welfare loss? *Journal of Economic Perspectives* 6(3):3–21.

Newhouse, J.P. 1993. An iconoclastic view of health cost containment. *Health Affairs* 12(Suppl):152–171.

Nyman, J.A. 1998. Theory of health insurance. *Journal of Health Administration Education* 16(1):41–66.

Pickett, J. P. et al., eds. 2000. *American Heritage Dictionary of the English Language*. 4th ed. Boston: Houghton Mifflin Company.

Price, F., and D. Farley. 2005, February 28. A winning hand: PPS for commercial populations. *For the Record* 17(5):16–19.

Redling, B. 2007, February. Double exposure: Higher deductibles, uninsured patients add to administrators' challenges. *MGMA Connexion/Medical Group Management Association* 7(2):28–32.

Rosenthal, M., and A. Milstein. 2004, August. Awakening consumer stewardship of health benefits: Prevalence and differentiation of new health plan models. *Health Services Research* 39(4) Part II:1055–1070.

Rowell, J. C. 2000. *Understanding Health Insurance: A Guide to Professional Billing,* 5th ed. Albany, N.Y.: Delmar.

State Health Plan for North Carolina. 2005. Available online from www.statehealthplan.state.nc.us.

Thorpe, K.E., C.S. Florence, D.H. Howard, and P. Joski. 2005, January–June. The rising prevalence of treated disease: Effects on private health insurance spending. *Health Affairs Suppl Web Exclusives* 24:W5-317–W5-325.

Woolhandler, S., and D.U. Himmelstein. 2007, June. Consumer directed healthcare: Except for the healthy and wealthy it's unwise. *Journal of General Internal Medicine* 22(6):879–881.

Chapter 4
Government-Sponsored Healthcare Programs

Objectives

- To differentiate among and to identify the various government-sponsored healthcare programs

- To understand the history of the Medicare and Medicaid programs in America

- To recognize the impact that government-sponsored healthcare programs have on the American healthcare system

Key Terms

Beneficiary

Centers for Medicare and Medicaid Services (CMS)

Civilian Health and Medical Program: Veterans Administration (CHAMPVA)

Federal Employees' Compensation Act of 1916 (FECA)

Indian Health Service (IHS)

Medicaid

Medicare

Medicare Advantage

Medicare Modernization Act of 2003 (MMA)

Medicare Part A

Medicare Part B

Medicare Part C

Medicare Part D

Medigap

Programs of All-Inclusive Care for Elderly (PACE)

Social Security Act

State Children's Health Insurance Program (SCHIP)

Temporary Assistance for Needy Families Program (TANF)

TRICARE

Workers' Compensation

Introduction

The various levels of government administer several health plans for various populations as mandated by laws and regulations. Perhaps the most well-known is **Medicare** for persons who qualify for social security benefits and are 65 years of age or older. This chapter discusses Medicare and several other federal and state sponsored programs.

Medicare

The **Social Security Act** was amended in 1965 to create the Medicare program (Title XVIII). Medicare is a national health insurance program that provides health services to elderly and other qualifying persons. Medicare benefits are available for persons:

*   Sixty-five years or older who are eligible for Social Security or Railroad Retirement benefits

*   Individuals entitled to Social Security or Railroad Retirement disability benefits for at least twenty-four months

*   Government employees with Medicare coverage who have been disabled for more than twenty-nine months

*   Insured workers (and their spouses) with end-stage renal disease

*   Children with end-stage renal disease

The most significant recent legislative change to Medicare was the **Medicare Modernization Act of 2003 (MMA).** MMA created an outpatient prescription drug benefit, provided beneficiaries with expanded coverage choices, and improved benefits.

Medicare is divided into four parts: Part A, Part B, Part C, and Part D.

Medicare Part A for Inpatients

Medicare Part A, inpatient hospital insurance, is provided with no premiums to most beneficiaries.

Most services covered under this benefit require an annual deductible and copayment to be paid by the **beneficiary.** Services included in this benefit are:

*   Inpatient hospitalization

*   Long-term care hospitalization

*   Skilled nursing facility services

*   Home health services

*   Hospice care

Each site of service has specific limitations with regard to cost-sharing provisions per benefit period (see table 4.1).

Medicare Part B

Medicare Part B, supplemental medical insurance, is an optional insurance package that beneficiaries may purchase. For 2008, the monthly premium is $96.40 (CMS 2007a, 110–113). Part B insurance covers physician services, medical services, and medical supplies not covered by Part A. Most of these services are provided on an outpatient basis. In addition to the monthly premium, beneficiaries are responsible for an annual deductible and service copayments. Table 4.2 provides a summary of the services and cost-sharing provisions.

Medicare Part C

Several services are excluded from Part A and Part B Medicare coverage. Beneficiaries can purchase additional coverage or choose **Medicare Part C** coverage, a managed care option known as **Medicare Advantage,** to gain insurance for these services. The Part A and Part B excluded services which are provided under Part C are:

*   Long-term nursing care

*   Custodial care

*   Dental services

*   Vision services

- Routine examinations, except initial preventive medicine examination added by MMA

- Health and wellness education

- Acupuncture

- Hearing aids

Medicare Part C, Medicare Advantage, is available for beneficiaries participating in Part A, B, and D (drug benefit) coverage. In addition to the Part B premium, members of an approved Medicare Advantage program pay an additional premium for the full scope of services offered by the program that are not typically covered by Medicare.

Example:

Routine physical examinations and vision services are excluded from Medicare Parts A and B. However, these services are provided by Medicare Advantage programs.

Table 4.1.   Part A services 2008

Site of Service	Benefit Period	Patient Responsibility
Hospital Inpatient and Long-Term Care Hospital	First 60 days Days 61–90 Days 91–150 (lifetime reserve days*) Beyond 150 (lifetime reserve days*)	$1,024 annual $256 per day $512 per day All costs
Skilled nursing facility	First 20 days Days 21–100 Beyond 100 days	Nothing $128 per day All costs
Home health	No time limit—based on medical necessity criteria	Nothing for services, 20% for durable medical equipment (DME)
Hospice	No time limit—based on physician certification	Limited costs for outpatient drugs and inpatient respite care

*Nonrenewable lifetime reserve of up to 60 additional days of inpatient hospital care.

Table 4.2.   Part B services 2008

Site of Service	Benefit	Patient Responsibility
Medical services	Physician services, medical and surgical services and supplies, DME Mental health care Occupational, physical, and speech therapy	$135 annual deductible, plus 20% of approved amount (excludes hospital outpatient, see below) 50% of most care 20% of approved amount
Clinical laboratory services	Blood tests, urinalysis, and more	Nothing
Home health	Intermittent skilled care, home health aide service, DME and supplies, and other services	Nothing for services, 20% for durable medical equipment (DME)
Outpatient hospital services	Services for diagnosis and/or treatment of an illness or injury	$135 deductible, plus established copayment amount per covered service 100% charges for noncovered services

MMA revised several components of the Medicare Advantage program including a new process for determining beneficiary premiums. Monthly premiums range from $50 to $350 depending on the scope of service the beneficiary elects to purchase.

Medicare Part D

Medicare Part D, Medicare drug benefit, was created by the MMA of 2003. The benefit was fully implemented on January 1, 2006. The program offers outpatient drug coverage provided by private prescription drug plans and Medicare Advantage. The National base premium for 2008 is $27.93. Additionally, beneficiaries have an annual deductible and make copayments for their prescriptions. Low-income beneficiary provisions are built into the program for seniors who cannot afford the standard copayment amounts. MMA also established improved access to pharmacies, an up-to-date formulary, and emergency access for Medicare beneficiaries.

Medigap

Medicare beneficiaries may elect to purchase private insurance policies to supplement their Medicare Part A and/or Part B coverage. This supplemental insurance, known as **Medigap,** covers most cost-sharing expenses as shown in tables 4.1 and 4.2. Medigap policies must meet federal standards and are offered by various private insurance companies.

Medicaid

Originally known as the Medical Assistance Program, **Medicaid** (Title XIX) was added to the Social Security Act in 1965. Medicaid is a joint program between the federal and state governments to provide healthcare benefits to low-income persons and families. This program is designed to allow each individual state to develop and maintain a Medicaid program unique to its state. Each state determines specific eligibility requirements and services to be offered. Therefore, coverage varies greatly from state to state. A person qualifying for services in one state may not qualify in any other state. Further, coverage

determination for services is state-specific. Federal funds allocated to each state are based on the average income per person for that state. However, for a state to qualify to receive Medicaid federal funds, the state's program must provide coverage to at least the following groups:

- Low-income families with children including those who meet eligibility for **Temporary Assistance for Needy Families (TANF)**
- Supplemental Security Income recipients (or others who meet criteria in more restrictive states)
- Infants born to Medicaid-eligible pregnant women
- Children under the age of six whose family income is at or below 133 percent of the federal poverty level
- Recipients of adoption assistance and foster care (Title IV-E of the Act)
- Certain Medicare beneficiaries
- Special protected groups

Additionally, the state program must offer a designated set of services to members in order to receive federal matching funds (see figure 4.1). Eligibility and services may be expanded by individual

Figure 4.1. Medicaid-required services

Inpatient hospital services	Rural health clinic services
Outpatient hospital services	Laboratory and x-ray services
Physician services	Pediatric and family nurse practitioner services
Medical and surgical dental services	Federally-qualified health center services
Nursing facility services for individuals aged 21 or older	Nurse-midwife services
Home health care for persons eligible for nursing facility services	Early and periodic screening, diagnosis, and treatment services for individuals under age 21
Family planning services and supplies	

states based on that state's laws and regulations. For example, states may elect to provide members with optometry services and eyeglasses, or dental services. States are also afforded the flexibility to determine cost-sharing (in terms of deductible and copayments) terms for their programs for certain services and members. For example, family planning services are exempt from cost-sharing as well as services to pregnant women and children under the age of eighteen. State programs may also offer managed care options. In 2004, 60.68 percent of all Medicaid enrollees chose the managed care option; that is up from 32.1 percent in 1995 (CMS 2005b; 2005c).

Check Your Understanding 4.1

1. Match each Medicare part with the type of benefits it provides:
   a. Part A   ____ Medicare drug benefit
   b. Part B   ____ Supplemental medical insurance
   c. Part C   ____ Inpatient hospital services
   d. Part D   ____ Medicare Advantage

2. What types of costs do Medigap policies cover?

3. Why is Medicaid coverage not identical in New Jersey, California, and Idaho?

Other Government-Sponsored Healthcare Programs

Other government-sponsored healthcare programs include the following:

- The Temporary Assistance for Needy Families (TANF) program
- **Programs of All-Inclusive Care for the Elderly (PACE)**
- **The State Children's Health Insurance Program (SCHIP)**
- **TRICARE Programs**
- **Civilian Health and Medical Program: Veterans Administration (CHAMPVA)**

- **Indian Health Services (IHS)**
- **Worker's Compensation**

Each of these programs serves a specific target group and has specific eligibility requirements, plan requirements, and participant benefits.

The Temporary Assistance for Needy Families Program

The Personal Responsibility and Work Opportunity Reconciliation Act of 1996 (also known as welfare reform) brought about many changes to Medicaid eligibility. For example, welfare reform repealed the Aid to Families with Dependent Children (AFDC) program. AFDC was replaced with the TANF program which provides states with grant money designated to provide low-income families with case assistance. However, because welfare reform made significant changes to eligibility, individuals may not realize that they are eligible for Medicaid benefits under this program (CMS 2005d).

Programs of All-Inclusive Care for the Elderly

The Balanced Budget Act of 1997 (BBA) authorized the creation of Programs of All-Inclusive Care for the Elderly (PACE). PACE is a joint Medicare–Medicaid venture that offers states the option of creating and administering this managed care option for the frail elderly population (DHHS 1999). PACE was designed to enhance the quality of life for the frail elderly population by enabling them to live in their own homes and communities, and to preserve and support their family units.

States electing to administer PACE must be approved and provide designated services (see figure 4.2). States must provide services in at least one facility in a geographical service area. The facilities must be accessible and offer adequate services to meet the needs of all participants in the programs. Additional facilities must be staffed and supply a full range of services when warranted by the growth of the PACE population in a service

Figure 4.2.   PACE-required services

Multidisciplinary assessment and treatment plan	Medical specialty services
	Laboratory and x-ray services
Primary care services	Drugs and biologicals
Social work services	Prosthetics and DME
Physical, occupational, and speech therapies	Acute inpatient care
	Nursing facility care
Personal care and supportive services	All Medicaid covered services
Nutritional counseling	
Recreational therapy	
Transportation	
Meals	

Services in the first column must be provided at each PACE facility.

area. Participants may frequent the facility as determined by the multidisciplinary team and the patient's needs. Each facility must have in place a multidisciplinary team consisting of at least the following members (DHHS 1999):

- Primary care physician
- Registered nurse
- Social worker
- Physical therapist
- Occupational therapist
- Recreation therapist or activity coordinator
- Dietician
- PACE center coordinator
- Home care coordinator
- Personal care attendants or representatives
- Drivers or representatives

Beneficiaries of PACE, frail elderly persons, must meet the following eligibility requirements:

- Minimum age of fifty-five
- Resident in the PACE service area

- Assessed by the PACE multidisciplinary team
- Certified by the State Medicaid Agency as eligible for nursing home level of care

PACE programs are not offered in all states or even all service areas within states.

State Children's Health Insurance Program

The State Children's Health Insurance Program (SCHIP) or Title XXI of the Social Security Act, was created in 1997 by the Balanced Budget Act (BBA). SCHIP is a state/federal partnership that targets the growing number of children not covered by health insurance. It is designed to provide health insurance to children of families whose income level is too high to qualify for Medicaid, but too low to afford private healthcare insurance. Specifically, to qualify for the program, the child must reside with a family whose income is below 200 percent of the federal poverty level or whose family has an income no more than 50 percent higher than the state's Medicaid eligibility threshold.

SCHIP varies from state to state. Each state may determine how it would like to deliver the healthcare benefit to qualifying persons. The state may elect to expand Medicaid eligibility to children who would qualify for SCHIP. The state may design a separate program to provide the benefit. Or the state may combine the Medicaid expansion and separate program concepts. Regardless of the individual program design, state plans and revisions must be approved by the **Centers for Medicare and Medicaid Services (CMS)**. By September 30, 1999, each state and territory had an approved SCHIP plan in place (CMS 2005e). States must provide the following services to SCHIP beneficiaries:

- Inpatient hospital services
- Outpatient hospital services

- Physicians' medical and surgical services

- Laboratory and radiology services

- Well-baby/child care services, including immunizations

States may impose cost-sharing provisions on individuals who are enrolled in the program. The cost-sharing cannot exceed 5 percent of a family's gross or net income. States cannot impose cost-sharing for preventive or immunization services. Further, American Indian/Alaskan native children who are members of a federally recognized Tribe may not be charged any cost-sharing fees.

TRICARE

The Department of Defense provides a healthcare program for active duty and retired members of one of the seven uniformed services of the United States: Air Force, Army, Coast Guard, Marine Corps, Navy, National Oceanic and Atmospheric Administration (NOAA) Commissioned Corps, and Public Health Service Commissioned Corps. Additionally, coverage is provided for their families and survivors. The healthcare program is now titled TRICARE, replacing Civilian Health and Medical Program of the Uniformed Services (CHAMPUS) that was enacted in 1966 by amendments to the Dependents Medical Care Act. There is only one program option for active duty members, but several for active duty family members, retirees, and their family members and survivors.

TRICARE Prime and TRICARE Prime Remote

TRICARE Prime and TRICARE Prime Remote are the program's managed care options. All active duty service members (ADSMs) are automatically covered by one of these programs, although the individual must complete an enrollment form and submit it to the regional contractor. TRICARE Prime is required when ADSMs live and work within fifty miles or an hour's drive of a military treatment facility.

TRICARE Prime Remote is required when ADSMs live and work in remote areas. In this option, the member may access primary care from a non-network provider if network providers are unavailable in the area. There are no enrollment fees, deductibles, or copayments for authorized medical services and prescriptions with either TRICARE option.

Active duty family members (ADFMs) may also enroll in TRICARE Prime or TRICARE Prime Remote. This is the most economical program available for military families because there are no enrollment, deductible, or copayment fees for covered services. In order to participate in the managed care option, ADFMs must enroll during an open enrollment period.

TRICARE Standard and TRICARE Extra

If ADFMs do not want to enroll in the managed care options, they can participate in TRICARE Standard or TRICARE Extra. TRICARE Standard requires members to pay an annual deductible as well as a 25 percent cost-share of allowed charges. Participants in this program may receive care from any TRICARE authorized provider. TRICARE Extra also requires an annual deductible, but only requires a 20 percent copayment for negotiated codes. Care must be provided by a TRICARE network provider. With this option, there are no claims to file by the beneficiary. The ADFM does not need to enroll in either of these programs. Rather, each family member enrolls in the Defense Enrollment Eligibility Reporting System (DEERS), which outlines eligibility dates. Service members are responsible for maintaining up-to-date information in DEERS.

Military retirees under age sixty-five and their families may enroll in TRICARE Prime or participate in TRICARE Standard or TRICARE Extra. TRICARE Standard and TRICARE Extra require deductibles and copayments for covered services. TRICARE Prime for retirees and their families requires an annual enrollment fee ($230 per individual or $460 per family) and a $12 per visit copayment for in-network providers. There is no copayment for covered services at a military treatment facility.

In addition to health services, TRICARE provides dental services for ADFMs and members of the Individual Ready and Selected Reserve and their families. There are single and family plans that consist of monthly premiums and copayments for covered services. Additionally, TRICARE provides a dental program for retirees and their families. Single, two-party, and family plans are available with monthly premiums, deductibles, and copayments for covered services.

The National Defense Authorization Act for federal fiscal year 2005 expanded TRICARE coverage to be available for Reserve Component (RC) members and their dependents when the RC member is called to active duty (on orders) for more than thirty consecutive days. RC dependents become eligible for TRICARE Standard or TRICARE Extra on the first day of the RC member's orders if the orders are for more than thirty days. RC dependents may choose to enroll in TRICARE Prime or TRICARE Prime Remote any time during the first month of the RC member's activation.

TRICARE for Life

TRICARE for Life (TFL) is TRICARE's secondary coverage for beneficiaries who become entitled to Medicare Part A. TRICARE becomes the secondary payer to Medicare. Members are required to participate in Medicare Part B and pay Medicare Part B premiums.

CHAMPVA

The Department of Veterans Affairs provides covered healthcare services and supplies to eligible beneficiaries through the Civilian Health and Medical Program of the Department of Veterans Affairs (CHAMPVA). This benefits program is available for the spouse or widow(er) and for the children of a veteran who meets one of the following criteria:

- Is permanently and totally disabled due to a service-connected disability

- Was permanently and totally disabled due to a service-connected condition at the time of death

- Died of a service-connected disability

- Died on active duty

Persons eligible for TRICARE benefits cannot participate in CHAMPVA. This program covers most healthcare services and supplies that are medically and psychologically necessary. CHAMPVA becomes a secondary payer when another health insurance benefit is available. For example, when a beneficiary reaches the age of 65, Medicare is the primary payer and CHAMPVA becomes the secondary payer.

The Indian Health Service

The Indian Health Service (IHS) was created to uphold the federal government's obligation to promote healthy American Indian and Alaskan native people, communities, and cultures (IHS 2005). A government-to-government relationship between the United States and Indian tribes was established in 1787 based on Article I, Section 8, of the U.S. Constitution. From this relationship came the provision of health services for members of federally recognized tribes. Principal legislation for authorizing federal funds for Indian Health Services is the Snyder Act of 1921. The IHS is an agency within the Department of Health and Human Services.

Following are the functions of the IHS:

- Assists Indian tribes in the development of their own health programs

- Facilitates and assists Indian tribes in coordinating health planning

- Promotes using health resources available through federal, state, and local programs

- Provides comprehensive healthcare services

Healthcare services offered by the IHS include inpatient and outpatient care, preventive and rehabilitative services, and development of community sanitation facilities. The federal IHS healthcare delivery system consists of hospitals, health centers, health stations, and residential treatment centers.

Workers' Compensation

The workers' compensation benefit is provided to most employees to cover healthcare costs and lost income that results from a work-related injury or illness. Federal government employees are covered under the **Federal Employees' Compensation Act (FECA).** Other employees are covered under state workers' compensation insurance funds if that program is established in the state in which the employees work.

FECA was established in 1916 and ensures that civilian employees of the federal government are provided medical, death, and income benefits for work-related injuries and illnesses. FECA is administered by the Office of Workers' Compensation Programs (OWCP), a division of the Department of Labor. OWCP also administered the Longshore and Harbor Workers' Compensation Act of 1927 and the Black Lung Benefits Reform Act of 1977.

State workers' compensation insurance funds are established by each state. Benefits may include burial, death, income, and medical. Rather than contracting individually with insurance companies for coverage, employers pay premiums into the nonprofit workers' compensation fund for their state. This allows the workers' compensation premiums to remain low and affordable for small business owners.

In states where no fund is mandated for workers' compensation, employers must purchase insurance from private carriers or provide self-insurance coverage. (LaTour and Eichenwald, 296–297).

Check Your Understanding 4.2

1. Match each TRICARE program on the left with its description on the right:
   a. ADFMs with deductible and 20% copay   ____ TRICARE for Life (TFL)
   b. ADFMs with deductible and 25% cost-share   ____ TRICARE Prime
   c. Managed care for ADSMs   ____ TRICARE Extra
   d. Secondary coverage for Medicare beneficiaries   ____ TRICARE Standard

2. When a CHAMPVA beneficiary reaches the age of 65, Medicare is the primary payer and CHAMPVA becomes the secondary payer. True or false?

3. Services offered by the IHS to Indian tribes include all of the following except:
   a. Rehabilitative services
   b. Death benefits
   c. Outpatient care
   d. Development of sanitation facilities

Summary

Government-sponsored healthcare plans such as Medicare, Medicaid, TANF, PACE, the TRICARE programs, CHAMPVA, the IHS, and workers' compensation make affordable healthcare options available to many people who would otherwise go without coverage and the quality healthcare services they need. The market for government-sponsored healthcare plans is large and growing, with federally sponsored programs now covering more than 60 million beneficiaries. Such programs, due to their size, have a unique and pervasive influence on private insurance plans and other public-sector plans in terms of coverage, quality of care, and cost-effectiveness, as well as the processes employed in healthcare reimbursement.

Chapter 4 Review Quiz

1. Which program replaced the Aid to Families with Dependent Children (AFDC)?

2. What recent legislation made a substantive change to Medicare benefits, and how did they change?

3. List at least three types of Medicaid recipients required for states to qualify for federal matching funds.

4. How was the PACE venture designed to enhance the quality of life for the frail elderly population?

5. What is the target population of the State Children's Health Insurance Program (SCHIP) (Title XXI)?

6. Which TRICARE program is the most economical program for military families, and why is it less expensive than the other options?

7. What program covers healthcare costs and lost income from work-related injuries or illness of federal government employees?

8. Individuals eligible for Railroad Retirement disability or retirement benefits are ineligible for Medicare. True or false?

9. Individuals who are eligible may choose between TRICARE benefits and CHAMPVA. True or false?

10. In states having no mandated workers' compensation fund, employers must purchase insurance from private carriers or provide self-insurance coverage. True or false?

References and Bibliography

Centers for Medicare and Medicaid Services. 2005a. Available online from www.cms.hhs.gov/providerupdate/regs/cms8027N.pdf.

Centers for Medicare and Medicaid Services. 2005b. Available online from www.cms.hhs.gov/medicaid/managedcare/pctoftot.pdf.

Centers for Medicare and Medicaid Services. 2005c. Available online from www.cms.hhs.gov/medicaid/managedcare/trends04.pdf.

Centers for Medicare and Medicaid Services. 2005d. State requirements and options under Federal Medicaid law. Available online from www.cms.hhs.gov/medicaid/welfareref/welfare.asp#ch1State.

Centers for Medicare and Medicaid Services. 2005e. State Children's Health Insurance Program (SCHIP). Available online from www.cms.hhs.gov/schip/about-SCHIP.asp.

Centers for Medicare and Medicaid Services. 2007a. Medicare & You 2008. Available online from www.medicare.gov.

Centers for Medicare and Medicaid Services. 2007b. Fact Sheet – Strong Competition and Beneficiary Choices Contribute to Medicare Drug Coverage with Lower Costs Than Predicted. Available online from www.cms.hhs.gov/apps/files/FactSheetPartDBenchmark.pdf.

Department of Health and Human Services. 1999. *Federal Register*. Medicare and Medicaid programs: Programs of all-inclusive care. 64 (226): 66233–66304.

Indian Health Service. 2005. www.ihs.gov.

LaTour, K., and S. Eichenwald, eds. 2002. *Health Information Management: Concepts, Principles, and Practice*. Chicago: American Health Information Management Association.

Chapter 5
Managed Care Plans

Objectives

- To describe origins of managed care

- To trace evolution of managed care

- To describe types of managed care plans

Key Terms

Bad debt

Capitation

Carve out

Case management

Charity care

Cherry picking

Closed panel

Community rating

Cost-sharing

Disease management

Episode-of-care reimbursement

Evidence-based clinical practice guidelines

Exclusive provider organization (EPO)

Fee-for-service reimbursement

Gatekeeper

Global payment

Group practice model

Health maintenance organizations (HMOs)

Independent practice association (IPA)

Integrated delivery system

Managed care

Managed care organizations (MCOs)

Medical foundation

Network

Network model

Out-of-pocket

Per member per month (PMPM)

Point-of-service (POS) healthcare insurance plan

Preadmission certification

Preadmission review

Preauthorization

Preauthorization (precertification) number

Precertification

Preferred provider organizations (PPOs)

Prescription management

Primary care provider

Prior approval (authorization)

Second opinion

Staff model

Subcapitation

Third opinion

Uncompensated care

Utilization review

Withhold

Withhold pool

Introduction to Managed Care

The purpose of **managed care** is to provide affordable, high-quality healthcare. Managed care systematically merges clinical, financial, and administrative processes to manage access, cost, and quality of healthcare.

Managed care traces its origins to the early 1900s. As early as 1910, Western Clinic in Tacoma, Washington, offered its members medical services for $0.50 per month (American College of Managed Care Medicine 2005). The first Blue Cross plan, established in Dallas, Texas, was a form of managed care. In 1929, schoolteachers in this plan prepaid $6 per year for twenty-one days of hospitalization (Starr 1982, 295). In the 1930s, Kaiser Construction Company established a plan for its workers (American College of Managed Care Medicine 2005). Today, as Kaiser Permanente, the healthcare plan enrolls over 8 million members (Kaiser Permanente 2007).

In the United States between 1966 and the early 1970s, the costs of healthcare escalated quickly (Foster 2000). To control costs and provide affordable quality healthcare, federal legislation encouraged the growth of **health maintenance organizations (HMOs)**. The Health Maintenance Organization (HMO) Act of 1973 provided federal grants and loans for new HMOs.

Through the 1980s and 1990s, additional economic constraints encouraged the growth of HMOs and other types of managed care as employers sought to reduce their healthcare costs. Contributing to the growth of hybrid types were the consumers' desires for freedom of choice and access to specialists. The result is that there are numerous types of managed care.

Managed Care Organizations

Managed care organizations (MCOs) are healthcare plans that attempt to manage care. In the Balanced Budget Act of 1997, these plans are termed coordinated care plans. MCOs implement provisions to manage both the costs and outcomes of healthcare. Managed care plans integrate the financing and delivery of specified healthcare services.

Benefits and Services of MCOs

MCOs offer differing levels of benefits, depending on the cost of their premiums and copayments. Typical covered services include:

- Physician services (inpatient and outpatient)
- Inpatient care
- Preventative care and wellness, such as immunizations, well-child examinations, adult periodic health maintenance examinations, and pap smears
- Prenatal care
- Emergency services
- Diagnostic and laboratory tests
- Certain home health services

Access to mental and behavioral health and specialty care is through referral from the **primary care provider.**

Characteristics of MCOs

Managed care organizations share characteristics associated with providing quality care and cost-effective care (table 5.1 and table 5.2). The lines between quality care and cost-effective care blur considerably. Moreover, these characteristics are not unique to MCOs; other payers also implement them. However, these characteristics are often associated with MCOs because of the characteristics' prevalence and extent of use in MCOs. MCOs coordinate and control healthcare services to improve quality and to contain expenditures.

Quality Patient Care

Managed care organizations focus on providing quality patient care. They achieve this goal through careful selection of providers, an emphasis on the health of their populations of members, use of care management tools, and maintenance of accreditation or participation in quality improvement programs.

Table 5.1. Managed care characteristics associated with quality care

Characteristic	Description
Selection Criteria for Providers	Criteria include quality, scope of services, cost, and location
	Credentialing and periodic recredentialing
	Procedural selection process at senior clinical staff level
Population	Responsible for delivery of healthcare services on continuum of care (prevention, wellness, acute, and chronic)
	Population receives recommended preventive care and appropriate care for chronic conditions
	Health and wellness management
Care Management Tools	Coordination of care by primary care provider
	Evidence-based clinical practice guidelines
	Disease management
Quality Assessment and Improvement	Entities accredited and engage in performance improvement
	The Joint Commission
	National Committee for Quality Assurance (NCQA)
	URAC (formerly Utilization Review Accreditation Commission)
	CAHPS®*
	HEDIS®**
	Member Satisfaction

*CAHPS® is a registered trademark of the Agency for Healthcare Research and Quality (AHRQ) and private research organizations.

**HEDIS® is a registered trademark of the National Committee for Quality Assurance (NCQA).

Table 5.2. Managed care characteristics associated with cost-effective care

Characteristic	Description
Service Management Tools	Medical necessity review
	Utilization management
	Case management
	Prescription management
Episode-of-Care Reimbursement	Capitated reimbursement
	Global payment
Financial Incentives	Providers to meet fiscal targets
	Members to use providers associated with the plan

Selection of Providers

MCOs stress the use of criteria in their selection of providers. Senior clinicians in the upper echelons of the MCO select providers using pre-established procedures and standards. These criteria are based on quality, scope of services, cost, and location. Timelines for credentialing and recredentialing are followed. This emphasis ensures their members' access to superior and eminent providers throughout a geographic area.

Services Across the Continuum of Care

Managed care organizations emphasize the health of their entire populations of members. These organizations are responsible for the delivery of healthcare services across the continuum of care in terms of setting and type. Examples of settings include the physicians' offices, home health agencies, and hospitals. Examples of types of care are preventative, wellness-oriented, acute, and chronic. The MCO is clinically responsible for the health outcomes of its population.

Preventive Care

Members receive appropriate testing for preventive care, such as timely mammograms and pap smears. Moreover, members with chronic conditions receive appropriate assessment and therapeutic procedures, as recommended by **evidence-based**

clinical practice guidelines. In addition, managed care organizations often support their members' participation in health and wellness management. Wellness programs are one component of health and wellness management. These programs stress the habits of healthy lifestyles, such as exercise and proper nutrition. Other aspects of health and wellness management include smoking cessation, alcohol moderation, and harm reduction.

Care Management Tools

Care management tools include coordination of care, **disease management,** and the application of evidence-based clinical practice guidelines. Together, these tools foster continuity of healthcare services and accessibility and reduce fragmentation and misuse of resources and facilities.

Coordination of care is achieved through the use of primary care providers (PCPs). In many managed care organizations, one PCP provides, supervises, or arranges for a patient or client's healthcare and makes necessary and appropriate referrals. Primary care providers may be physicians, nurse practitioners, or physician assistants (Felt-Lisk 1996, 97–98). Primary care physicians are often family practitioners, general practitioners, internists, pediatricians, and obstetricians/gynecologists.

Disease management focuses on preventing exacerbations of chronic diseases and promoting healthier lifestyles for patients and clients with chronic diseases. In disease management, patients are monitored to promote adherence to treatment plans and to detect early signs and symptoms of exacerbations. Disease management programs often focus on diabetes, congestive heart failure, coronary heart disease, chronic obstructive pulmonary disease, and asthma. Often the management of chronic diseases requires treatment plans and complex medication regimens involving multiple healthcare providers. Therefore, disease management is closely aligned with coordination of care because the efforts of multiple providers must be synchronized.

As a disease management initiative, a healthcare system began a frail elderly program (Baseman and Truxell 2000, 33). Characteristics of the 73 frail elders enrolled in the program included: being diagnosed with three or more comorbid, chronic conditions; having been hospitalized two or more times within the preceding 12-month period; and being functionally or cognitively impaired (Baseman and Truxell 2000, 35). Cost savings after one year were $396 per member per month (Baseman and Truxell 2000, 36) with a 36 percent reduction in the number of inpatient admissions. Thus, disease management programs are able to produce significant savings as well as the positive impact on enrollee's health.

Evidence-based clinical practice guidelines are the foundation of members' care for specific clinical conditions. Evidence-based clinical practice guidelines are explicit statements that guide clinical decision making. They outline the

- Key diagnostic indicators
- Timelines
- Alternatives in interventions and treatments
- Potential outcomes

They have been systematically developed from scientific evidence and clinical expertise to answer clinical questions. Other terms for these guidelines are evidence-based guidelines, clinical practice guidelines, clinical guidelines, clinical pathways, clinical criteria, and medical protocols. Sources of these guidelines are the Agency for Healthcare Research and Quality (AHRQ), the Centers for Disease Control and Prevention, the National Guideline Clearinghouse, and specialty organizations, such as the American College of Cardiology, the American Academy of Family Physicians, the American Academy of Ophthalmology, and the American College of Obstetricians and Gynecologists. These guidelines are benchmarks of best practices in the care and treatment of patients and clients.

These guidelines are used to manage the wellness of members and to direct the care of acute illnesses and chronic conditions. The guidelines typically address:

- Entire plan of care across multiple delivery sites

- Appropriate diagnostic and therapeutic procedures for given diseases and conditions

- Reasons for referrals to specialists

- Clinical decision factors and decision points

Therefore, evidence-based clinical practice guidelines serve as a means to standardize optimum care for all patients and to deliver comprehensive, coordinated care across multiple providers.

Accreditation Processes and Performance Improvement Initiatives

Managed care organizations also participate in rigorous accreditation processes and in performance improvement initiatives. Organizations with accreditation standards for managed care include the National Committee for Quality Assurance (NCQA), the URAC (formerly the Utilization Review Accreditation Commission), and the Accreditation Association for Ambulatory Health Care (AAAHC, also known as the Accreditation Association). Effective January 1, 2006, the Joint Commission (formerly known as the Joint Commission on Accreditation of Healthcare Organizations, JCAHO) discontinued its network accreditation program for integrated delivery systems, managed care organizations, managed behavioral healthcare organizations, and preferred provider organizations. However, the Joint Commission will continue to provide support and oversight to organizations accredited under the network program until the end of each organization's accreditation cycle

(Joint Commission 2007). Plans also participate in performance improvement initiatives, such as the AHRQ's CAHPS® (formerly Consumer Assessment of Health Plans) project and the NCQA's Health Plan Employer Data and Information Set (HEDIS®). Often as a part of HEDIS, managed care organizations also survey their members to assess members' feedback on such issues as:

- Satisfaction with administrative, clinical services, and customer services

- Perceptions of the plan's strengths and weaknesses

- Suggestions for improvements

- Intentions regarding re-enrollment

In addition to surveying members, MCOs conduct satisfaction surveys of patients, physicians, providers, customers, employers, and disenrolled members. Commitment to accreditation and performance improvement demonstrates MCOs' dedication to their members and to the delivery of quality healthcare.

Cost Controls

Managed care plans implement various forms of cost controls. These cost controls include service management tools, the method of reimbursement, and financial incentives. Examples of service management tools are review of medical necessity, utilization management, and case and prescription management. The method of reimbursement is **episode-of-care reimbursement** with its inherent features of cost reduction. Financial incentives include those for both providers and members. The MCO is fiscally accountable for the health outcomes of its population.

Medical Necessity and Utilization

Several cost controls are related to medical necessity and utilization. These cost controls contain and monitor use of healthcare services by evaluating the need for and intensity of the service prior to it being provided. As stated in chapter 3, medical necessity can be defined as:

> A service or supply provided for the diagnosis, treatment, cure, or relief of a health condition, illness, injury, or disease. The service or supply must not be experimental, investigational, or cosmetic in purpose. It must be necessary for and appropriate to the diagnosis, treatment, cure, or relief of a health condition, illness, injury, disease, or its symptoms. It must be within generally accepted standards of medical care in the community. It must not be solely for the convenience of the insured, the insured's family, or the provider (State health plan 2005, 7).

Utilization review assesses the appropriateness of the setting for the healthcare service in the continuum of care and the level of service. Also factored in are patients' severity of illness and other medical conditions and illnesses. Review of medical necessity and utilization are often performed concomitantly.

MCOs and other insurers review medical necessity and utilization in a three-step process: initial clinical review, peer clinical review, and appeals consideration (Table 5.3). Steps two and three are only implemented if the previous step results in a negative decision. If a step results in a positive decision, the process stops at that step.

Table 5.3.   Review of medical necessity and utilization

Step	Responsible Party	Activity or Resource
Clinical Review	Licensed health professional	Review against established criteria
Peer Clinical Review	Peer clinician	Clinician qualified to render clinical opinion performs clinical review
Appeals Consideration	Qualified, expert clinician in same specialty	Clinician not involved in initial decision and qualified to render clinical opinion performs clinical review

Medical necessity and utilization are reviewed using objective, clinical criteria. Multiple sets of criteria exist:

- Intensity of Service, Severity of Illness, and Discharge Screens (ISD)
- Appropriateness Evaluation Protocol (AEP)
- Managed Care Appropriateness Protocol (MCAP) (Kalant et al. 2000, 1809)
- Milliman and Robertson (M&R) guidelines (Rutledge 1998, 579)
- Solucient (formerly HCIA-Sachs) length of stay guidelines
- American Society of Addiction Medicine's Patient Placement Criteria, Second Edition-Revised (ASAM PPC-2R)
- Federal and state-specific guidelines

Medical necessity and utilization are often reviewed for the following services:

- Confinement in acute care hospital, long-term acute care facility, long-term care facility psychiatric hospital, partial-day hospital, hospice, and rehabilitation services
- Surgical procedures
- Emergency room services
- Emergent care received from out-of-**network** (out-of-plan) providers
- High-cost or high-risk diagnostic, interventional, or therapeutic outpatient procedures
- Physical, occupational, speech, and other rehabilitative therapies
- Mental health and chemical dependency care
- Home health services, private duty nurses, and referrals to medical specialists

- Durable medical equipment, prosthetic and orthotic appliances, medical supplies, blood transfusions and administration, and medical transport

Gatekeeper Role of Primary Care Provider

The **gatekeeper** role of the primary care provider is a cost control. As the coordinator of all the healthcare a member may access, the primary care provider determines whether referrals are warranted. These referrals may be to (a) medical specialists, (b) other healthcare sites for diagnostic or therapeutic procedures, or (c) hospitals or other healthcare facilities. Gatekeepers determine the appropriateness of the healthcare service, the level of healthcare personnel, and the setting in the continuum of care.

Prior Approval

Prior approval (authorization) is also a cost control. Prior approval is the formal administrative process of obtaining prior approval for healthcare services. Alternate terms for this process are **preauthorization** and **precertification.** Terms for prior approval specific to inpatient services are **preadmission review** and **preadmission certification.** Inpatient admissions, surgeries, visits to medical specialists, elective procedures, and expensive or sophisticated diagnostic tests are all types of services requiring prior approval. Occasionally, for healthcare services such as mental or behavioral health, providers must submit entire treatment plans for prior approval. A **preauthorization** or **precertification number** is issued when the healthcare service is approved. Managed care organizations may deny coverage and third party payers may deny payment for healthcare services for which required prior approval was not obtained. Policies identify the healthcare services for which prior approval must be obtained.

Second/Third Opinions

Second and **third opinions** are cost containment measures to prevent unnecessary tests, treatments, medical devices, or surgical procedures. Second or third opinions are obtained from medical experts within the healthcare plan. They are particularly sought when the:

- Test, treatment, medical device or surgical procedure is high risk or high cost

- Diagnostic evidence is contradictory or equivocal

- Experts' opinions are mixed about efficacy

Utilization Review

Utilization review is also a means of cost control that evaluates both effectiveness and efficiency. Utilization review answers the following two questions:

- Should this healthcare service occur?

- If yes, then what setting is the most efficient in terms of delivery and cost?

Utilization review determines the medical necessity of a procedure and the appropriate setting (inpatient or outpatient), given the severity of a patient's illness. For example, utilization review assesses whether the services could be provided more efficiently and economically in an ambulatory setting rather than in the inpatient hospital. Generally, then, utilization review saves money through its prevention of overutilization. Overutilization is the unnecessary consumption of healthcare services or the consumption of unnecessarily expensive or sophisticated healthcare services.

Case Management

Case management coordinates an individual's care, especially in complex and high-cost cases. Individuals are assigned case managers who are typically nurses or physicians. With patients or clients and their families, case managers coordinate the efforts of multiple healthcare providers at multiple sites over time. Consultants, specialists, primary care providers, ancillary services, ambulatory care, inpatient services, and long-term care may all be involved. Case managers are often assigned to patients or clients with catastrophic illnesses or injuries, such as severe head injury. Workers' compensation cases may involve a case manager. Goals of case management include continuity of care, cost-effectiveness, quality, and appropriate utilization.

Prescription Management

Prescription management is also a cost control measure. Prescription management expands the use of a **formulary** (chapter 3) to a comprehensive approach to medications and their administration. This approach includes patient education; electronic screening, alert, and decision-support tools; expert and referent systems, especially related to drug-drug interactions, food-drug interactions, and cross-sensitivities; and criteria for drug utilization. Some electronic prescription management systems include point-of-service order entry, electronic transmission of the prescription to the pharmacy, and patient-specific medication profiles. As discussed in chapter 3, generic, less-expensive drugs are preferred to brand-name, expensive drugs. However, the comprehensive approach also enhances quality patient care. Considering the cost of medications, prescription management is a powerful tool of cost containment.

Episode-of-Care Reimbursement Method

Managed care organizations utilize the episode-of-care reimbursement method. The purpose of the episode-of-care reimbursement method is to reduce the inflation of costs in a **fee-for-service reimbursement** environment. Episode-of-care reimbursement pays providers one predetermined amount for all the care a patient or client may receive during a period. The MCO does not increase payments for the complexity or extent of healthcare services. Therefore, the incentive to provide higher volumes of services to generate higher reimbursements is eliminated.

Episode-of-care reimbursement is based upon averages. On average, the majority of enrolled members will rarely or never use healthcare services within a period. These low or nonusers offset the acutely or chronically ill members. In the aggregate, the low or nonusers balance out the heavy users. Managed care organizations most commonly use two of the episode-of-care payment methods: **capitation** and **global payment**.

Capitation

In capitation, providers are reimbursed a predetermined, fixed amount per member per period. The common phrase is **"per member per month"** (PMPM). The volume of services and their expense does not affect the reimbursement. Typically, capitation involves a group of physicians or an individual physician.

Global Payment

Global payment extends the scale of capitation. In global payment, providers in an **integrated delivery system** or other type of network receive one fixed amount for members of the MCO. These providers include physicians, hospitals, and other care providers. The single payment is divided among all the providers. Therefore, in global payment, the scale of capitation is increased from the single group to an entire delivery system.

Financial Incentives

Financial incentives exist for both providers and members. These incentives prevent the waste of financial resources through the provision of excessive or unnecessarily expensive healthcare services.

For providers, these incentives involve the provision of cost-efficient care. Incentives involve meeting targets for cost-efficiency. The following types of healthcare services were the focus of incentives (Grumbach et al. 1998, 1517):

- Referrals to specialists
- Use of laboratory or other ancillary services

- Inpatient admissions or days

- Settings of care, such as office preferred to emergency room

- Productivity, in terms of number of visits per day

- Pharmaceuticals

For example, primary care providers in MCOs may order less expensive generic drugs rather than the more expensive brand-name drugs. Medicaid managed care organizations also set targets, such as "the number of emergency room visits for mental health or substance abuse treatment shall not exceed 8.5 visits per 1000 enrollee months" (Carlson 2000, 13–14).

Incentives can be both positive and negative. As a positive incentive, providers may receive bonuses for meeting cost-containment targets. Conversely, a penalty may be assessed as a negative incentive (disincentive). Examples of penalties include percentage reduction of the PCP's salary if the provider does not meet the target or the loss of withholds (also known as physician contingency reserve [PCR]). A **withhold** is a part of the provider's capitated payment that the MCO deducts and holds to pay for excessive expenditures for expensive healthcare services, such as referrals to specialists. Withholds transfer risk to the providers. For a group practice, the withholds from individual providers are combined to form a **withhold pool**. At the end of period, surplus withheld funds are dispersed for meeting efficiency (utilization) or performance targets. Providers who do not meet targets do not receive their withholds at the end of the period.

It should be noted that, effective January 1, 1997, a federal rule governs financial incentives in managed care Medicaid and Medicare plans (Gallagher, Alpers, and Lo 1998, 409). This rule is Medicare and Medicaid Programs: Requirements for Physician Incentive Plans in Prepaid Health Care Organizations. The rule prohibits incentives that limit medically necessary referrals and requires

MCOs to report information about financial incentives regarding referrals to the CMS and state Medicaid offices. Moreover, the rule mandates that MCOs disclose summaries about financial incentives to Medicare and Medicaid members who ask.

As financial incentives to members, MCOs set varying rates of **cost-sharing**. For example, MCOs require higher **out-of-pocket** payments when members use out-of-plan providers than in-plan providers. Other MCOs offer members levels of prescription drug benefits. The drug benefit with the most restrictive formulary is the least expensive while the member's cost-sharing increases with the liberality of the formulary. Incentives influence members' behavior without eliminating freedom of choice.

Contract Management

Contract management is critical in the episode-of-care reimbursement method. Providers and plans must be able to accurately project their expenditures in order to negotiate contracts that cover the costs of treating members. If a provider or plan underestimates the costs to treat plan members, the provider or plan loses money. Moreover, once the contract is established, entities must monitor and evaluate utilization and costs to assess whether projections align with reality. If variances are detected, the plan or provider must implement corrective interventions on a timely basis.

Carve outs are contracts that separate out ("carve out") services or populations of patients or clients to decrease risk and costs. These services and populations are carved out of the global capitated payment. The types of services or populations that are carved out typically require long-term management, are high-cost, can be managed by one group of specialists, and are not usually managed by primary care providers (See figure 5.1). The use of carve outs has been increasing since the mid-1980s (Garnick et al. 2001, 1502). The provision of care for these services or to these populations is contracted out to vendors.

Figure 5.1. Examples of carved-out services or populations

Chronically ill children
  Asthma
  Cancer
  Cerebral palsy
  Chromosomal and metabolic anomalies
  Congenital defects
  Cystic fibrosis
  Diabetes mellitus (Type I)
  Down syndrome
  Epilepsy
  Hemophilia
  Muscular dystrophy
  Organ transplantation
  Rheumatoid arthritis
  Sickle cell disease and other hemoglobinopathies
  Spina bifida and other neural tube defects
Dental care
Diseases or conditions
  Acquired immunodeficiency syndrome/human immuno-
    deficiency virus (AIDS/HIV)
  Alcoholism
  Behavioral health
  Cancer
  Chronic pain
  Congestive heart failure
  End-stage renal disease
  Mental health
  Quadriplegia or paraplegia
  Substance abuse
Prescription drug (pharmacy benefit)
Specialty services
  Cardiology
  Cardiovascular surgery
  Neurology
  Neurosurgery
  Occupational medicine
  Oncology
  Ophthalmology
  Orthopedics
  Physical therapy
  Radiology
  Rehabilitation
Vision care

Contracts for carved out services vary greatly. However, contracted functions may include:

- Maintenance of a provider network

- Processing claims

- Utilization management and case management

- Operation of quality improvement programs (Garnick et al. 2001, 1503).

The payment methods for carved out services and populations also vary greatly. A common payment for specialists' services is **subcapitation** (Alexander 1999, 9). Under subcapitation, the healthcare plan reimburses the specialists with a portion of the capitated rate. This portion is known as the subcapitation. Other methods of reimbursement for contracted vendors are administrative fees, prepayment (capitation based on per member per month), and fee-for-service (Blumenthal and Buntin 1998, SP53; Garnick et al. 2001, 1507). Given the variability in the diseases and their costs, experts advise that healthcare plans pay contracted vendors on a disease by disease or a population by population basis (Blumenthal and Buntin 1998, SP53).

Advantages of carve outs include reduction of **cherry picking** (targeting the enrollment of healthy patients to minimize healthcare costs), increased quality due to volume of services, and increased cost savings due to economies of scale (Blumenthal and Buntin 1998, SP46).

Potential disadvantages of carve outs include fragmentation of care and decreased access. The benefits of managed care's coordination of care are negated without close synchronization between the gatekeeper and the provider of carved out services. Care could become fragmented as seen in fee-for-service. Moreover, the geographic dispersion of vendors of specialized services, such as behavioral health or substance abuse counseling, may be less wide-spread than primary care providers. For example, vendors of behavioral health or substance abuse counseling may be clustered in large population centers rather than evenly distributed across urban and rural counties. Travel time and distance to these vendors may be increased for patients and clients who live in rural areas. Also, potential patients and clients who live on the opposite side of a very large city from the vendor may face problems related to travel. Moreover, the cost of travel may act as a barrier to services for these potential patients and clients. Thus, the lack of geographic dispersion may prevent utilization of specialized services by all persons who need them. Thus, carve outs that require use of specialized vendors may curtail access.

Types of MCOs

As managed care has evolved, lines have blurred among the types of MCOs. The blurring across types makes a continuum a better conceptualization of managed care than individual, separate categories. The different types of MCOs can be placed on a continuum of control. On this continuum, the HMOs represent the most controlled and the **preferred provider organizations** (PPOs), represent the least controlled. This chapter discusses several managed care plans across the continuum of control.

Health Maintenance Organization

Health maintenance organizations (HMOs) combine the provision of healthcare insurance and the delivery of healthcare services. The HMO Act of 1973 was an initiative to control healthcare costs. Subsequent amendments were enacted in 1976, 1978, and 1981 implementing regulations (42 CFR Part 417). Included in the act were conditions for becoming a federally qualified health HMO. The conditions were a minimum benefits package, open enrollment, and **community rating.** In community rating, the rates for healthcare premiums are determined by geographic area (community) rather than by age, health status, or company size.

The act recognized three basic types of HMOs. These basic types are the **staff model**, the **group practice model**, and the **independent practice association (IPA).** Since the 1970s, the **network model** HMO has developed. In some types of HMOs, the HMO hires the healthcare providers and owns the hospitals and other facilities. In other types of HMOs, the plans contract with providers, such as physicians, hospitals, and other healthcare professionals, to provide service. The negotiated payment rates in the contract are discounted. Providers accept the discounted rate because of the increased certainty of referrals and income. The different types of HMOs reflect these differing means of compensation.

HMOs share the following characteristics:

- Organized system of healthcare delivery to a geographic area

- Established set of basic and supplemental health maintenance and treatment services

- Voluntarily enrolled members

- Predetermined, fixed, and periodic prepayments for enrollees

HMOs emphasize preventive care in the belief that, in the long term, preventive care saves money by preventing acute illness and chronic conditions. HMOs are the most restrictive form of managed care because they allow patients and clients the least freedom in choosing a provider. Offsetting this loss of freedom is the reduced out-of-pocket expenses and wide range of benefits.

Staff Model
The staff model HMO provides hospitalization and physicians' services through its own staff. It owns its facility. Its physicians are employees of the HMO and paid on salary or on a capitated basis. Both the staff model and the group model are sometimes called **closed panel.**

The staff model is the most controlled of the HMOs. Primary care physicians strictly control referrals to specialists within the HMO. Members who seek healthcare services outside the HMO receive no compensation for their healthcare costs.

Group Practice Model

In the group practice model, the HMO contracts with a medical group. The health professionals in this medical group provide services on a fee-for-service or capitation basis. The medical group bears the risk.

Network Model

A network model is the same as a group model HMO except that a network model contracts with two or more independent group practices.

Independent Practice Model

The independent (individual) practice association (IPA) (or organization, IPO) is a type of MCO in which participating physicians maintain their private practices. In the independent practice model, the HMO contracts with the IPA. The IPA, in turn, contracts with individual health providers. The HMO reimburses the IPA on a capitated basis. However, the IPA may reimburse the physicians on a capitated basis or a on a fee-for-service basis. The participating physicians have patients and clients who are members of the HMO as well as patients and clients who are not members. Existing facilities of the independent health professionals are used rather than a free-standing facility. Local, county, or state medical societies may sponsor this type of HMO.

Preferred Provider Organization

A preferred provider organization (PPO) is an entity that contracts with employers and insurers to render healthcare services to a group of members. Its common characteristics are as follows:

- Virtual rather than physical entity

- Decentralized

- Flexibility of choice for members

- Negotiated fees (may include discounts)

- Financial incentives to induce members to choose preferred option

- No prepaid capitation (retains aspects of fee-for-service)

- Not subject to regulatory requirements of HMOs

- Limited financial risk for providers

The PPO also contracts with providers for healthcare services at fixed or discounted rates. The providers are a network of physicians, hospitals, and other healthcare providers. Members can choose to use the healthcare services of any physician, hospital, or other healthcare provider. However, the PPO influences members to use the healthcare services of in-network (in-plan) providers. Members' out-of-pocket expenses are lower if they use in-network providers; members' out-of-pocket expenses are higher if they use the services of out-of-network (out-of-plan) providers. A PPO may be a separate legal entity or it may be a functional unit of another MCO, such as an HMO. A PPO may also be a functional unit of a larger indemnity insurer. The PPO may be sponsored by the network of physicians, hospitals, and other healthcare providers. PPOs offer greater freedom of choice for patients and clients than HMOs. Because there is greater uncertainty about the number of referrals, PPOs typically reimburse providers at a higher rate than HMOs.

Point-of-Service Plan

A **point-of-service (POS) healthcare insurance plan** is one in which members choose how to receive services at the time they need the services. For example, members can choose "at the point of service" whether they want an HMO, a PPO, or a fee-for-service plan. They do not need to make this decision during an open enrollment period. These healthcare insurance plans are also known as open-ended HMOs. Patients' out-of-pocket costs are increased if they receive services outside a referral network (out-of-network or out-of-plan).

Similar to a point-of-service plan is the provider-sponsored organization (PSO). The PSO differs from the point-of-service plan in that the physicians that practice in a regional or community hospital organize the plan. Various levels of benefits are offered, including aggressiveness of gatekeeping, cost-sharing for out-of-network healthcare services, and prescription drug benefits.

Exclusive Provider Organization

An **exclusive provider organization (EPO)** is an MCO that is sponsored by self-insured (self-funded) employers or associations. The EPO is very much a hybrid. Along a continuum of freedom of choice, EPOs feature characteristics of both HMOs and PPOs. Similar to operations of HMOs, a small network of primary care physicians frequently act as gatekeepers. Similar to the system of PPOs, many EPOs reimburse providers on a discounted fee schedule. A few EPOs, however, do reimburse providers through capitation. Members are influenced to seek healthcare services from in-network providers. Patients or clients who choose to receive care outside the network receive lower, and in some cases, no, recompense. Contracts are created between the EPO and providers. Because they offer greater choice, EPOs ensure cost efficiency by aggressively reviewing medical necessity and utilization.

Medicare Advantage

Medicare Advantage, or Medicare Part C (formerly Medicare+Choice), is a form of MCO for Medicare beneficiaries. Medicare beneficiaries who are entitled to Part A and enrolled in Part B have the option to switch to a Medicare Advantage plan, if a plan exists in their area. Types of plans available include HMOs, POSs, PPOs, and PSOs.

Deductibles and copayments are lower in Medicare Advantage. Other benefits may include:

- Preventative care
- Prescription drug plan
- Eyeglasses and hearing aids

- Day care, respite care, assisted care, and long-term care insurance
- Health transport
- Education and health promotion programs

Because the elderly often present complex medical conditions, Medicare Advantage plans may incorporate case management and disease management.

Check Your Understanding 5.1

1. How does a member of an MCO plan obtain coverage for an oncologist?

2. List three types of care delivered by MCOs.

3. _____ supported by MCOs stress the habits of healthy lifestyles, such as exercise and proper nutrition.

Integrated Delivery Systems

Stephen Shortell, a leader in health services management, defines an integrated delivery system (IDS) as "various components that work together in an integrated fashion to provide a continuum of healthcare to a defined patient population" (Manus 1995, 24). *Integrated delivery system* is a generic term referring to the collaborative integration of healthcare providers. Financial agreements, contracts, or both underpin the legal entity. The goal of the IDS is the seamless delivery of care along the continuum of care. Other terms for IDS are health delivery network, horizontally integrated system, integrated services network (ISN), and vertically integrated system.

Shortell states that there are four types of integrated delivery systems, differentiated by who organizes or leads them (Manus 1995, 24), as follows:

- Hospital-led IDS. This type of IDS is the most common. In addition to hospitals and physicians, this system may include group practices; home health agencies; hospices; nursing homes; ambulatory surgery, outpatient care centers, and urgicenters; and ancillary providers, such as podiatrists, psychologists, and others.

- Physician-led IDS. An example of a physician-led IDS is the Mayo Clinic in Rochester, Minnesota (Manus 1995, 24).

- Physician-hospital organization (PHO). In this hybrid of the hospital-led and physician-led IDSs, hospitals and physicians share leadership.

- Insurance-led IDS. The fourth type is led by a healthcare insurance company.

Shortell states that integrated delivery systems are evolving and various "permutations" of these generic types exist (Manus 1995, 25). The permutations are based on specifics of accountability and organization. Examples of these various permutations include:

- Network or horizontal integration
- Vertical integration
- With-or-without healthcare plan

The existence of the healthcare plan alters the regulations under which the entity operates. If the IDS includes a healthcare plan, the IDS is governed by applicable state and federal regulations for healthcare plans, insurance, or HMOs, as relevant. If the IDS does not include a healthcare plan, the IDS is governed by the regulations for each type of organization in the entity. Hospital regulations govern hospitals; clinic regulations govern clinics.

The variance in the degree of integration adds more complexity to this sector of the healthcare industry. Scanlan describes four degrees of integration: affiliation, acquisition, consolidation, and merger (Scanlan 1995, 33–34). The least binding is affiliation. In affiliation, the components influ-

ence one another. In acquisition, one component purchases part or all the assets of the other component. Consolidation is a catch-all term in which operations are legally combined. In a merger, two similar components permanently combine to form one unit. Finally, partnership is a term that can refer to all four of the degrees of integration and any other integrative effort (Scanlan 1995, 34).

This section describes the following models of integration including the integrated provider organization, the group practice without walls, the physician-hospital organization, the management service organization, and the medical foundation.

Integrated Provider Organization

An integrated provider organization (IPO) is an entity that includes one or more hospitals, a large physician group practice, other healthcare organizations, or various configurations of these businesses. An IPO is the corporate umbrella for the management of an IDS.

Group Practice Without Walls

A group practice without walls (PWW) or clinic without walls (CWW) is a group practice in which the physicians have maintained their separate practices and offices in a geographic area. The individual practices share administrative systems to form the group practice. The PWW is similar to an independent practice association. The purpose of the PWW is to gain bargaining power in the negotiation of managed care contracts. Economies of scale also accrue from the centralization of administrative systems.

Physician-Hospital Organization

A physician-hospital organization (PHO) is a legal entity formed by a hospital and a group of physicians. The single corporate umbrella gives the PHO bargaining power when the provider organization negotiates contracts with managed care organizations. The PHO also fosters the delivery of seamless healthcare to its patients and clients.

Management Service Organization

A management service organization or medical service organization (MSO) is a specialized entity that provides management services and administrative and information systems to one or more physician group practices or small hospitals. An MSO may be owned by a hospital, physician group, PHO, IDS, or investors. The MSOs' services and systems are infrastructure for the smaller healthcare organizations. Patient billing and claims management are examples of services that an MSO provides.

Medical Foundations

A **medical foundation** is a nonprofit service organization. Members include physicians and other healthcare providers. Medical foundations are typically geographically based, such as a local organization or county organization. Medical foundations have many purposes other than serving as a managed care organization. For example, medical foundations may be involved with offering continuing medical education for their members. Medical foundations have, though, also involved themselves in some aspects of managed care. Medical foundations have established PPOs, EPOs, and MSOs. As physician-led organizations, the common characteristics are freedom of choice and preservation of the physician–patient relationship.

Future Trends

Monitoring access to health services under managed care is an ongoing trend. Another trend is the ongoing evaluation of utilization of health services under managed care.

Access

Analysts have monitored access to health services under managed care from several perspectives. This section reports on access from three perspectives: uncompensated hospital care, racial disparities, and maternal care.

Uncompensated Care

Uncompensated care represents a significant cost to healthcare organizations. For example, U.S. hospitals bore costs of uncompensated care totaling $26.9 billion in 2004, an increase of 8 percent over 2003 (Evans 2005, 4).

Uncompensated care is an overall measure of services provided for which no payments were received from the patient, client, or third party payer (American Hospital Association 2006, 1). It is the sum of the healthcare organization's **bad debts** and **charity care** (American Hospital Association 2006, 1). Bad debts are services for which healthcare organizations expected, but did not receive, payment (American Hospital Association 2006, 2). Charity care consists of services for which healthcare organizations did not expect payment because they had previously determined the patients' or clients' inability to pay (American Hospital Association 2006, 2). Thus, uncompensated care is healthcare organizations' total costs for unreimbursed services to medically indigent or underinsured patients and clients (American Hospital Association 2006, 2).

A study of data from Florida hospitals found that managed care had a negative effect on the provision of uncompensated care, taking into account other factors (McKay and Meng 2007, 121). Thus, as the number of managed care patients and clients receiving hospital care increased, the number of medically indigent and underinsured patients and clients receiving hospital care decreased (McKay and Meng 2007, 121). The researchers explained that hospitals offset the revenues lost because of discounts to managed care plans by providing less uncompensated care (McKay and Meng 2007, 122). While the magnitude of the decrease was modest, it had significant implications (McKay and Meng 2007, 122). Provision of uncompensated care is a key element under which not-for-profit hospitals maintain their tax exemption (McKay and Meng 2007, 122). Finally, reductions in uncompensated care translate into reduced access to healthcare.

Racial Disparities

Racial disparities in healthcare access exist (Cook 2007, 125). One researcher evaluated the effect of Medicaid Managed Care on racial disparities in access to healthcare (Cook 2007, 128). Studying this topic with data from Medicaid Managed Care is appropriate because of the numbers of Medicaid recipients enrolled in managed care programs. In 2004, approximately 60 percent of Medicaid recipients or 27 million people were enrolled in managed care (Centers for Medicare and Medicaid Services 2006). Forty-seven states enroll their Medicaid recipients in some form of managed care (Centers for Medicare and Medicaid Services 2006). Analysis showed that enrollment in Medicaid Managed Care significantly reduced disparities between African Americans and whites in having a doctor visit (Cook 2007, 138). However, no change was seen in the disparity between Hispanics and whites in having a doctor visit (Cook 2007, 138). The disparity for having a usual source of care was eliminated for both African Americans and Hispanics (Cook 2007, 138). However, enrollment in Medicaid Managed Care was associated with an exacerbation of the disparity between African Americans and whites in use of the emergency room (Cook 2007, 138). A reverse disparity existed between Hispanics and whites in use of the emergency room as Hispanics used the emergency room less than whites (Cook 2007, 138). The researcher concluded that Medicaid Managed Care contributed to reducing disparities in seeing a doctor and having a usual source of care and that the findings related to use of emergency rooms required further study (Cook 2007, 138). Therefore, overall Medicaid Managed Care improved access to care for members of underserved populations.

Maternal Care

Comparing maternal services presents another perspective on the effect of managed care on access to healthcare services. Analysts compared services provided to pregnant women covered under fee-for-service healthcare insurance and services provided to pregnant women covered under managed care (Turcotte et al. 2006, 1514). The analysts focused on four services: ultrasound, induction/stimulation of birth, electronic fetal monitor, and Cesarean delivery (Turcotte et al. 2006, 1514). Pregnant women covered under managed care were more likely to receive ultrasounds and fetal monitoring than women covered under fee-for-service healthcare insurance (Turcotte et al. 2006, 1523.). Managed care enrollees were less likely to have Cesarean deliveries or induced/stimulated deliveries than fee-for-service enrollees. The researchers noted that the literature indicates that Cesarean deliveries are overutilized and that induced/stimulated deliveries are elective (Turcotte et al. 2006, 1523). Thus, overall managed care had not adversely affected the treatment of pregnant women by limiting access to services.

Utilization

On an ongoing basis, health economists analyze the effect of managed care on utilization of services. Trending these data is important as healthcare is 16 percent of the gross domestic product and managed care is a growing sector of the healthcare industry. Health economists compared utilization of healthcare services in two national surveys from the same time period (Deb et al. 2006, 743). The two surveys were the Medical Expenditure Panel Survey (MEPS) and the Community Tracking Survey (CTS) (Deb et al. 2006, 743). The two surveys allowed cross-checking of findings. Using data from the MEPS, HMO enrollees are predicted to have 2.52 more doctor visits annually and 0.12 more emergency room visits annually than enrollees in nonmanaged care plans (Deb et al. 2006, 756). Similarly, using data from CTS, HMO enrollees are predicted to have 1.89 more doctor visits annually and 0.09 more emergency room visits annually than enrollees in nonmanaged care plans (Deb et al. 2006, 756). Even accounting for adverse selection, enrollment in managed care is associated with higher utilization of healthcare services than enrollment in nonmanaged care plans (Deb et al. 2006, 757). Health professionals can expect that this utilization pattern will continue to be studied as it relates to healthcare policy.

Check Your Understanding 5.2

1. Which type of integrated delivery system is most common, and what types of providers may be included?

2. List the four types of integration models.

3. Name two ways that practices having integrated structures lower their overhead costs.

Summary

Managed care is the provision of cost-effective, quality healthcare through the integration of administrative, financial, and clinical systems. Managed care organizations (MCOs) implement the concepts and techniques of managed care to both deliver and finance healthcare. Managed care organizations share characteristics associated with providing quality care, such as an emphasis on coordination of care, techniques of disease management, application of evidence-based clinical practice guidelines, and maintenance of accreditation. MCOs also share characteristics associated with cost efficiency, such as review of medical necessity and utilization and financial incentives. Also associated with cost savings is capitation, a reimbursement method common to MCOs in which the providers share risk. Multiple types of MCOs exist on a continuum of control with health maintenance organizations representing the most controlled and preferred provider organizations, the least controlled. An integrated delivery system is a separate legal entity that healthcare providers have formed to offer a comprehensive set of healthcare services to a population. In the future, health professionals can expect that health policy analysts will continue to trend access to and utilization of health services under managed care.

Review Quiz

1. Describe at least three ways in which MCOs work toward their goal of quality patient care.

2. From where do evidence-based clinical guidelines originate?

3. List at least two reasons that MCOs survey their members for feedback.

4. Name the three steps in medical necessity and utilization review.

5. Describe three types of cost controls used by MCOs.

6. Which type of HMO offers patients the least selection in referrals to specialists?

7. List at least five types of services or populations that are common examples of "carve outs."

8. Disease management is closely associated with coordination of care tools of MCOs because efforts of multiple providers must be synchronized in disease management. True or false?

9. Integrated delivery systems typically have horizontal rather than vertical integration of services. True or false?

10. The least binding degree of healthcare service integration is affiliation, and the highest degree of integration is the merger. True or false?

References and Bibliography

Alexander, J.M. 1999. Managed care contracting for specialists. *Healthcare Financial Management* 52(12 Suppl): S6–S10.

American College of Managed Care Medicine. 2005. A history of managed care. Available online from www.managing managedcare.com/Resources/HxMgdCare.htm.

American Hospital Association. 2006, October. Uncompensated hospital care cost fact sheet. Accessed at http://www.aha.org/aha/content/2006/pdf/uncompensatedcarefs2006.pdf 19 September 2007.

Baseman, S., and R. Truxell. 2000, February. Developing an IDS-based disease-management program for the frail elderly. *Healthcare Financial Management* 54(2):33–36.

Blue Cross. 2005. www.brainyencyclopedia.com/encyclopedia/b/bl/blue_cross.html.

Blumenthal, D., and M.B. Buntin. 1998, June 25. Carve outs: Definition, experience, and choice among candidate conditions. *American Journal of Managed Care* 4(Suppl):SP45–SP57.

Carlson, B. 2000. Many state Medicaid agencies use financial incentives to boost quality. *Managed Care* 9 (4): 13–14.

Centers for Medicare and Medicaid Services. 2006. Overview. Available at http://www.cms.hhs.gov/MedicaidManagCare/ 19 September 2007.

Cook, B.L. 2007, February. Effect of Medicaid managed care on racial disparities in health care access. *Health Services Research* 42(1 Pt 1):124–145.

Deb, P., C. Li, P.K. Trivedi, and D.M. Zimmer. 2006, July. The effect of managed care on use of health care services: Results from two contemporaneous household surveys. *Health Economics* 15(7):743–760.

Evans, M. 2005, November 28. Bearable burden: Hospital spending on poor moderate in 2005. *Modern Healthcare* 35(48):4.

Felt-Lisk, S. 1996. How HMOs structure primary care delivery. *Managed Care Quarterly* 4 (4): 96–105.

Foster, R. S. 2000. Trends in Medicare expenditures and financial status, 1966–2000. *Health Care Financing Review* 22 (1): 35–49.

Gallagher, T., A. Alpers, and B. Lo. 1998. Health Care Financing Administration's new regulations for financial incentives in Medicaid and Medicare managed care: One step forward? *American Journal of Medicine* 105 (5): 409–415.

Garnick, D. W., C.M. Horgan, D. Hodgkin, E.L. Merrick, D. Goldin, G. Ritter, and K.C. Skwara. 2001, November. Risk transfer and accountability in managed care organizations' carve-out contracts. *Psychiatric Services* 52(11): 1502–1509.

Grumbach, K., et al. 1998. Primary care physicians' experience of financial incentives in managed-care systems. *New England Journal of Medicine* 339 (21): 1516–1521.

Joint Commission. 2007. Discontinuation of Network Accreditation Programs. Accessed at http://www.jointcommission.org/AccreditationPrograms/Networks 14 December 2007.

Kaiser Permanente. 2007. Accessed at http://www.individual-health-plans.com/kaiserpermanente.htm 19 September 2007

Kalant, N., M. Berlinguet, J. Diodati, L. Dragatakis, and F. Marcotte. 2000. How valid are utilization review tools in assessing appropriate use of acute care beds? *Canadian Medical Association Journal* 162 (13): 1809–1813.

Manus, P. and S. Shortell. 1995. The future of integrated systems. *Healthcare Financial Management* 49 (1): 24–30.

McKay, N.L., and X. Meng. 2007, Spring. The effect of managed care on hospitals' provision of uncompensated care. *Inquiry-Excellus Health Plan* 44(1):114–124.

Rutledge, R.. 1998. An analysis of 25 Milliman & Robertson guidelines for surgery: Data-driven versus consensus-derived clinical practice guidelines. *Annals of Surgery* 228 (4): 579–587.

Scanlan, L. 1995. Building consensus for integration. *Healthcare Financial Management* 49 (1): 32–43.

Starr, P. 1982. *The Social Transformation of American Medicine*. New York: Basic Books.

State health plan for North Carolina. 2005. Available online from statehealthplan.state.nc.us/yourbenefits/benefits.pdf.

Turcotte, L., J. Robst, and S. Polachek. 2006, July 20. Medical interventions among pregnant women in fee-for-service and managed care insurance: A propensity score analysis. *Applied Economics* 38(13):1513–1525.

Chapter 6
Medicare-Medicaid Prospective Payment Systems for Inpatients

Objectives

- To differentiate major types of Medicare and Medicaid prospective payment systems for inpatients

- To define basic language associated with reimbursement under Medicare and Medicaid prospective payment systems

- To explain common models and policies of payment for inpatient Medicare and Medicaid prospective payment systems

Key Terms

Add-ons
Arithmetic mean length of stay (AMLOS)
Average length of stay (ALOS)
Base payment rate
Case mix
Case mix group (CMG)
Case mix index (CMI)
Clean claim
Code range
Complication or comorbidity (CC)
Cost reports
Cost-of-living adjustment (COLA)
Diagnosis related groups (DRGs)
Encounter
Etiologic diagnosis
Fiscal intermediaries (FI)
Fiscal year (FY)
Functional independence assessment tool
Functional status
Geometric mean length of stay (GMLOS)
Grouper (pricer)

High-cost outliers
Hospital within hospital (HwH)
Impairment group code (IGC)
Indirect medical education (IME) adjustment
Inpatient Rehabilitation Validation and Entry (IRVEN)
Interrupted stays
Labor-related share
Long-term care hospital (LTCH)
Major complication/comorbidity (MCC)
Major diagnostic categories (MDCs)
Market basket
Market basket index
Medicare Administrative Contractor (MAC)
Medicare-severity diagnosis related group (MS-DRG)
Medicare-severity long-term care diagnosis related group (MS-LTC-DRG)
Minimum data set (MDS)
New technology
Noncase-mix adjusted component
Noncase-mix component
Noncase mix therapy component

Nonlabor share
Nursing component
Nursing per diem amount
Nursing index
Outliers
Prospective payment systems (PPSs)
Qualifying OR procedure
Quintile
Rehabilitation impairment category (RIC)
Relative weight (RW)
Resource utilization groups (RUGs)

Short-stay outliers
Sole-community hospital
Standard federal rate
Standardized payment
Teaching hospitals
Therapy component
Therapy per diem amount
Therapy index
Title
Transfer
Trim points

Introduction to Inpatient Prospective Payment Systems (PPSs)

Federal legislators are demanding that healthcare costs be controlled. These demands have led to federal healthcare reimbursement reform. Reform in the federal method of reimbursing providers for healthcare services resulted from three trends:

- Rising healthcare payments using the funds in the Medicare Trust at a rate faster than U.S. workers were contributing dollars

- Fraud and abuse in the system, which wasted funding

- Payment rules that were not uniformly applied across the nation

Federal analysts noted that the inpatient **prospective payment system** (PPS), implemented in 1983, had successfully curbed payments for inpatient charges. In the first three years of the prospective payment system, the rate of growth of Medicare Part A payments decreased from 7.3 percent in the five years prior to its implementation to 4 percent (Lave 1989, 152). Reporting on longer time periods, the staff of the Office of the Inspector General wrote that Medicare hospital payments increased by 88 percent between 1970 and 1980 (Gottlober 2001, 3) and the payment rates decreased by 52 percent between 1985 and 1990; and by 37 percent between 1990 and 1995.

This success of the inpatient prospective payment system prompted Congress to authorize the Department of Health and Human Services (DHHS) to develop and implement prospective payment systems across the continuum of care. Today, the original acute care PPS has been augmented by prospective payment systems for all types of inpatients through the skilled nursing facility prospective payment system, long-term care hospital prospective payment system, inpatient rehabilitation prospective payment system, and inpatient psychiatric facility prospective payment system. Also, Chapter 7 describes reimbursement systems for ambulatory **encounters** and physicians.

Acute Care Prospective Payment System

The inpatient prospective payment system (IPPS) is the Medicare reimbursement system for inpatient services provided in an acute care setting. The system provides payment to facilities but does not include payment for professional services.

Conversion from Cost-Based Payment to Prospective Payment

From the implementation of the Medicare Program in 1966 until 1983, Medicare hospital inpatient claims were reimbursed based on the cost of services, reasonable cost, and/or per-diem costs (LaTour and Eichenwald 2006, 303). This meant a hospital was reimbursed for approximately 80 percent of their costs for treating Medicare beneficiaries. From the hospital's perspective, there was no incentive to reduce costs—if its costs associated with patient care increased, so did its payments. By the late 1970s, healthcare costs, hand in hand with Medicare reimbursement payments, were sharply on the rise. The steep increase in healthcare costs had a dramatic impact on the Medicare Program, as illustrated by the following facts (Averill 2001, 105):

- Medicare payments to hospitals grew on average by 19 percent annually (three times the average overall rate of inflation).

- The Medicare hospital deductible expanded, creating a burden for Medicare beneficiaries.

- The solvency of the Medicare Trust Fund was endangered due to the increase of hospital costs.

- The increase in Medicare expenditures for hospital inpatient care jeopardized the ability of Medicare to fund other needed health programs.

- Under the variable cost-based payment system, Medicare paid up to sixfold differences across hospitals for comparable services.

- The reporting requirements of the cost-based system were some of the most burdensome in the federal government

In response to the rising healthcare costs, Medicare administrators began to search for a different payment mechanism in the early 1970s to help control the rising healthcare costs.

Concept of Prospective Payment

The system that they began to investigate was based on the concept of prospective payment. In 1972, Congress authorized CMS (then HCFA) to begin prospective payment demonstration projects (Averill 2001, 83). The demonstration projects had to follow four guiding principles of prospective payment in their study:

- Payment rates are to be established in advance and fixed for the fiscal period to which they apply.

- Payment rates are not automatically determined by the hospital's past or current actual cost.

- Prospective payment rates are considered to be payment in full.

- The hospital retains the profit or suffers a loss resulting from the difference between the payment rate and the hospital's cost, thus creating an incentive for cost control (Averill 2001, 106).

Demonstration Projects

Between 1972 and 1983, Connecticut, Maryland, Massachusetts, New Jersey, New York, Rhode Island, Washington, and Wisconsin implemented prospective payment systems (PPSs) by participating in the demonstration projects (Averill 2001, 106). Based on these demonstration projects, CMS concluded:

- Prospective payment itself was effective in reducing the rate of increase in hospital costs.

- All state systems required consideration of hospital **case mix.**

- Failure to adequately address the case mix issue results in an active appeals process.

- Small rural hospitals frequently required special exceptions unless case mix was explicitly recognized in the payment system.

- Prospective payment rates were established through use of actual hospital costs for a base year.

- Successful systems had a firm legal basis with strict enforcement and could not be manipulated by the hospitals.

- Individual hospitals' budget review systems were often managed by exceptions and were complex to administer.

- All prospective payment systems had some inherent undesirable incentives that required the insertion of countermeasures.

The projects proved that hospital costs could be controlled under a prospective payment system and still allow for adequate reimbursement of hospital services rendered to Medicare beneficiaries.

New Jersey Model

Medicare chose the New Jersey model, which was based on **diagnosis related groups (DRGs)** as the prospective payment system to use. The DRG system was created at Yale University in the late 1960s through early 1970s. The initial charge for the DRG developers was to create a classification system that would monitor quality of care and use of services in a hospital setting. Although DRGs can be used to monitor quality and utilization, they are best known for their use as the foundation for the Medicare Inpatient Prospective Payment System implemented in 1983.

Prospective Payment Legislation

The Tax Equity and Fiscal Responsibility Act of 1982 (TEFRA) mandated extensive changes to the Medicare program. Many of the changes focused on controlling the rising costs of healthcare. TEFRA called for the implementation of a prospective payment system for hospital inpatients (Johns 2002, 256). In 1983, Public Law 98–21 amended Sections 1886(d) and 1886(g) of the Social Security Act (the Act) and mandated DRGs as the prospective payment system for the operating and capital-related costs of acute care hospital inpatient stays under Medicare Part A (DHHS 2004e, 48920).

Diagnosis Related Group Classification System

The diagnosis related group (DRG) system takes into consideration the role that a hospital case mix plays in influencing costs (Averill 2001, 83). Each DRG is assigned a relative weight that is intended to represent the resource intensity of the clinical group. It is also used to determine the payment level for the group. **Case mix index** (CMI) is an average of the sum of the **relative weights** of all patients treated during a specified time period. It should be noted that case mix is defined in many different ways, based on one's healthcare perspective. From a clinician's or physician's perspective, case mix complexity or description of the patient population can refer to the severity of illness, risk of mortality, prognosis, treatment difficulty, or need for intervention. This viewpoint uses sickness as a proxy for resource consumption.

However, from the DRG perspective, the case mix complexity is a direct measure of the resource consumption and, therefore, the cost of providing care. A high case mix in the DRG system means patients are consuming more resources, and, therefore, the cost of care is higher. However, it is a

weak measure of the severity of illness, risk of mortality, prognosis, treatment difficulty, or need for intervention for the patient population (Averill 2001, 84). Therefore, this case mix complexity viewpoint allows DRGs to be an adequate system for hospital reimbursement because it measures the resources consumed for clinically-like patients.

Classification System Development

The hospital inpatient business is vast, with great variation in the types of diseases treated and procedures performed. Consequently, the task of creating a classification system to encompass the industry was understandably daunting. After statistical analysis and physician consultation, four guidelines were established as guiding principles for the DRG system's formation:

- The patient characteristics used in the definition of the DRGs should be limited to information routinely collected on the hospital billing form.

- There should be a manageable number of DRGs, which encompass all patients seen on an inpatient basis.

- Each DRG should contain patients with a similar pattern of resource intensity.

- Each DRG should contain patients who are similar from a clinical perspective (that is, each class should be clinically coherent) (Averill 2001, 85).

Medicare has been successful at implementing the DRG system because it strictly adheres to these guiding principles. All hospitals are able to compute a DRG because they routinely collect all data needed to calculate the DRG assignment. Version 25.0 (effective dates October 1, 2007–September 30, 2008) of the DRG system includes 745 **Medicare-severity diagnosis groups (MS-DRGs),** which is a reasonable number of groupings for hospitals to evaluate and manage. Linking like-patients with like resource consumption allows hospitals to perform cost management by DRG or DRG groupings. In addition, because DRGs were developed to monitor quality of care and resource use, hospitals can benchmark by DRG and continually improve upon their quality and resource indicators.

Only one DRG can be assigned and reimbursed for a single admission. All hospital services performed during an admission are packaged into this single DRG payment. The payment provided for the DRG is intended to cover the costs of all hospital services performed during the patient stay. Therefore, individual tests, services, pharmaceuticals, and supply items are not paid separately from the DRG payment. One component of a prospective payment system is that the predetermined payment for the clinical group is considered payment in full. Therefore, hospitals accept profit or loss based on their cost of providing services. The fully packaged concept drives facilities to practice cost management for inpatient services. Physician services are separately reimbursed under RBRVS and are not included in the DRG reimbursement to the hospital.

Structure of the DRG System

The DRG system is hierarchal in design. (See figure 6.1.) The highest level in the hierarchy is **major diagnostic categories (MDCs),** which represent the body systems treated by medicine. At the system's inception, there were twenty-three MDCs, plus a group for DRGs associated with all MDCs and the preMDC. However, in Version 8.0 (October 1, 1990–September 30, 1991) two new MDCs were added to represent the Human Immunodeficiency Virus Infections and Multiple Significant Trauma categories (see table 6.1). The next level in the hierarchy divides each MDC group into surgical and medical sections. The third and final level in the

Figure 6.1.   Hierarchical DRG system

Table 6.1.   Major diagnostic categories

MDC	Title
	DRGs associated with all MDCs and the PreMDC
1	Diseases and disorders of the nervous system
2	Diseases and disorders of the eye
3	Diseases and disorders of the ear, nose, mouth, and throat
4	Diseases and disorders of the respiratory system
5	Diseases and disorders of the circulatory system
6	Diseases and disorders of the digestive system
7	Diseases and disorders of the hepatobiliary system and pancreas
8	Diseases and disorders of the musculoskeletal system and connective tissue
9	Diseases and disorders of the skin, subcutaneous tissue, and breast
10	Endocrine, nutritional and metabolic diseases and disorders
11	Diseases and disorders of the kidney and urinary tract
12	Diseases and disorders of the male reproductive system
13	Diseases and disorders of the female reproductive system
14	Pregnancy, childbirth, and the puerperium
15	Newborns and other neonates with conditions originating in the perinatal period
16	Diseases and disorders of the blood and blood-forming organs and immunological disorders
17	Myeloproliferative diseases and disorders and poorly differentiated neoplasms
18	Infectious and parasitic diseases
19	Mental diseases and disorders
20	Alcohol/drug use and alcohol/drug-induced organic mental disorders
21	Injury, poisoning, and toxic effects of drugs
22	Burns
23	Factors influencing health status and other contacts with health services
24	Multiple significant trauma
25	Human immunodeficiency virus infections

hierarchy divides the DRGs into the surgical or medical sections amongst the twenty-five MDC groups. Table 6.2 presents the ten DRGs reported to Medicare most frequently in fiscal year 2006.

Each version of the DRG system defines the same components: **title**, **geometric mean length of stay (GMLOS)**, **arithmetic mean length of stay (AMLOS)**, **relative weight (RW)**, and ICD-9-CM **code range** that drives the DRG assignment. (See figure 6.2.) The code range may consist of the principal diagnosis, operating room (OR) procedure, or a diagnosis/procedure combination.

Severity Refinement to DRGs

In FY 2008 (October 1, 2007 through September 30, 2008) CMS adopted Medicare-severity DRGs (MS-DRGs) for use in the IPPS. The Medicare Payment Advisory Commission (MedPAC) and the hospital community at large greatly influenced CMS to migrate to a severity-adjusted DRG system. Specifically, the 2005 MedPAC *Report to Congress on Physician Owned Specialty Hospitals* provided several recommendations regarding how CMS could add a severity component to IPPS. One of the biggest criticism of the DRG system over the years was the lack of severity, many felt the refinement was necessary for CMS to be able to adequately reimburse a facility for the more complex and resource intensive cases.

Table 6.2.   Medicare top 10 MS-DRGs based on FY 2006 data

MS-DRG	MS-DRG Title	Volume	Relative Weight
470	Major joint replacement or reattachment of lower extremity w/o MCC	420,832	1.9871
392	Esophagitis, gastroent & misc digest disorders w/o MCC	332,818	0.7121
194	Simple pneumonia & pleurisy w CC	295,268	1.0235
247	Perc cardiovasc proc w drug-eluting stent w/o MCC	280,971	2.1255
293	Heart failure & shock w/o CC/MCC	246,773	0.8765
313	Chest pain	233,216	0.5489
292	Heart failure & shock w CC	232,661	1.0134
690	Kidney & urinary tract infections w/o MCC	219,743	0.8000
192	Chronic obstructive pulmonary disease w/o CC/MCC	218,500	0.8145
871	Septicemia w/o MV 96+ hours w MCC	213,339	1.7484

Figure 6.2.   MS-DRG components

MS-DRG 293	
Title: Heart Failure and Shock w/o CC/MCC	
Geometric Mean Length of Stay (GMLOS):	3.1
Arithmetic Mean Length of Stay (AMLOS):	3.7
Relative Weight:	0.8765
Principal Diagnosis	
Failure, heart, congestive, rheumatic	398.91
Hypertensive heart disease, malignant, with heart failure	402.01
Hypertensive heart disease, benign, with heart failure	402.11
Hypertensive heart disease, unspecified, with heart failure	402.91
Hypertensive heart and renal disease, malignant, with failure, heart	404.01
Hypertensive heart and renal disease, malignant, with failure, heart and renal	404.03
Hypertensive heart and renal disease, benign, with failure, heart	404.11
Hypertensive heart and renal disease, benign, with failure, heart and renal	404.13
Hypertensive heart and renal disease, unspecified, with failure, heart	404.91
Hypertensive heart and renal disease, unspecified, with failure, heart and renal	404.93
Failure, heart	*428
Shock, unspecified, without mention of trauma	785.50
Shock, cardiogenic	785.51

*Entire code range is included.

The MS-DRG system is a refinement of the DRG system, which uses **major complication/comorbidity (MCC)** diagnosis codes and **complication/comorbidity (CC)** diagnosis codes to establish a greater number of subclassifications or MS-DRGs. The greater number of classifications is intended to better differentiate between the levels of resource consumption within a base MS-DRG group. Figure 6.3 shows the four types of subclassification breakouts under MS-DRGs.

Along with the development of MS-DRGs, CMS revised the CC list. The CC list had not had a major revision since its inception; the only updates to the list were made based on code additions and deletions from the ICD-9-CM code system. New criteria were established for the CC list. For each diagnosis the following questions were posed:

Does this condition require intensive monitoring?

Does this condition result in the use of expensive and technically complex services?

Does this condition result in extensive care requiring a greater number of caregivers?

Figure 6.3   Example subclassification breakouts under MS-DRGs

Example 3 subgroups	
MS-DRG 190 COPD with MCC	RW 1.1138
MS-DRG 191 COPD with CC	RW 0.9405
MS-DRG 192 COPD without MCC/CC	RW 0.8145
Example 2 subgroups	
MS-DRG 231 Coronary bypass with PTCA with MCC	RW 7.2993
MS-DRG 232 Coronary bypass with PTCA without MCC	RW 6.1947
Example 2 subgroups	
MS-DRG 131 Cranial/facial procedures with CC/MCC	RW 1.6300
MS-DRG 132 Cranial/facial procedures without CC/MCC	RW 1.2054
Example 1 subgroup	
MS-DRG 313 Chest pain	RW 0.5489

Over 730 codes were removed from the CC list for FY 2008. Chronic conditions without an acute manifestation were removed from the list. What remained on the list or were added included significant acute diseases, acute exacerbations of chronic conditions, advanced or end stage chronic diseases, and chronic diseases associated with extensive debility. In addition, each code that remained on the list after the revision was designated as either a CC or a MCC; so the CC list became two different lists for use with MS-DRGs. The revision of the CC list has a drastic impact on the percent of patients assigned to a higher-weighted MS-DRG within a MS-DRG set. Table 6.3 provides a scenario which provides a comparison of the FY 2007 CC list and the revised FY 2008 CC and MCC lists.

Assigning MS-DRGs

Computer programs that assign patients to case mix groups are generically called **groupers** or **pricers.** Groupers have internal logic, or an algorithm, that determines the patients' groups. Although groupers are available and widely used for MS-DRG assignment, a good understanding of the assignment process is necessary to help coding and reimbursement professionals ensure proper payment for services communicated. A four-step process is used to assign MS-DRGs for hospital inpatient encounters. (See figure 6.4.)

Table 6.3   Comparison of FY 2007 CC list and FY 2008 CC and MCC lists

	2007 CC List	2008 CC List
Codes designated as a CC	3,326	2,583
Percent of patients with one or more CCs	77.66%	40.34%
Percent of patients with no CC	22.34%	59.66%
Average charge of patients with one or more CCs	$24,538	$31,451
Average charge of patients with no CCs	$14,795	$16,215

Source: Table E, *Federal Register* 72 (85): 47154.

Figure 6.4.   Excerpt of MS-DRG decision tree for surgical MDC 06

Step One: PreMDC Assignment

The pre-MDC assignment step was added during the version 8 revision of DRGs. A set of procedures was identified that crossed all MDCs. The principal diagnosis is not considered for MS-DRG assignment; rather, the principal ICD-9-CM procedure is used to assign the DRG. These procedures, transplants, and tracheostomies can be performed for diagnoses from multiple MDCs. Once the encounter has been determined to qualify for preMDC assignment, the MS-DRG assignment is made and the process is complete. No other steps are taken to assign the payment group. The thirteen MS-DRGs that qualify for preMDC assignment are displayed in table 6.4. If the MS-DRG assignment is made during step one, all other steps are ignored.

Step One Example:

A pancreas transplant can be performed for a variety of clinical conditions including diabetes with renal, ophthalmic, neurological, or peripheral circulatory manifestations (MDC 10), hypertensive renal disease (MDC 05), chronic pancreatitis (MDC 06), chronic renal failure (MDC 11), and complications of transplanted organs (MDC 21). The diagnoses that warrant a pancreas transplant can be found in multiple MDCs. In order to maintain a manageable number of MS-DRGs and to adhere to the concept of like-resource consumption groupings, there is only one MS-DRG for all pancreas transplants regardless of the principal diagnosis. Therefore, the patient who received a pancreas transplant would be assigned to MS-DRG 010 regardless of the principal diagnosis.

Step Two: MDC Determination

The principal diagnosis assigned to an encounter is the reason "established after study to be chiefly responsible for occasioning the admission of the patient to the hospital for care" (Schraffenberger 2005, 49). The principal diagnosis is used to place the encounter into one of the 25 MDCs. (See table 6.1.) Once the MDC is established for the encounter, step two is complete and the case moves on to step three.

Table 6.4.   PreMDC assignment for MS-DRGs

MS-DRG	Title
001	Heart transplant or implant of heart assist system with MCC
002	Heart transplant or implant of heart assist system without MCC
003	ECMO or tracheostomy with mechanical ventilation 96+ hours or principal diagnosis except face, mouth, and neck diagnoses with major OR procedure
004	Tracheostomy with mechanical ventilation 96+ hours or principal diagnosis except face, mouth, and neck diagnoses without major OR procedure
005	Liver transplant with MCC or intestinal transplant
006	Liver transplant without MCC
007	Lung transplant
008	Simultaneous pancreas/kidney transplant
009	Bone marrow transplant
010	Pancreas transplant
011	Tracheostomy for face, mouth & neck diagnoses with MCC
012	Tracheostomy for face, mouth & neck diagnoses with CC
013	Tracheostomy for face, mouth & neck diagnoses without CC/MCC

Step Two Example:

Patient A presents and is treated for pneumonia due to Streptococcus, Group A. The ICD-9-CM code for Group A Streptococcus pneumonia is 482.31 and is assigned to MDC 04, Diseases and Disorders of the Respiratory System.

Step Three: Medical/Surgical Determination

The next step is to determine if an OR procedure was performed. If a **qualifying OR procedure** was performed, the case is assigned a surgical status. Many ICD-9-CM code books provide a flag or indicator for procedure codes that qualify as valid OR procedures. Minor procedures and testing are not qualifying procedures. If a qualifying OR procedure was not performed, the case is assigned a medical status.

Step Three Example:

Patient A presents and is treated for an acute myocardial infarction of the anterolateral wall, initial episode (heart attack). The ICD-9-CM code for this diagnosis is 410.01 and is assigned to MDC 05, Diseases and Disorders of the Circulatory System (step two). During the hospital stay a percutaneous transluminal coronary angioplasty (PTCA) is performed on the right coronary artery. In this example, code 00.66 is assigned for the PTCA and is a valid OR procedure. Therefore, this case is a surgical case in MDC 05.

Patient B is also evaluated for an acute myocardial infarction of the anterolateral wall, initial episode (heart attack). The ICD-9-CM code for this diagnosis is 410.01 and is assigned to MDC 05, Diseases and Disorders of the Circulatory System (step two). However, no procedures were performed for this patient during the hospital stay. This case is a medical case in MDC 05.

Once the medical/surgical status is assigned, step three is complete, and the case proceeds to step four.

Step Four: Refinement
Step four uses various refinement questions to isolate the correct MS-DRG assignment. This refinement process allows for the MS-DRG system to group together like patients from the clinical perspective with like resource consumption. The refinement questions group patients by like resource consumption. The refinement questions are:

- Is a major complication or comorbidity (MCC) present?
- Is a complication or comorbidity (CC) present?
- Is the principal diagnosis complicated?
- Is a major complication or complex diagnosis present?

- What is the patient's sex?
- What is the patient's discharge disposition (alive, expired, or against medical advice)?
- For neonates, what is the birth weight of the baby?

Step Four Surgical Example:

Patient A is sixty-seven years old and is admitted for a duodenum fistula closure procedure. The patient also has malignant essential hypertension. The ICD-9-CM diagnosis codes are 537.4 (Duodenum fistula) and 401.0 (hypertension), and the ICD-9-CM procedure code is 46.72. Code 537.4 is assigned to MDC 06, Diseases and Disorders of the Digestive System (step two). Code 46.72 is a valid OR procedure (step three). Therefore, the case is a surgical MDC 06 case.

There are two applicable pathway questions for this encounter. First, is there a major complication or comorbidity present? The answer is no, code 401.0 is not on the MCC list. Second, is there a complication or comorbidity present? Malignant essential hypertension is a comorbidity; therefore, the answer is yes. Now that all the refinement questions have been answered, the MS-DRG assignment can be made. The MS-DRG assignment for this case is MS-DRG 327, Stomach, Esophageal, and Duodenal Procedures.

Step Four Medical Example:

Patient B is sixty-eight years old and is admitted for cellulitis of the right ankle. Nonexcisional debridement is performed on the right ankle. The patient also has chronic obstructive pulmonary disease (COPD). The ICD-9-CM diagnosis codes are 682.6 (Cellulitis of leg, except foot) and 496 (COPD) and the ICD-9-CM procedure code is 86.28. Code 682.6 is assigned to MDC 09, Diseases and Disorders of the Skin, Subcutaneous Tissue and Breast (step two). Code 86.28 is not a valid OR procedure (step three). Therefore, the case is a medical MDC 09 case.

There is one applicable pathway question for this encounter. Is there a major complication or comorbidity present? COPD is not a major complication or comorbidity; therefore, the answer is no. Now that all the refinement questions have been answered, the MS-DRG assignment can be made. The MS-DRG assignment for this case is MS-DRG 603, Cellulitis without MCC.

Invalid Coding and Data Abstraction

Accurate diagnosis/procedure coding and healthcare information abstracting are vital to MS-DRG assignment. When invalid codes or data are submitted on the patient claim form, one of two MS-DRGs is assigned. MS-DRG 998, Principal Diagnosis Invalid as Discharge Diagnosis, is assigned when the principal diagnosis reported is not specific enough for MS-DRG assignment. MS-DRG 999, Ungroupable, is assigned when an invalid diagnosis code, age, sex, or discharge status code is reported. Payment for each of these MS-DRGs is $0. The claim is returned to the provider and should be corrected, then resubmitted to Medicare.

Provisions of the MS-DRG System

The MS-DRG system uses provisions to provide additional payments for specialized programs and unusual admissions that historically have added significant cost to patient care. Without the additional payments associated with these provisions, it may not be feasible for acute care facilities to provide all services to Medicare beneficiaries.

Disproportionate Share Hospital

Effective for discharges occurring on or after May 1, 1986, Disproportionate Share Hospital (DSH) status was enacted for facilities with a high percentage of low-income patients (CMS n.d). Additional payment is provided for these hospitals because they experience a financial hardship by providing treatment for patients who are unable to pay for the services rendered. There are two methods of qualification for this provision. First, a hospital may qualify by exceeding 15 percent on the statutory formula. The statutory formula takes into consideration Medicare inpatient days for patients eligible for Medicare Part A, Medicare Advantage, and Supplemental Security Income (SSI), and total inpatient days for patients eligible for Medicaid but not Medicare Part A.

The second method for DSH qualification applies to large urban hospitals. If large urban hospitals are able to demonstrate that more than 30 percent of their total net inpatient care revenues come from state and local governments for indigent care (excluding Medicare and Medicaid) then they can be granted DSH status (CMS 2005). The DSH payment adjustment is hospital-specific and is based on a formula that incorporates the hospital bed size and hospital type (rural, **sole-community**, urban). The SSI/Medicare Part A Disproportionate Share Percentage File is updated once a year for the IPPS Final Rule and can be found on the Medicare Web site at www.cms.hhs.gov.

Indirect Medical Education

Approved **teaching hospitals** are provided an **indirect medical education (IME) adjustment.** The hospitals must have residents in an approved graduate medical education (GME) program. Teaching hospitals experience an increased patient care cost in comparison to nonteaching hospitals. Therefore, Medicare provides IME hospitals with additional reimbursement to help offset the costs of providing education to new physicians. The IME payment adjustment is hospital-specific. The adjustment factor is based on the hospital's ratio of residents to beds and a multiplier established by Congress. This formula is traditionally described as "a certain percentage increase in payment for every 10 percent increase in the resident-to-bed ratio."

Several acts of Congress have decreased the percentage increase during the past nine years. The most recent, Benefits Improvement and Protection Act (BIPA) of 2000, established the transition to a 5.5 percent increase to take effect in 2003. The percent increase of 5.5 percent in IME payment for every 10 percent increase in the resident-to-bed ratio is effective for FY 2005 and subsequent years.

High-Cost Outlier Cases

Because the Medicare payment for inpatient services is prospective, hospitals will experience profit or loss for individual cases whose reimbursements exceed or fall short of the cost incurred for a particular case. The payment provided to facilities is an average amount, meaning that some cases will result in a profit and some, a loss. For the most part, costs are covered if reasonable cost management is performed. However, there are extreme cases, **outliers,** for which the costs are very high when compared to the average costs for cases in the same MS-DRG. The outlier payment provision provides some financial relief for those cases.

For an encounter to qualify for an outlier payment, the hospital's Medicare-approved charges reported on the claim are converted to costs, using the cost-to-charge ratio (CCR), and compared to the threshold limit established for that **fiscal year (FY)**. If the threshold is exceeded, additional payment is made. The payment is 80 percent of the difference between the hospital's entire cost for the stay and the threshold amount (CMS 2005). Outlier payments for the Burn MS-DRGs (MS-DRGs 927–929 and 933–935) are 90 percent rather then 80 percent.

New Medical Services and New Technologies

New medical services, new technologies, and innovative methods for treating patients are often very costly. A **new technology** is an advance in medical technology that substantially improves, relative to technologies previously available, the diagnosis or treatment of Medicare beneficiaries (CMS 2005). Applicants for the status of new technology must submit a formal request, including a full description of the clinical applications of the technology and the results of any clinical evaluations demonstrating that the new technology represents a substantial clinical improvement, along with data to demonstrate the technology meets the high-cost threshold.

Providing these innovative services in a prospective system could, in many cases, lead to inadequate payments. These financial losses may prohibit a facility from offering new and innovative services to patients because they are simply not affordable. Therefore, in order to ensure that new and innovative services and technologies are provided to Medicare beneficiaries, the IPPS allows additional payments to be made for new medical services and new technologies. This payment provision allows for the full MS-DRG payment plus 50 percent of the cost for the new technology or service.

Payment

Medicare provides a six-step methodology for calculating total MS-DRG payment (CMS 2005). **Fiscal intermediaries or Medicare Administrative Contractors** use **grouper (pricer)** software to calculate the MS-DRG and payment for each hospital encounter.

Step One: MS-DRG Assignment

Hospitals must submit a claim to Medicare for payment using an electronic claim to its designated Medicare fiscal intermediary. The fiscal intermediary performs electronic auditing of the claim to ensure that the claim contains correct information (also referred to as **clean claim**) based on edits found in the Medicare Code Editor (MCE). Once the claim is deemed clean, the grouper software assigns a MS-DRG based on the demographic and coded data submitted.

Step Two: Establishment of Initial Payment Rate

A **base payment rate** is established for each Medicare-participating hospital for each fiscal year (FY). The base payment rate is a per encounter rate that is based on historic claims data. The standardized amounts are derived from 1981 hospital costs per Medicare discharge figures. The 1981 costs established the base year amount that was adjusted to explain differences among facilities for case mix, wage rates, DSH status, IME status, and certain hospital costs. The base-year amount has been updated each year since 1981 by an update factor that is established by Congress and is intended to account for inflation.

Each year, the standardized amount is divided into a labor-related portion and a nonlabor portion.

The **labor-related share** is adjusted by the wage index for the hospital's geographic location based on core based statistical areas (CBSA). The **non-labor share** is modified by a **cost-of-living adjustment (COLA)** if the hospital is located in Alaska or Hawaii. These adjustments establish the base payment rate for the effective fiscal year. A listing of the wage index and COLA values can be found in the IPPS Final Rule released each year via the Federal Register. Past and current *Federal Register* publications can be located via the government printing office at www.gpoaccess.gov. Current prospective payment system rules are also posted on the Medicare Web site at www.cms.hhs.gov.

The base payment rate is multiplied by the relative weight for the MS-DRG that was assigned in step one.

Example:

Patient A was seen for congestive heart failure (428.0) and no OR procedures were performed. MS-DRG 293 is assigned for the encounter. The relative weight for MS-DRG 293 is 0.8765. The hospital base rate is $7,325. In order to calculate the initial payment rate, the relative weight is multiplied by the hospital base rate. The initial payment rate for this case is $6,420.37 (0.8765 × $7,325).

Step Three: Add-on for Disproportionate Share Hospital
If the hospital has DSH status, the established percentage for that year for that facility is added on to the initial payment rate.

Step Four: Add-on for Indirect Medical Education
If the hospital qualifies for IME payments, then the established percentage for that year for that facility is added on.

Step Five: Add-on for High Cost Outlier
The costs incurred for providing services for the encounter are calculated and examined to determine whether the case qualifies for an outlier payment. If an outlier payment is warranted, the additional payment is added on during this step.

Step Six: Add-on for New Medical Service and Technology
The encounter is reviewed to determine whether any qualifying new services or technology were used during the course of patient treatment. If a new service or technology was used, the costs are calculated for the service or supply. Fifty percent of the calculated costs are added onto the payment.

Pricer Software
The pricer software is used to completes steps two through six. When the six steps are completed, payment is made to the facility and the data from the encounter is included in the National Claims History File. The Medicare Provider Analysis Review (MedPAR) file, an extract from the National Claims History File, is used for statistical analysis and research.

Transfer Cases
There are two types of **transfer** cases under the IPPS. The first category is a patient transfer between two IPPS hospitals. A type 1 transfer is when a patient is discharged from an acute IPPS hospital and is admitted to another acute IPPS hospital on the same day. If a patient leaves an acute IPPS hospital against medical advice (AMA) and is admitted to another acute IPPS hospital on the same day, this situation is treated the same as a transfer between two IPPS hospitals.

Payment is altered for the transferring hospital and is based on a per-diem rate methodology. The MS-DRG is established for the case and the full payment rate is calculated. This payment rate is divided by the GMLOS established for the MS-DRG, thus creating a per-diem rate. The transferring facility receives double the per-diem rate for the first day plus the per-diem rate for each day thereafter for the patient LOS. DHS, IME, and outlier **add-ons** are applied after the per-diem rate is established. The receiving facility receives full PPS payment for the case. The one exception to this rule is MS-DRG 789, Neonates Died or Transferred to Another Acute Care Facility. The payment and GMLOS established for MS-DRG 789 are based on historical data; no reduction is necessary because it is a transfer-related MS-DRG.

A transfer that occurs from an IPPS hospital to a hospital or unit excluded from IPPS is known as a type 2 transfer. For this type of transfer case, the full PPS payment is made to the transferring hospital and the receiving hospital or unit is paid on a reasonable cost basis or under prospective payment, whichever is applicable for that setting (CMS 2004, 1). However, there are exceptions to the payment policy, known as the post-acute care transfer policy, for type 2 transfer cases. Of the 273 MS-DRGs (see table 6.5) that qualify for the post-acute care transfer policy, a discharge from an acute IPPS hospital to an excluded IPPS hospital or unit is considered a type 1 transfer rather than a discharge. The facilities that are excluded from IPPS are:

- Inpatient rehabilitation facilities or units
- Long-term care hospitals
- Psychiatric hospitals and units
- Children's hospitals
- Cancer hospitals

Additionally, the case is considered a transfer instead of a discharge when a patient is discharged from an acute IPPS hospital and is admitted to a skilled nursing facility (SNF) or is sent home with a written plan of care for home health services that will begin within three days after discharge from the IPPS hospital. In these three situations, the same transfer payment provision used for IPPS-to-IPPS transfer cases (type 1 transfer cases) is enacted and followed for the 248 of the 273 qualifying MS-DRGs. For the remaining twenty-five MS-DRGs, there is a special payment policy which allows for 50 percent of the full MS-DRG payment plus the per diem amount to be made for the first day of stay, and then 50 percent of the per diem amount each day thereafter. These twenty-five MS-DRGs have significantly higher costs upon admission. Creating this special payment policy better reimburses facilities in the post-acute care transfer situation for these twenty-five MS-DRGs.

The post-acute care transfer policy ensures that an incentive is not created for hospitals to discharge patients early in order to reduce costs while still receiving full MS-DRG payment. Additionally, this concept allows for proper reimbursement levels when the full course of treatment is divided across two healthcare settings.

Maintenance of the MS-DRG System

CMS is responsible for updating the MS-DRG system. Each payment rate for each MS-DRG is intended to reimburse the costs for average resources required to care for encounters grouping to that MS-DRG. Therefore, adjustments are made to the MS-DRG system to account for changes in treatment patterns, technology, and other elements that influence resource cost. Section 1886(d)(4)(C) of the Act requires that MS-DRG classifications and relative weights are adjusted at least annually (DHHS 2004e, 48925). Claims from the MedPAR file are used to evaluate possible changes to the system. NonMedPAR issues are also considered. Interested parties (such as hospitals, supply companies, and national associations representing healthcare groups) can submit change requests to Medicare. NonMedPAR issues should be submitted to CMS no later than December for consideration for the next federal fiscal year (FY), which begins annually on October 1. The group adjustments and recalibration of group weights are published in the *Federal Register* at least forty-five days prior to the start of the new federal FY.

Summary

The IPPS for hospital inpatient services provided to Medicare beneficiaries was successfully implemented in 1983. The concept of prospective payment has spread to other third party payers, and many have implemented payment systems using DRGs or a modified version of DRGs. In response, hospitals have adopted cost analysis and containment practices in order to remain profitable under prospective systems. IPPS was the first prospective payment system and has paved the way for the implementation of many other systems in other healthcare settings, such as skilled nursing, rehabilitation, and for a variety of outpatient services, as described in Chapter 7.

Table 6.5.   Postacute-care transfer MS-DRGs for FY 2008

MS-DRG	MS-DRG Title	Weights	Geometric Mean LOS
003	ECMO or trach w MV 96+ hrs or PDX exc face, mouth & neck w maj O.R.	18.7707	33.4
004	Trach w MV 96+ hrs or PDX exc face, mouth & neck w/o maj O.R.	11.4219	23.8
025	Craniotomy & endovascular intracranial procedures w MCC	4.2362	10.3
026	Craniotomy & endovascular intracranial procedures w CC	3.1582	6.5
027	Craniotomy & endovascular intracranial procedures w/o CC/MCC	2.3259	3.5
028*	Spinal procedures w MCC	4.2339	10.8
029*	Spinal procedures w CC or spinal neurostimulators	2.8356	5.3
030*	Spinal procedures w/o CC/MCC	1.7617	2.8
031	Ventricular shunt procedures w MCC	3.2226	9.2
032	Ventricular shunt procedures w CC	1.9342	3.8
033	Ventricular shunt procedures w/o CC/MCC	1.4281	2.3
040*	Periph/cranial nerve & other nerv syst proc w MCC	3.2550	10.0
041*	Periph/cranial nerve & other nerv syst proc w CC or periph neurostim	2.3595	5.4
042*	Periph/cranial nerve & other nerv syst proc w/o CC/MCC	1.8710	2.5
054	Nervous system neoplasms w MCC	1.4228	5.3
055	Nervous system neoplasms w/o MCC	1.1213	3.8
056	Degenerative nervous system disorders w MCC	1.2820	5.8
057	Degenerative nervous system disorders w/o MCC	0.8951	3.9
064	Intracranial hemorrhage or cerebral infarction w MCC	1.5470	5.6
065	Intracranial hemorrhage or cerebral infarction w CC	1.1901	4.3
066	Intracranial hemorrhage or cerebral infarction w/o CC/MCC	1.0303	3.1
070	Non-specific cerebrovascular disorders w MCC	1.6212	6.0
071	Non-specific cerebrovascular disorders w CC	1.2522	4.5
072	Non-specific cerebrovascular disorders w/o CC/MCC	0.9586	2.9
085	Traumatic stupor & coma, coma <1 hr w MCC	1.6946	5.7
086	Traumatic stupor & coma, coma <1 hr w CC	1.2337	4.0
087	Traumatic stupor & coma, coma <1 hr w/o CC/MCC	0.9235	2.6
091	Other disorders of nervous system w MCC	1.3242	4.7
092	Other disorders of nervous system w CC	0.9529	3.5
093	Other disorders of nervous system w/o CC/MCC	0.7710	2.6

MS-DRG	MS-DRG Title	Weights	Geometric Mean LOS
100	Seizures w MCC	1.2500	4.7
101	Seizures w/o MCC	0.8258	2.9
163	Major chest procedures w MCC	4.0452	12.2
164	Major chest procedures w CC	2.8081	6.9
165	Major chest procedures w/o CC/MCC	2.4106	4.5
166	Other resp system O.R. procedures w MCC	3.2677	10.1
167	Other resp system O.R. procedures w CC	2.4151	6.5
168	Other resp system O.R. procedures w/o CC/MCC	1.8181	4.0
175	Pulmonary embolism w MCC	1.4152	6.1
176	Pulmonary embolism w/o MCC	1.1580	4.7
177	Respiratory infections & inflammations w MCC	1.8444	7.2
178	Respiratory infections & inflammations w CC	1.5636	6.0
179	Respiratory infections & inflammations w/o CC/MCC	1.2754	4.6
186	Pleural effusion w MCC	1.4542	5.8
187	Pleural effusion w CC	1.1947	4.2
188	Pleural effusion w/o CC/MCC	0.9745	3.2
190	Chronic obstructive pulmonary disease w MCC	1.1138	5.1
191	Chronic obstructive pulmonary disease w CC	0.9405	4.2
192	Chronic obstructive pulmonary disease w/o CC/MCC	0.8145	3.4
193	Simple pneumonia & pleurisy w MCC	1.2505	5.5
194	Simple pneumonia & pleurisy w CC	1.0235	4.5
195	Simple pneumonia & pleurisy w/o CC/MCC	0.8398	3.5
196	Interstitial lung disease w MCC	1.3781	5.8
197	Interstitial lung disease w CC	1.1458	4.4
198	Interstitial lung disease w/o CC/MCC	0.9654	3.5
205	Other respiratory system diagnoses w MCC	1.0636	4.2
206	Other respiratory system diagnoses w/o MCC	0.7848	2.7
207	Respiratory system diagnosis w ventilator support 96+ hours	5.1231	12.6
216	Cardiac valve & oth maj cardiothoracic proc w card cath w MCC	9.3040	15.9
217	Cardiac valve & oth maj cardiothoracic proc w card cath w CC	7.5813	10.9
218	Cardiac valve & oth maj cardiothoracic proc w card cath w/o CC/MCC	6.8595	8.3

(Continued on next page)

MS-DRG	MS-DRG Title	Weights	Geometric Mean LOS
219*	Cardiac valve & oth maj cardiothoracic proc w/o card cath w MCC	7.2072	11.7
220*	Cardiac valve & oth maj cardiothoracic proc w/o card cath w CC	5.7278	7.6
221*	Cardiac valve & oth maj cardiothoracic proc w/o card cath w/o CC/MCC	5.2463	6.0
228	Other cardiothoracic procedures w MCC	6.7400	12.0
229	Other cardiothoracic procedures w CC	5.3191	7.9
230	Other cardiothoracic procedures w/o CC/MCC	4.7847	5.6
233	Coronary bypass w cardiac cath w MCC	6.4496	12.4
234	Coronary bypass w cardiac cath w/o MCC	4.9216	8.2
235	Coronary bypass w/o cardiac cath w MCC	5.1381	9.7
236	Coronary bypass w/o cardiac cath w/o MCC	3.7307	6.1
239	Amputation for circ sys disorders exc upper limb & toe w MCC	3.9454	12.1
240	Amputation for circ sys disorders exc upper limb & toe w CC	2.9983	8.4
241	Amputation for circ sys disorders exc upper limb & toe w/o CC/MCC	2.4709	5.7
242	Permanent cardiac pacemaker implant w MCC	3.2586	6.9
243	Permanent cardiac pacemaker implant w CC	2.5483	3.8
244	Permanent cardiac pacemaker implant w/o CC/MCC	2.1367	2.2
255	Upper limb & toe amputation for circ system disorders w MCC	2.1486	7.3
256	Upper limb & toe amputation for circ system disorders w CC	1.6847	5.8
257	Upper limb & toe amputation for circ system disorders w/o CC/MCC	1.3990	3.7
264	Other circulatory system O.R. procedures	2.4840	5.9
280	Acute myocardial infarction, discharged alive w MCC	1.7391	5.9
281	Acute myocardial infarction, discharged alive w CC	1.3126	4.0
282	Acute myocardia infarction, discharged alive w/o CC/MCC	1.0617	2.6
288	Acute & subacute endocarditis w MCC	2.9143	9.6
289	Acute & subacute endocarditis w CC	2.3075	7.1
290	Acute & subacute endocarditis w/o CC/MCC	1.9733	5.2
291	Heart failure & shock w MCC	1.2585	5.1
292	Heart failure & shock w CC	1.0134	4.1
293	Heart failure & shock w/o CC/MCC	0.8765	3.1
299	Peripheral vascular disorders w MCC	1.2220	5.2
300	Peripheral vascular disorders w CC	0.9451	4.1

MS-DRG	MS-DRG Title	Weights	Geometric Mean LOS
301	Peripheral vascular disorders w/o CC/MCC	0.7183	3.1
314	Other circulatory system diagnoses w MCC	1.5606	5.1
315	Other circulatory system diagnoses w CC	1.1720	3.5
316	Other circulatory system diagnoses w/o CC/MCC	0.9075	2.4
326	Stomach, esophageal & duodenal proc w MCC	5.1660	13.4
327	Stomach, esophageal & duodenal proc w CC	3.2941	8.1
328	Stomach, esophageal & duodenal proc w/o CC/MCC	1.8017	3.3
329	Major small & large bowel procedures w MCC	4.5059	12.8
330	Major small & large bowel procedures w CC	2.8935	8.4
331	Major small & large bowel procedures w/o CC/MCC	1.8415	5.4
332	Rectal resection w MCC	3.7139	12.2
333	Rectal resection w CC	2.5787	7.8
334	Rectal resection w/o CC/MCC	1.7856	4.9
335	Peritoneal adhesiolysis w MCC	3.4785	11.8
336	Peritoneal adhesiolysis w CC	2.4776	7.7
337	Peritoneal adhesiolysis w/o CC/MCC	1.6984	4.4
356	Other digestive system O.R. procedures w MCC	3.3790	9.6
357	Other digestive system O.R. procedures w CC	2.4946	6.1
358	Other digestive system O.R. procedures w/o CC/MCC	1.7333	3.4
371	Major gastrointestinal disorders & peritoneal infections w MCC	1.6263	6.6
372	Major gastrointestinal disorders & peritoneal infections w CC	1.3059	5.5
373	Major gastrointestinal disorders & peritoneal infections w/o CC/MCC	1.1109	4.2
374	Digestive malignancy w MCC	1.7229	6.5
375	Digestive malignancy w CC	1.3337	4.6
376	Digestive malignancy w/o CC/MCC	1.0268	3.1
377	G.I. hemorrhage w MCC	1.3367	5.0
378	G.I. hemorrhage w CC	1.0195	3.7
379	G.I. hemorrhage w/o CC/MCC	0.8476	2.9
380	Complicated peptic ulcer w MCC	1.4334	5.5
381	Complicated peptic ulcer w CC	1.1302	4.2
382	Complicated peptic ulcer w/o CC/MCC	0.9662	3.0

(Continued on next page)

MS-DRG	MS-DRG Title	Weights	Geometric Mean LOS
388	G.I. obstruction w MCC	1.2860	5.5
389	G.I. obstruction w CC	0.9533	4.0
390	G.I. obstruction w/o CC/MCC	0.7260	3.0
405	Pancreas, liver & shunt procedures w MCC	4.8273	12.8
406	Pancreas, liver & shunt procedures w CC	3.3149	7.1
407	Pancreas, liver & shunt procedures w/o CC/MCC	2.2443	4.2
414	Cholecystectomy except by laparoscope w/o c.d.e. w MCC	3.0942	9.7
415	Cholecystectomy except by laparoscope w/o c.d.e. w CC	2.2749	6.6
416	Cholecystectomy except by laparoscope w/o c.d.e. w/o CC/MCC	1.5398	4.1
441	Disorders of liver except malig,cirr,alc hepa w MCC	1.3973	5.1
442	Disorders of liver except malig,cirr,alc hepa w CC	1.0935	4.0
443	Disorders of liver except malig,cirr,alc hepa w/o CC/MCC	0.9079	3.1
459	Spinal fusion except cervical w MCC	4.8679	7.8
460	Spinal fusion except cervical w/o MCC	3.4870	3.8
463	Wnd debrid & skn grft exc hand, for musculo-conn tiss dis w MCC	3.9615	12.3
464	Wnd debrid & skn grft exc hand, for musculo-conn tiss dis w CC	2.8821	7.8
465	Wnd debrid & skn grft exc hand, for musculo-conn tiss dis w/o CC/MCC	2.3417	4.6
466	Revision of hip or knee replacement w MCC	3.5408	7.6
467	Revision of hip or knee replacement w CC	2.7523	4.8
468	Revision of hip or knee replacement w/o CC/MCC	2.4545	3.7
469	Major joint replacement or reattachment of lower extremity w MCC	2.6664	7.1
470	Major joint replacement or reattachment of lower extremity w/o MCC	1.9871	3.7
474	Amputation for musculoskeletal sys & conn tissue dis w MCC	2.8432	9.5
475	Amputation for musculoskeletal sys & conn tissue dis w CC	2.1308	6.6
476	Amputation for musculoskeletal sys & conn tissue dis w/o CC/MCC	1.6799	3.8
477*	Biopsies of musculoskeletal system & connective tissue w MCC	2.6555	9.6
478*	Biopsies of musculoskeletal system & connective tissue w CC	1.9836	4.8
479*	Biopsies of musculoskeletal system & connective tissue w/o CC/MCC	1.6784	1.9
480*	Hip & femur procedures except major joint w MCC	2.4027	8.0
481*	Hip & femur procedures except major joint w CC	1.8485	5.4
482*	Hip & femur procedures except major joint w/o CC/MCC	1.5644	4.5

MS-DRG	MS-DRG Title	Weights	Geometric Mean LOS
483	Major joint & limb reattachment proc of upper extremity w CC/MCC	1.9905	3.5
484	Major joint & limb reattachment proc of upper extremity w/o CC/MCC	1.7376	2.2
488	Knee procedures w/o pdx of infection w CC/MCC	1.6584	4.1
489	Knee procedures w/o pdx of infection w/o CC/MCC	1.4512	2.7
492*	Lower extrem & humer proc except hip,foot,femur w MCC	2.2413	6.9
493*	Lower extrem & humer proc except hip,foot,femur w CC	1.7186	4.4
494*	Lower extrem & humer proc except hip,foot,femur w/o CC/MCC	1.2752	2.8
495	Local excision & removal int fix devices exc hip & femur w MCC	2.5765	8.3
496	Local excision & removal int fix devices exc hip & femur w CC	1.7792	4.6
497	Local excision & removal int fix devices exc hip & femur w/o CC/MCC	1.2301	2.3
500*	Soft tissue procedures w MCC	2.4096	8.1
501*	Soft tissue procedures w CC	1.5598	4.4
502*	Soft tissue procedures w/o CC/MCC	1.0342	2.3
510	Shoulder,elbow or forearm proc,exc major joint proc w MCC	1.6616	5.0
511	Shoulder,elbow or forearm proc,exc major joint proc w CC	1.2512	3.1
512	Shoulder,elbow or forearm proc,exc major joint proc w/o CC/MCC	0.9602	1.7
515*	Other musculoskelet sys & conn tiss O.R. proc w MCC	2.4858	8.1
516*	Other musculoskelet sys & conn tiss O.R. proc w CC	1.8307	4.4
517*	Other musculoskelet sys & conn tiss O.R. proc w/o CC/MCC	1.4192	2.0
533	Fractures of femur w MCC	1.1294	5.1
534	Fractures of femur w/o MCC	0.7560	3.2
535	Fractures of hip & pelvis w MCC	1.0836	4.8
536	Fractures of hip & pelvis w/o MCC	0.7340	3.4
539	Osteomyelitis w MCC	1.7648	7.7
540	Osteomyelitis w CC	1.4026	5.8
541	Osteomyelitis w/o CC/MCC	1.2101	4.4
542	Pathological fractures & musculoskelet & conn tiss malig w MCC	1.4877	6.8
543	Pathological fractures & musculoskelet & conn tiss malig w CC	1.1151	4.8
544	Pathological fractures & musculoskelet & conn tiss malig w/o CC/MCC	0.9395	3.7
545	Connective tissue disorders w MCC	1.8330	6.5
546	Connective tissue disorders w CC	1.2092	4.3

(Continued on next page)

MS-DRG	MS-DRG Title	Weights	Geometric Mean LOS
547	Connective tissue disorders w/o CC/MCC	0.9054	3.2
551	Medical back problems w MCC	1.1632	5.5
552	Medical back problems w/o MCC	0.7839	3.4
557	Tendonitis, myositis & bursitis w MCC	1.2171	5.4
558	Tendonitis, myositis & bursitis w/o MCC	0.8480	3.5
559	Aftercare, musculoskeletal system & connective tissue w MCC	1.2104	5.1
560	Aftercare, musculoskeletal system & connective tissue w CC	0.8521	3.6
561	Aftercare, musculoskeletal system & connective tissue w/o CC/MCC	0.6753	2.1
562	Fx, sprn, strn & disl except femur, hip, pelvis & thigh w MCC	1.1163	5.0
563	Fx, sprn, strn & disl except femur, hip, pelvis & thigh w/o MCC	0.6981	3.1
573	Skin graft &/or debrid for skn ulcer or cellulitis w MCC	2.7483	10.1
574	Skin graft &/or debrid for skn ulcer or cellulitis w CC	2.0177	7.2
575	Skin graft &/or debrid for skn ulcer or cellulitis w/o CC/MCC	1.4216	4.7
579	Other skin, subcut tiss & breast proc w MCC	2.3093	8.1
580	Other skin, subcut tiss & breast proc w CC	1.4256	3.6
581	Other skin, subcut tiss & breast proc w/o CC/MCC	0.9124	1.9
592	Skin ulcers w MCC	1.4555	6.6
593	Skin ulcers w CC	1.1060	5.2
594	Skin ulcers w/o CC/MCC	0.9335	3.9
602	Cellulitis w MCC	1.1522	5.5
603	Cellulitis w/o MCC	0.8087	3.9
616	Amputat of lower limb for endocrine,nutrit,& metabol dis w MCC	3.1449	12.6
617	Amputat of lower limb for endocrine,nutrit,& metabol dis w CC	2.2071	7.2
618	Amputat of lower limb for endocrine,nutrit,& metabol dis w/o CC/MCC	1.7554	4.9
622	Skin grafts & wound debrid for endoc, nutrit & metab dis w MCC	2.7257	9.7
623	Skin grafts & wound debrid for endoc, nutrit & metab dis w CC	2.0065	6.8
624	Skin grafts & wound debrid for endoc, nutrit & metab dis w/o CC/MCC	1.6056	4.6
628	Other endocrine, nutrit & metab O.R. proc w MCC	3.0602	7.8
629	Other endocrine, nutrit & metab O.R. proc w CC	2.4730	7.0
630	Other endocrine, nutrit & metab O.R. proc w/o CC/MCC	1.7767	3.7
637	Diabetes w MCC	1.0891	4.6

MS-DRG	MS-DRG Title	Weights	Geometric Mean LOS
638	Diabetes w CC	0.8021	3.4
639	Diabetes w/o CC/MCC	0.6742	2.5
640	Nutritional & misc metabolic disorders w MCC	0.9793	4.1
641	Nutritional & misc metabolic disorders w/o MCC	0.7248	3.1
643	Endocrine disorders w MCC	1.3926	6.0
644	Endocrine disorders w CC	1.0638	4.3
645	Endocrine disorders w/o CC/MCC	0.8310	3.2
653	Major bladder procedures w MCC	4.5710	13.3
654	Major bladder procedures w CC	3.1860	8.8
655	Major bladder procedures w/o CC/MCC	2.7075	5.8
659	Kidney & ureter procedures for non-neoplasm w MCC	2.8119	8.2
660	Kidney & ureter procedures for non-neoplasm w CC	2.0605	4.8
661	Kidney & ureter procedures for non-neoplasm w/o CC/MCC	1.4004	2.6
682	Renal failure w MCC	1.4664	5.3
683	Renal failure w CC	1.1942	4.5
684	Renal failure w/o CC/MCC	0.9835	3.1
689	Kidney & urinary tract infections w MCC	1.0587	5.0
690	Kidney & urinary tract infections w/o MCC	0.8000	3.6
698	Other kidney & urinary tract diagnoses w MCC	1.3017	5.1
699	Other kidney & urinary tract diagnoses w CC	1.0352	3.8
700	Other kidney & urinary tract diagnoses w/o CC/MCC	0.8232	2.7
840	Lymphoma & non-acute leukemia w MCC	2.1454	6.8
841	Lymphoma & non-acute leukemia w CC	1.6444	5.0
842	Lymphoma & non-acute leukemia w/o CC/MCC	1.2188	3.2
853	Infectious & parasitic diseases w O.R. procedure w MCC	5.1840	12.8
854	Infectious & parasitic diseases w O.R. procedure w CC	3.9291	9.1
855	Infectious & parasitic diseases w O.R. procedure w/o CC/MCC	3.3662	5.6
856	Postoperative or post-traumatic infections w O.R. proc w MCC	3.9257	12.1

(Continued on next page)

MS-DRG	MS-DRG Title	Weights	Geometric Mean LOS
857	Postoperative or post-traumatic infections w O.R. proc w CC	2.4919	6.8
858	Postoperative or post-traumatic infections w O.R. proc w/o CC/MCC	2.0996	4.7
862	Postoperative & post-traumatic infections w MCC	1.5454	6.2
863	Postoperative & post-traumatic infections w/o MCC	1.0560	4.2
867	Other infectious & parasitic diseases diagnoses w MCC	2.1971	7.2
868	Other infectious & parasitic diseases diagnoses w CC	1.5258	4.6
869	Other infectious & parasitic diseases diagnoses w/o CC/MCC	1.3611	3.5
870	Septicemia w MV 96+ hours	5.7579	12.6
871	Septicemia w/o MV 96+ hours w MCC	1.7484	5.6
872	Septicemia w/o MV 96+ hours w/o MCC	1.3783	4.7
884	Organic disturbances & mental retardation	0.8431	4.0
896	Alcohol/drug abuse or dependence w/o rehabilitation therapy w MCC	1.0419	4.8
897	Alcohol/drug abuse or dependence w/o rehabilitation therapy w/o MCC	0.6145	3.3
907	Other O.R. procedures for injuries w MCC	3.1030	8.1
908	Other O.R. procedures for injuries w CC	2.1865	5.0
909	Other O.R. procedures for injuries w/o CC/MCC	1.4112	2.7
917	Poisoning & toxic effects of drugs w MCC	1.1717	3.7
918	Poisoning & toxic effects of drugs w/o MCC	0.6886	2.1
945	Rehabilitation w CC/MCC	1.1005	8.4
946	Rehabilitation w/o CC/MCC	1.0143	7.0
947	Signs & symptoms w MCC	0.8767	3.8
948	Signs & symptoms w/o MCC	0.6542	2.7
956*	Limb reattachment, hip & femur proc for multiple significant trauma	3.4854	7.6
981	Extensive O.R. procedure unrelated to principal diagnosis w MCC	4.5168	11.9
982	Extensive O.R. procedure unrelated to principal diagnosis w CC	3.5417	7.8
983	Extensive O.R. procedure unrelated to principal diagnosis w/o CC/MCC	2.9737	3.9
987	Non-extensive O.R. proc unrelated to principal diagnosis w MCC	2.8500	9.9
988	Non-extensive O.R. proc unrelated to principal diagnosis w CC	2.0134	5.9
989	Non-extensive O.R. proc unrelated to principal diagnosis w/o CC/MCC	1.6310	2.9

Skilled Nursing Facility Prospective Payment System

Section 4432 of the Balanced Budget Act of 1997 mandated a prospective payment system (PPS) and consolidated billing for skilled nursing facilities (SNFs). Under the PPS, SNFs are paid through per-diem prospective, case mix adjusted payment rates applicable to all covered SNF services. These payment rates cover all the costs of furnishing covered skilled nursing services. Included in the payment rates are routine care, ancillary services, and capital costs. Operational costs associated with defined, approved educational activities are excluded. The payment system was effective for cost reporting periods beginning on or after July 1, 1998.

Consolidated billing requires the SNF to pay for outpatient services that a resident may receive from outside vendors. Outside vendors will no longer bill Medicare for services provided to the SNF for a resident with Part A benefits. The laboratory, x-ray service, and pharmacy must bill the SNF and the SNF is responsible for paying for the services. Emergency services, inpatient services, and other extensive procedures (such as radiation therapy) are not consolidated.

Data Collection

Since the late 1980s, CMS has required SNFs to prepare the **Minimum Data Set (MDS).** The MDS is an extensive database of clinical data. These clinical data include comprehensive assessments and treatment plans and are reported within prescribed timeframes. The PPS treatment plan is integral; thus, services outside the scope of the treatment plan may be excluded from payment. The PPS also requires SNFs to use HCPCS coding.

The MDS data determine the classification into one of fifty-three refined **resource utilization groups (RUGs).** Until refinements in 2006, the resource utilization groups, version III (RUG-III) formed a schema that classified nursing home residents into forty-four homogeneous groups. Effec-tive January 2006, CMS refined the system creating nine new RUGs for a total of fifty-three. Residents within groups are similar in terms of their health characteristics and use of resources. The refined RUG-III schema is hierarchical with the first level being eight categories. The second hierarchical level is the fifty-three groups. The groups are allocated among the eight categories:

- Rehabilitation Plus Extensive Services (nine refined RUG-III groups) (DHHS 2005b, 45030)

- Rehabilitation (fourteen refined RUG-III groups)

- Extensive services (three refined RUG-III groups)

- Special care (three refined RUG-III groups)

- Clinically complex (six refined RUG-III groups)

- Impaired cognition (four refined RUG-III groups)

- Behavior function (four refined RUG-III groups)

- Physical function (ten refined RUG-III groups)

CMS analysts believe that MDS data that classify patients into one of the upper thirty-five RUGs (rehabilitation plus extensive services, rehabilitation, extensive services, special care, and clinically complex) justify the patients' admissions to SNFs. These patients by definition require skilled care. The coverage of patients classified into the lower eighteen RUGs (impaired cognition, behavior function, and physical function) is determined on an individual basis.

Grouping and Payment

The PPS uses per-diem federal payment rates based on mean SNF costs that are updated for inflation.

The payment rates were calculated using allowable costs from SNF **cost reports.** Cost reports are reports that providers are required to submit to Medicare. The base year of the cost reports was 1995. Separate payment rates were established for urban and rural areas. Annually, the rates are adjusted using the SNF **market basket index. A market basket** is a mix of goods and services. The market basket index is a relative measure that averages the costs of an appropriate mix of goods and services for the SNF PPS. Effective January 1, 2006, CMS refined the payment system to more accurately represent the consumption of services and expenditures (DHHS 2005b, 45030–45031).

The fifty-three refined RUG-III groups are derived from data in the resident assessments of the MDS. The per-diem rates are case-mix adjusted using the resident classification system, RUG III. The three components of the adjustment include:

- **Nursing component**

- **Therapy component**

- **Noncase-mix adjusted component** (See table 6.6)

These three components drive the rate for each of the fifty-three groups (See table 6.7). Therefore, federal payment is then based on the RUG.

A fifty-fourth default group also exists. This group represents patients for whom the SNF has made an error in assessment or has missed a deadline.

In addition, the rates are adjusted for geographic variations in wages. The total federal rate includes both the labor-related portion and the nonlabor-related portion (table 6.8), which vary from year to year.

Example:

In 1999, the labor and nonlabor portions for the RVC category were $245.23 and $57.20, respectively (DHHS 1999, 41686). In 2008, the corresponding rates were $288.25 and $122.64 (DHHS 2007a, 43421).

To adjust for local geographic variations in wages, the labor portion is multiplied by the local wage index that also varies from year to year. Finally, to calculate the payment, the wage-adjusted total federal rate is multiplied by the number of covered Medicare days. (See the sample calculation in table 6.9.)

A federal act initiated an additional temporary payment adjustment. This act was the Medicare Prescription Drug, Improvement, and Modernization Act of 2003 (MMA) (P.L. 108–173)

The adjustment authorized by this act is termed an **add-on.**

Table 6.6.   Components of case-mix adjusted per diem rates of SNF PPS

Nursing component	**Nursing per diem amount** is the standard amount which includes direct nursing care and the cost of nontherapy ancillary services
	Nursing index is the ratio based on the amount of staff time, weighted by salary levels, associated with each refined RUG-III group; applying this ratio to the nursing per diem is the case-mix adjustment
Therapy component	**Therapy per diem amount** is a standard amount which includes physical, occupational, and speech-language therapy services provided to beneficiaries in a Part A stay
	Therapy index is the ratio based on the amount of staff time, weighted by salary levels, associated with each refined RUG-III group; applying this ratio to the therapy per diem is the case-mix adjustment
Non-case-mix adjusted component	**Noncase-mix therapy component** is the standard amount to cover the cost of therapy assessments of residents who were determined not to need continued therapy services; this amount is the therapy component for nonrehabilitation groups
	Noncase-mix component is the standard amount added to the rate for each refined RUG-III group to cover administrative and capital-related costs; this standard amount is added to all groups

Source: CMS 2005 (April 29). CMS Manual System, Pub 100-04 Medicare Claims Processing, Transmittal 540, Change Request 3774. Available on-line from https://www.cms.hhs.gov/transmittals/downloads/R540CP.pdf.

Table 6.7.   Case-adjusted skilled nursing facility rates by refined resource utilization groups, version III (refined RUG III)

No.	RUG III Category	Nursing Component	Therapy Component	Noncase Mix Therapy Comp	Noncase Mix Component	Total Rate $
			Urban Case-Mix Adjusted Federal Rate (Effective 2008)				
1	RUX	278.58	248.49		74.83	601.90
2	RUL	205.27	248.49		74.83	528.59
3	RVX	225.79	155.72		74.83	456.34
4	RVL	195.00	155.72		74.83	425.55
5	RHX	208.20	103.81		74.83	386.84
6	RHL	200.87	103.81		74.83	379.51
7	RMX	282.98	85.04		74.83	442.85
8	RML	246.32	85.04		74.83	406.19
9	RLX	192.07	47.49		74.83	314.39
10	RUC	187.67	248.49		74.83	510.99
11	RUB	145.15	248.49		74.83	468.47
12	RUA	123.16	248.49		74.83	446.48
13	RVC	180.34	155.72		74.83	410.89
14	RVB	159.82	155.72		74.83	390.37
15	RVA	120.23	155.72		74.83	350.78
16	RHC	178.88	103.81		74.83	357.52
17	RHB	162.75	103.81		74.83	341.39
18	RHA	137.82	103.81		74.83	316.46
19	RMC	168.61	85.04		74.83	328.48
20	RMB	159.82	85.04		74.83	319.69
21	RMA	152.48	85.04		74.83	312.35
22	RLB	167.15	47.49		74.83	289.47
23	RLA	124.63	47.49		74.83	246.95
24	SE3	272.71		14.54	74.83	362.08
25	SE2	218.46		14.54	74.83	307.83
26	SE1	184.74		14.54	74.83	274.11

(Continued on next page)

Table 6.7. (Continued)

No.	RUG III Category	Nursing Component	Therapy Component	Noncase Mix Therapy Comp	Noncase Mix Component	Total Rate $
27	SSC	180.34		14.54	74.83	269.71
28	SSB	165.68		14.54	74.83	255.05
29	SSA	161.28		14.54	74.83	250.65
30	CC2	178.88		14.54	74.83	268.25
31	CC1	155.42		14.54	74.83	244.79
32	CB2	143.69		14.54	74.83	233.06
33	CB1	133.42		14.54	74.83	222.79
34	CA2	131.96		14.54	74.83	221.33
35	CA1	117.30		14.54	74.83	206.67
36	IB2	108.50		14.54	74.83	197.87
37	IB1	105.57		14.54	74.83	194.94
38	IA2	89.44		14.54	74.83	178.81
39	IA1	82.11		14.54	74.83	171.48
40	BB2	107.03		14.54	74.83	196.40
41	BB1	101.17		14.54	74.83	190.54
42	BA2	87.97		14.54	74.83	177.34
43	BA1	76.24		14.54	74.83	165.61
44	PE2	124.63		14.54	74.83	214.00
45	PE1	120.23		14.54	74.83	209.60
46	PD2	114.36		14.54	74.83	203.73
47	PD1	111.43		14.54	74.83	200.80
48	PC2	104.10		14.54	74.83	193.47
49	PC1	101.17		14.54	74.83	190.54
50	PB2	80.64		14.54	74.83	170.01
51	PB1	79.17		14.54	74.83	168.54
52	PA2	77.71		14.54	74.83	167.08
53	PA1	73.31		14.54	74.83	162.68

Data Source: DHHS. 2007 (August 3). Medicare Program; Prospective Payment System and Consolidated Billing for Skilled Nursing Facilities for FY 2008; Final Rule. *Federal Register* 72(149):43418.

Table 6.8. Refined resource utilization groups, version III (refined RUG-III) and labor adjustments

				Total
No.	**RUG III Category**	**Labor ($)**	**NonLabor ($)**	**Federal Rate ($)**

Excerpt from Urban Case-Mix Adjusted Federal Rate Showing Labor and Nonlabor Portions (Effective 2008)

No.	RUG III Category	Labor ($)	NonLabor ($)	Total Federal Rate ($)
1	RUX	422.24	179.66	601.90
13	RVC	288.25	122.64	410.89
16	RHC	250.81	106.71	357.52
18	RHA	222.00	94.46	316.46
27	SSC	189.21	80.50	269.71
30	CC2	188.18	80.07	268.25
38	IA2	125.44	53.77	178.81
39	IA1	120.30	51.18	171.48
40	BB2	137.78	58.62	196.40
41	BB1	133.67	56.87	190.54

Source: Department of Health and Human Services. 2007 (August 3). *Federal Register.* 72(149):43421.

The MMA provided a temporary increase of 128 percent for SNF residents with acquired immune deficiency syndrome (AIDS; diagnosis code 042). The act identifies no particular RUG.

The pricer is the software program that has the logic to calculate payments for SNF PPS claims. The pricer's logic contains the following data items on rates and weight:

- Components of the federal rate for rural and urban areas, including a table of the nursing and therapy indices for each RUG

- Applicable wage index

- Changes, if applicable, to the labor and nonlabor portions

CMS updates these data items periodically, usually annually and in October. However, updates may also occur at other times in the year, as required by legislation. CMS publishes the updates in the *Federal Register.* Reimbursement analysts should monitor the *Federal Register* for these updates (CMS 2005).

Table 6.9. Generic calculation of skilled nursing facility payment

Sample Calculation of Wage-Adjusted Federal Payment

RUG III Category	Labor Portion ($)	Wage Index (Greenville, NC*)	Adj. Labor Portion ($)	Nonlabor Portion ($)	Adjusted Rate [Adj. Labor Portion + Nonlabor Portion] ($)	Medicare Days	Payment [Adj. Rate × Days] ($)
RUX	422.24	0.9402	396.99	179.66	576.65	50	28832.50
RVC	288.25	0.9402	271.01	122.65	393.66	50	19683.13
RHC	250.81	0.9402	235.81	106.71	342.52	100	34252.16
RHA	222.00	0.9402	208.72	94.46	303.18	16	4850.95
SSC	189.21	0.9402	177.90	80.50	258.40	30	7751.86
CC2	188.81	0.9402	177.52	80.07	257.59	10	2575.89
IA2	120.30	0.9402	113.11	51.81	164.92	30	4947.48

Adapted source: DHHS. 1999 (July 30). *Federal Register.* 64(146):41697; and 2007a (August 3). *Federal Register.* 72(149):43421.

*Greenville, NC is in the Core-Based Statistical Area (CBSA) 24780. DHHS. 2007a (August 3). *Federal Register.* 72(149):43446.

Other Applications

At the state level, Pennsylvania instituted a case mix reimbursement system for its Medicaid recipients in nursing facilities in 1994. This prospective case mix reimbursement system replaced a retrospective cost-based methodology. The purpose of the prospective payment system is to improve long-term care and to reduce payment for this care. The cost-based system reimburses nursing facilities at an interim payment cost per day during the fiscal year. Using the prospective case mix reimbursement system, the Department of Public Welfare (DPW) determines a payment rate based on the facility resident population, adjusted to reflect resource usage of the Medical Assistance population, administrative costs, and other costs. This payment rate is determined quarterly based on the resident population information provided to the DPW via the Commonwealth of Pennsylvania Access to Social Services (COMPASS). Each facility knows in advance its payment rate under the Medical Assistance system.

The case mix system enhances incentives for facilities to admit residents who require a more skilled, intensive type care. This system eliminates any incentives for providers to admit and care for the least disabled residents. The payment system was established at 120 percent of the median cost for each facility peer group. The rate of 120 percent directs a higher amount of revenue to those activities most related to resident care. The case mix reimbursement system also reimburses facilities for capital costs based on the appraised value rather than depreciation and interest.

Summary

In summary, Section 4432 of the Balanced Budget Act of 1997 mandated a skilled nursing facility prospective payment system (SNF PPS). The SNF PPS was implemented July 1, 1998. The SNF PPS reimburses skilled nursing facilities an all-inclusive, per diem rate. Based on refined resource utilization groups (RUGs), the payment system rewards facilities that can efficiently and effectively treat clinically complex cases.

Check Your Understanding 6.1

1. When and where was the DRG system created?

2. In the four-step DRG assignment process, if a coder is able to assign the DRG in step one, the preMDC assignment, all subsequent steps in the process are _____.

3. List two refinement questions that help coders group together patients with like resource consumption.

4. How are Medicare base payment rates increased to reflect inflation?

5. What tool does the SNF PPS use annually to adjust payment rates?

Long-Term Care Hospital Prospective Payment System

Prior to October 2002, Medicare reimbursed **long-term care hospitals (LTCHs)** under a cost-based (retrospective) payment system. LTCHs were exempt from the acute care hospital prospective payment system of diagnosis related groups (DRGs). On August 30, 2002, CMS published the final rule for PPS for LTCHs (DHHS 2002). Starting in October 2002, the LTCH PPS became effective as each LTCH began its new fiscal year. The PPS was phased in incrementally (20 percent per year) until full implementation in 2006.

The Balanced Budget Refinement Act (BBRA) of 1999 (P.L. 106–113), as amended by the Benefits Improvement and Protection Act (BIPA) of 2000 (P.L. 106–554) mandated that a budget neutral, per discharge PPS for LTCHs based on diagnosis related groups (DRGs) be implemented for cost reporting periods beginning on or after October 1, 2002. This LTCH PPS replaced the reasonable cost-based payment system mandated by the Tax

Equity and Fiscal Responsibility Act (TEFRA) of 1982.

Covered Organizations

Long-term care hospitals treat groups of patients who have longer than average lengths of stay. Some patients have chronic diseases, such as tuberculosis and respiratory ailments. Other patients have acute diseases requiring long-term therapy, such as cancer and head trauma. LTCHs can provide both general acute care and specialized services, such as comprehensive rehabilitation and ventilator-dependent therapy.

A facility can meet the Centers for Medicare and Medicaid Services (CMS) definition of long-term care hospital (LTCH) in two ways (DHHS 2002, 55957):

- Its **average length of stay (ALOS)** is twenty-five days or more. The calculation is based only on the lengths of stay of Medicare patients and it includes both covered and noncovered days. In addition, the calculation must be based on data from the past six months.

- It was excluded from the diagnosis related group (DRG) PPS on or after August 5, 1997, and has an ALOS of twenty days or more for both Medicare and nonMedicare patients. In addition, 80 percent of the hospital's annual inpatient Medicare discharges in the fiscal year had principal diagnoses of neoplastic diseases, such as cancer.

Approximately 388 LTCHs meet these qualifying circumstances (Medicare Payment Advisory Commission 2007, 227). LTCHs can be freestanding or located within hospitals (**hospitals within hospitals,** HwH; Medicare Payment Advisory Commission 2007, 223). Excluded from the LTCH PPS are Department of Veterans Affairs (VA) hospitals, hospitals reimbursed under state cost-control systems or authorized demonstration projects, and nonparticipating hospitals furnishing emergency services to Medicare beneficiaries.

Long-term care hospitalizations are covered under Part A Medicare. Beneficiaries have up to ninety days of hospital services within the benefit period. Admissions to both acute care hospitals and long-term care hospitals are counted in the benefit period. One inpatient deductible is required for each ninety-day benefit period. For the sixty-first through ninetieth days, a daily coinsurance payment is also required. The sixty lifetime reserve days may also be used after the ninetieth day (DHHS 2002, 55960–55961).

Long-Term Care Diagnosis Related Groups

The LTCH PPS is based on categorizing patients into classes with similar clinical characteristics. Generally, classes of patient discharges with similar clinical characteristics are called **case mix groups (CMGs).** For the LTCH PPS, these case mix groups are the **Medicare-severity long-term care diagnosis related groups (MS-LTC-DRGs).** The MS-LTC-DRGs are exactly the same as the acute care MS-DRGs. The number of MS-LTC-DRGs varies from year to year just as the number of acute care MS-DRGs varies. In 2003, there were 510 MS-LTC-DRGs (formerly known as LTC-DRGs) (DHHS 2002, 55979). In 2004, there were 518 MS-LTC-DRGs (DHHS 2004b, 25679). In 2008, there were 745 MS-LTC-DRGs (DHHS 2007c, 47280). Just like acute care MS-DRGs, MS-LTC-DRGs are based on:

- The principal diagnosis
- Up to eight additional diagnoses
- Up to six procedures
- Sex
- Discharge status

The difference between the acute care MS-DRGs and the MS-LTC-DRGs is the weight assigned to the groups. MS-LTC-DRGs have higher weights to account for the increased complexity of the patients' conditions (DHHS 2004b, 25678). Another difference is the grouping of low-volume MS-LTC-DRGs (less than 25 LTCH cases) in five **quintiles** based on average charge per discharge (DHHS 2004b, 25678). A third difference is the classification of **short-stay outliers.** A short-stay outlier is defined as an LTCH admission that is five-sixths of the geometric average length of stay (DHHS 2004b, 25678).

Grouping and Payment

A computer software program called a grouper classifies the patient discharges into MS-LTC-DRGs. Groupers have internal logic or an algorithm that determines the patients' groups. The groupers use the principal diagnosis, additional diagnoses, procedures, age, sex, and discharge status to determine the MS-LTC-DRG.

The principal diagnosis is the primary determinant of the MS-LTC-DRG. Additional (secondary) diagnoses also affect the assignment of the MS-LTC-DRG. Additional diagnoses represent comorbid conditions that were present at admission, conditions that occurred subsequent to admission, or both. These comorbid conditions or complications (CCs) group a patient's discharge to a higher weight MS-LTC-DRG.

MS-LTC-DRGs have assigned relative weights (table 6.10). These weights reflect the resources necessary to treat the medically complex LTCH patients. Patients who consume more resources are grouped to MS-LTC-DRGs that have higher relative weights. The weights are adjusted annually because changes in the delivery of healthcare change the resource consumption. For example, the relative weight of MS-LTC-DRG for pulmonary edema and respiratory edema decreased between 2002 and 2004 from 1.6597 to1.6513. On the other hand, the relative weight of MS-LTC-DRG for spinal disorders and injuries increased between 2002 and 2004 from 1.4118 to 1.5025.

Of the 745 MS-LTC-DRGs, 743 have weights. Two of the MS-LTC-DRGs are administrative and have no assigned weights (998, Principal Diagnosis is invalid and 999, Ungroupable). There are 303 low-volume MS-LTC-DRGs. They are divided into quintiles and each quintile has a specific relative weight. There are 185 no-volume MS-LTC-DRGs. No-volume MS-LTC-DRGs are crosswalked to one of the low-volume quintiles. Organ transplants should not occur at an LTCH. Therefore, CMS has assigned weights of 0.0000 to the MS-LTC-DRGs

Table 6.10.   Selected Medicare severity long-term care diagnosis related groups (MS-LTC-DRG) relative weights

Excerpts: MS-LTC DRG Relative Weights		
MS-LTC-DRG	Description	2008 Relative Weight
052	Spinal disorders & injuries w CC/MCC	1.0629
056	Degenerative nervous system disorders w MCC	0.7407
058	Multiple sclerosis & cerebellar ataxia w MCC	0.7305
067	Nonspecific CVA & precerebral occlusion w/o infarct w MCC	0.5472
189	Pulmonary edema & respiratory failure	0.9743
190	Chronic obstructive pulmonary disease w MCC	0.6858
191	Chronic obstructive pulmonary disease w CC	0.6256
192	Chronic obstructive pulmonary disease w/o CC/MCC	0.5832
207	Respiratory system diagnosis with ventilator support 96+ hours	2.0266
535	Fractures of hip & pelvis w MCC	0.7305

Source: DHHS. 2007c (August 22). Medicare Program; Changes to the Hospital Inpatient Prospective Payment Systems and Fiscal Year 2008 Rates; Final Rule. *Federal Register* 72(162):48143–48175.

for organ transplants. The weights of the MS-LTC-DRGs in the federal prospective payment system include the following costs:

- Operating

- Capital-related

- Routine

- Ancillary

Excluded from the prospective payment system are the following costs:

- Bad debts

- Approved educational activities

- Blood-clotting factors

- Anesthesia

- Photocopying costs for records sent to the quality improvement organization (QIO)

The LTCH can bill these costs separately to CMS. There are also adjustments for the following:

- Short stays

- Interrupted stays

- High cost outliers

- Area wage differences

- Co-location (HwH) or satellites

The unit of payment is the discharge. A budget-neutral conversion factor (CF) converts the MS-LTC-DRG weight into a payment. In the LTCH PPS, the CF is known as the **standard federal rate.** The standard federal rate is based on the costs of a market basket of goods, such as operating costs and capital costs. Given the complexity of the cases and their concomitant high costs, the standard federal rate is high. It is updated annually. In 2003, 2004, and 2008, the standard federal rates were \$34,956.15, \$35,726.18, and \$38,356.45, respectively (DHHS 2003a, 34134; DHHS 2004b, 25682; DHHS 2007b, 26890). The generic payment formula is:

MS-LTC-DRG weight $\times$ Standard federal rate
= Unadjusted LTCH PPS payment

For a patient discharged in 2008 with MS-LTC-DRG 058 Multiple sclerosis & cerebellar ataxia (0.7305):

0.7305 $\times$ \$38,356.45 [2008 standard federal rate]
= \$28,019.39 (DHHS 2007b, 26890)

Implementation

The importance of accurate coding for the LTCH PPS cannot be overstated. Correct ICD-9-CM diagnosis and procedure coding play an important role, along with other factors, in the way Medicare pays the claim. The ICD-9-CM coding terminology and definitions of principal diagnosis, other diagnoses, and principal procedure follow the requirements of the Uniform Hospital Discharge Data Set (UHDDS). For example, coders must be careful to record the code that occasioned the admission to the LTCH and not the code that occasioned the admission to the acute care hospital. For the case depicted in figure 6.5, correct LTCH coding results in MS-LTC-DRG 056. Incorrectly using the acute care codes would have resulted in MS-LTC-DRG 067 (as MS-LTC-DRGs match acute MS-DRGs). Most important, the relative weights of the MS-LTC-DRGs differ (DHHS 2007c, 48144):

MS-LTC-DRG 056 relative weight = 0.7407

MS-LTC-DRG 067 relative weight = 0.5472

The difference is 0.1935; while seemingly insignificant, when multiplied by the standard federal rate of \$38,356.45, the LTCH is overpaid \$7,421.97 per incorrectly coded discharge.

Figure 6.5.   Case study to calculate long-term care prospective payment system reimbursement

Patient suffers a stroke (ICD-9-CM 436, Acute, but ill-defined cerebrovascular disease) and is admitted to an acute care hospital.

The inpatient MS-DRG is 067, Nonspecific CVA & Precerebral occlusion w/o infarct w MCC.

Patient is discharged and then admitted to an LTC for further treatment of left-sided hemiparesis (ICD-9-CM 438.20, Late effects of cerebrovascular disease, hemiplegia affecting unspecified side) and dysphasia (ICD-9-CM 438.12, Late effects of cerebrovascular disease, dysphasia).

The MS-LTC-DRG is 056, Degenerative nervous system disorders w MCC.

Source: Department of Health and Human Services. 2007ć (August 22). Final Rule. *Federal Register.* 72(162):48144.

Summary

In summary, LTCHs are facilities certified under Medicare as acute-care hospitals that had been excluded from the federal inpatient prospective payment system. These facilities typically have an average inpatient length of stay of 25 days or more. The LTCH PPS, implemented October 1, 2002, replaced the previous reasonable cost-based payment system under which Medicare had previously reimbursed LTCHs.

Inpatient Rehabilitation Facility Prospective Payment System

Medicare has implemented a prospective payment system for Medicare beneficiaries residing in inpatient rehabilitation facilities: the inpatient rehabilitation facility (IRF) prospective payment system (PPS) or the IRF PPS.

According to CMS, the IRF PPS promotes:

- Quality of, access to, and continuity of care

- Efficient provision of rehabilitative services

- Fairness and equity to facilities, beneficiaries, and taxpayers. (DHHS 2001, 41320)

Background

In the past, Medicare paid rehabilitation services under a reasonable cost formula that factored in costs and demographic and geographic variations. Because inpatient rehabilitation services differ from acute care services, inpatient rehabilitation services had been excluded from the inpatient PPS that had been implemented in October 1983 and that used diagnosis related groups (DRGs). Both rehabilitation hospitals and rehabilitation units within acute care general hospitals were excluded from the DRG system.

Healthcare analysts recognized that to create a payment system for inpatient rehabilitation services, a special case mix classification was needed. This classification must account for the variation in resource use across patients in rehabilitation facilities. The Balanced Budget Act of 1997 (BBA) authorized the development of the IRF PPS and its concomitant classification. CMS phased in the IRF PPS as each inpatient rehabilitation facility began its new fiscal year on or after January 1, 2002. This implementation included the amendments to the IRF PPS from the Balanced Budget Refinement Act of 1999 (BBRA) and the Medicare, Medicaid, and SCHIP Benefits Improvement and Protection Act of 2000 (BIPA).

Today the IRF PPS applies to inpatient rehabilitation services that Medicare participating rehabilitation hospitals or distinct rehabilitation units in acute care hospitals provide to Medicare Part A fee-for-service patients. To meet CMS's definition of an IRF, facilities must have an inpatient population in which:

- At least 75 percent of the patients require intensive rehabilitation services

- For one of the following thirteen conditions:

    —Stroke

    —Spinal cord injury

    —Congenital deformity

—Amputation

—Major multiple trauma

—Fracture of the femur (hip fracture)

—Brain injury

—Neurological disorders

—Burns

—Active, polyarticular rheumatoid arthritis, psoriatic arthritis, and seronegative arthropathies

—Systemic vasculidities with joint inflammation (unresponsive to aggressive, sustained, and appropriate outpatient treatment)

—Severe or advanced osteoarthritis involving two or more major weight-bearing joints

—Knee or hip replacement with bilateral replacement, extreme obesity, or age eighty-five or older

This minimum percentage is known as the "compliance threshold" or "75 percent rule." (DHHS 2007d, 44287).

Excluded from the IRF PPS are Department of Veterans Affairs (VA) hospitals, hospitals reimbursed under state cost-control systems or authorized demonstration projects, and nonparticipating hospitals furnishing emergency services to Medicare beneficiaries. There are approximately 1,200 facilities that meet the definition of a participating IRF.

Key components of the IRF PPS are data collection, grouping via case mix, single payment per discharge, and electronic data submission. The foundation of the IRF PPS is the case mix group (CMG). CMGs are classes of discharges in functional related groups.

Data Collection

The IRF PPS features an eighty-five-item, rehabilitation-specific tool. This tool is the inpatient rehabilitation facility patient assessment instrument (IRF PAI). The IRF PAI collects the information that drives payment.

Types of Patient Information

The IRF PAI consists of nine different types of patient information. These types are:

- Identification information

- Admission information

- Payer information

- Medical information

- Medical needs

- Function modifiers

- Functional independence assessment information

- Discharge information

- Quality measures (for example, pressure ulcers or patient falls)

Assignment of Codes

The IRF PAI must be completed for each Medicare patient twice, upon admission and again at discharge.

By the fourth day of the inpatient admission, the IRF PPS requires the assignment of codes. These codes reflect:

- The reason for admission to the rehabilitation facility (using impairment group codes)

- The etiology of the impairment (using ICD-9-CM codes)

- Comorbidities and complications (using ICD-9-CM codes)

- The reason for interruption, transfer, or death (using an ICD-9-CM code)

The functional abilities of the patient must be assigned using the **functional independence assessment tool.**

The codes on the IRF PAI are used for research, for grouping patients into CMGs, and for determining the payment tier. It must be emphasized that the codes on the IRF PAI do not follow the UHDDS and the UB-04 guidelines.

Impairment Group Code
The reason for admission is coded using an **impairment group code (IGC).** (See table 6.11). CMS provides these codes in the manual. There are eighty-five IGCs. The IGC structure consists of a two-digit ID number, a decimal point, and one to four digits representing the subgroups. The IGC describes the primary reason that the patient is being admitted to the rehabilitation program.

Etiologic Diagnosis
The IRF PAI also reports the code for the etiology of the problem that led to the condition requiring the inpatient rehabilitation admission. The **etiologic diagnosis** is an ICD-9-CM code. Therefore, a principal diagnosis, as defined by the Uniform Hospital Discharge Data Set (UHDDS), is not reported on the IRF PAI.

Complications and Comorbidities
A comorbidity is a specific condition that the patient had at admission to the IRF. Comorbidities affect patients in addition to their etiologic diagnoses and their impairments. Because of these comorbidities, the IRFs must use additional resources (costs) to

Table 6.11.   Inpatient rehabilitation facility prospective payment system's impairment group code (IGC)

Example of Impairment Group Code (IGC)	
01.1	Stroke with left body involvement (right brain)
01.2	Stroke with right body involvement (left brain)
01.3	Stroke with bilateral involvement
01.4	Stroke with no paresis
01.9	Other stroke
02.21	Traumatic brain injury (TBI) with open injury
02.22	Traumatic brain injury (TBI) with closed injury
04.210	Traumatic spinal cord injury (TSCI) with paraplegia, unspecified
04.211	Traumatic spinal cord injury (TSCI) with paraplegia, incomplete
04.212	Traumatic spinal cord injury (TSCI) with paraplegia, complete
04.220	Traumatic spinal cord injury (TSCI) with quadriplegia, unspecified
04.2211	Traumatic spinal cord injury (TSCI) with quadriplegia, incomplete C1–4
04.2212	Traumatic spinal cord injury (TSCI) with quadriplegia, incomplete C5–8
04.2221	Traumatic spinal cord injury (TSCI) with quadriplegia, complete C1–4
04.2222	Traumatic spinal cord injury (TSCI) with quadriplegia, complete C5–8

Adapted Source: Department of Health and Human Services. 2001 (August 7). *Federal Register.* Final rule. 66 (152): 41342–41343.

treat these patients. Therefore, about 980 comorbid conditions affect the IRF PPS payment. ICD-9-CM coding of comorbid conditions is critical (Trela 2002, 48B). Up to ten ICD-9-CM codes for comorbid conditions may be reported on the PAI. Complications are comorbidities that occur after admission to the IRF (Trela 2002, 48B). Complications are reported both as comorbid conditions and as complications. Complications are also reported using ICD-9-CM codes.

These comorbid conditions are divided into three tiers by associated costs (table 6.12). CMS has linked the ICD-9-CM codes to their respective tiers. Tier 1 is high cost, tier 2 is medium cost, and tier 3 is low cost. On the table, a "1" is found in the respective tier. Conditions that are inherent to a specific **rehabilitation impairment category (RIC)** are excluded from the list of relevant comorbidities for that RIC. Excluded comorbidities do not affect the relative weight and, thus, do not increase the payment for that RIC.

Finally, the reason for transfer or death is reported by ICD-9-CM code on the IRF PAI.

Functional Independence Assessment

Another major element of the IRF PAI is the **functional independence assessment tool.** (See

table 6.13). This is an eighteen-item, rehabilitation-specific instrument that reflects the characteristics of patients. It captures patients' **functional status.** Functional status is a patient's ability to perform activities of daily living. CMS has organized this assessment by motor and cognitive functioning.

The functional independence measure tool was developed in the 1980s. About 75 percent of U.S. IRFs use this standardized instrument to measure the severity of patients' impairments. The eighteen items are measured on a seven-level scale that classifies patients according to their ability to perform certain activities. A score of 7 indicates complete independence. Conversely, a score of 1 indicates complete dependence. The IRF PAI added an eighth level, 0, for not assessed. Therefore, a higher score means that the patient has more functional abilities; a lower score means that the patient has fewer functional abilities. Patients with fewer functional abilities (lower scores) need more assistance from facilities' personnel and, thus, require more resources.

All the patient's scores for the motor items are totaled, and all the patient's scores for the cognitive items are totaled. With the patient's diagnosis, these two totals and the patient's age determine the exact case mix group. Completion of the indicators for medical needs and quality is voluntary.

Table 6.12. Comorbidities in inpatient rehabilitation facility prospective payment system

Excerpt from List of Comorbidities and Tiers (2001)					
ICD-9-CM Code	Abbreviated Description	Tier 1	Tier 2	Tier 3	Excluded RIC
011.02	TB Lung Infiltr-Exm Unkn	0	1	0	15
093.20	Syphil Endocarditis NOS	0	0	1	14
112.4	Candidiasis of Lung	1	0	0	15
342.92	Unsp Hmiplga Nondominant Side	0	0	1	01
204.00	Acute Lym Leuk w/o Rmsion	0	0	1	—
787.2	Dysphagia	0	0	1	01
V49.75	Status Amput Below Knee	0	0	1	10

Source: Department of Health and Human Services. 2001 (August 7). *Federal Register.* Final rule. 66 (152): 41414–41427.

Table 6.13.   Functional independence measure (FIM™) and inpatient rehabilitation facility prospective payment system

Functional Independence Measure (FIM™) Instrument		
CMS Motor Items		**Min = 0, Max = 84**
No.	**Description**	**Score (0, 1 to 7)***
1.	Eating	
2.	Grooming	
3.	Bathing	
4.	Dressing-Upper	
5.	Dressing-Lower	
6.	Toileting	
7.	Bladder Control	
8.	Bowel Control	
9.	Bed, Chair, Wheelchair Transfer	
10.	Toilet Transfer	
11.	Tub, Shower Transfer (CMS Excludes)	
12.	Walk/Wheelchair Locomotion	
13.	Stairs Locomotion	
CMS Cognitive Items		**Min = 0, Max = 35**
14.	Comprehension	
15.	Expression	
16.	Social Interaction	
17.	Problem Solving	
18.	Memory	

*1 = complete dependence, 7 = complete independence, 0 = not assessed [0 score is unique to PAI].

Adapted Source: Department of Health and Human Services. 2001 (August 7). *Federal Register.* Final rule. 66 (152): 41333, 41349.

IRF staff members must complete PAI within specific timeframes. However, if entries are incorrect, facilities may update data at any time prior to transmission of the IRF PAI.

Grouping

Case mix groups (CMGs) are classes of patient discharges of rehabilitation facilities. These groups represent similar functional-related patient discharges based on impairment, functional capability of the patient, age, and comorbidities. The CMG is derived from:

- The rehabilitation impairment category (RIC)
- Motor and cognitive scores from the functional independence assessment tool
- Age
- Comorbid conditions

As previously noted, the IRF PAI is completed twice, one time with admission data and a second time with discharge data. The admission assessment assigns patients to a CMG. The discharge assessment determines the weighting factors associated with comorbidities (if they are present and applicable).

In the admission assessment, patients are assigned to a CMG based upon admission data and clinical characteristics. Patients are classified into CMGs based on the expected improvement of the patient's functional status as reflected by the functional independence assessment tool. IRFs must complete admission assessments that are the basis for CMG assignment according to a specific timetable (Trela 2002, 48C).

The CMS software that assigns patients to case mix groups is called the pricer. The pricer uses the impairment group codes (IGCs) on the PAI to classify patients into one of twenty-one RICs (table 6.14).

Table 6.14.   Rehabilitation impairment categories (RICs) and associated impairment group codes (IGCs)

RIC	Description	IGC	Description
01	Stroke (Stroke)	01.1	Left body involvement (right brain)
		01.2	Right body involvement (left brain)
		01.3	Bilateral involvement
		01.4	No paresis
		01.9	Other stroke
02	Traumatic brain injury (TBI)	02.21	Open injury
		02.22	Closed injury
04	Traumatic spinal cord injury (TSCI)	04.210	Paraplegia, unspecified
		04.211	Paraplegia, incomplete
		04.212	Paraplegia, complete
		04.220	Quadriplegia, unspecified
		04.2211	Quadriplegia, incomplete C1–4
		04.2212	Quadriplegia, incomplete C5–8
		04.2221	Quadriplegia, complete C1–4
		04.2222	Quadriplegia, complete C5–8

Source: Department of Health and Human Services. 2001 (August 7). *Federal Register.* Final rule. 66 (152): 41342–41344.

RICs are clusters of similar impairments and diagnoses (table 6.15). It should be noted that staff members at IRFs enter the IGC on the PAI; they do not enter the RIC. The pricer calculates the RIC from the IGC. RICs, in turn, assign patients to CMGs (table 6.16). In RIC 1 Stroke (01), there are fourteen CMGs (0101, 0102 to 0114).

To summarize: IGC ➞ RIC ➞ CMG.

Within a RIC, the numbering of the CMGs is hierarchical. Therefore, a case mix group of 0101 is a less serious than a group 0102; 0102 is a less serious CMG than 0114. Moreover, lower CMGs tend to use fewer resources than higher CMGs.

There are 100 CMGs. Ninety-five are clinical (typical) and five are administrative (special). CMGs are four-digit codes, such as 0101 and 5104. The CMGs are assigned relative weights to account for the comparative difference in resource use. Within a RIC (the two leading digits of the CMG number), higher CMG numbers are associated with higher weights.

Each of the ninety-five clinical CMGs has four payment weights. Comorbid conditions determine the payment weight. There is one rate for cases without a comorbid condition and three rates for cases with comorbid conditions (table 6.17). The three rates with comorbid conditions correspond to the three tiers. The pricer selects the condition that assigns the case to the tier with the highest payment.

The five administrative (special) CMGs are for case-level adjustments. There is one CMG for short-stay cases. Short stays comprise three days or less (including patient expirations) and do not meet the definition of a transfer. There are four CMGs for expired patients. These four CMGs are determined by the condition (orthopedic or nonorthopedic) and by the lengths of stay (Greater than or equal to 4–13 or Greater than or equal to 14).

Table 6.15. Rehabilitation impairment categories (RICs)

RIC	Description
01	Stroke (Stroke)
02	Traumatic brain injury (TBI)
03	Nontraumatic brain injury (NTBI)
04	Traumatic spinal cord injury (TSCI)
05	Nontraumatic spinal cord injury (NTSCI)
06	Neurological (Neuro)
07	Fracture of lower extremity (FracLE)
08	Replacement of lower extremity joint (Rep1LE)
09	Other orthopedic (Ortho)
10	Amputation, lower extremity (AMPLE)
11	Amputation, other (AMP–NLE)
12	Osteoarthritis (OsteoA)
13	Rheumatoid, other arthritis (RheumA)
14	Cardiac (Cardiac)
15	Pulmonary (Pulmonary)
16	Pain syndrome (Pain)
17	Major multiple trauma, no brain injury or spinal cord injury (MMT–NBSCI)
18	Major multiple trauma, with brain injury or spinal cord injury (MMT–BSCI)
19	Guillain Barre (GB)
20	Miscellaneous (Misc)
21	Burns (Burns)

Information source: Department of Health and Human Services. 2001 (August 7). *Federal Register.* Final rule. 66 (152): 41342–41344.

Table 6.16.   Case mix groups (CMGs): numbers and descriptions

CMG	Description
0101	Stroke with motor score from 69–84 and cognitive score from 23–35.
0102	Stroke with motor score from 59–68 and cognitive score from 23–35.
0103	Stroke with motor score from 59–84 and cognitive score from 5–22.
0104	Stroke with motor score from 53–58.
0105	Stroke with motor score from 47–52.
0106	Stroke with motor score from 42–46.
0107	Stroke with motor score from 39–41.
0108	Stroke with motor score from 34–38 and patient is 83 years old or older.
0109	Stroke with motor score from 34–38 and patient is 82 years old or younger.
0110	Stroke with motor score from 12–33 and patient is 89 years old or older.
0111	Stroke with motor score from 27–33 and patient is between 82 and 88 years old.
0112	Stroke with motor score from 12–26 and patient is between 82 and 88 years old.
0113	Stroke with motor score from 27–33 and patient is 81 years old or younger.
0114	Stroke with motor score from 12–26 and patient is 81 years old or younger.

Source: Department of Health and Human Services. 2001 (August 7). *Federal Register.* Final rule. 66 (152): 41345–41347.

Table 6.17.   Comorbidity codes

A	Without comorbidities
B	Comorbidity in tier 1
C	Comorbidity in tier 2
D	Comorbidity in tier 3

Reimbursement

CMS reimburses IRFs for each discharge, with all costs of covered inpatient services included (Trela 2002, 48A). Thus, the unit of measure of the system is the discharge. There is a single payment for each discharge. CMS's pricer software also determines the payment.

Payments are based on the weight of the CMG. Higher CMGs are associated with higher relative weights. Therefore, the weight and associated payment for CMG 0114 is higher than the weight and associated payment for 0101. (See table 6.18.) Comorbid conditions increase the weight. The relative weights of the CMGs were calculated using cost report data from fiscal years 1996 through 1997. CMS may periodically adjust the case mix groups and weighting factors to reflect changes in:

- Treatment patterns
- Technology
- Number of discharges
- Other factors affecting the relative use of resources

IRFs report the health insurance prospective payment system (HIPPS) code on the claim. The HIPPS code collapses the information about the case mix group and comorbidity into one code. Only one HIPPS code is allowed per claim.

The HIPPS code is a five-character alphanumeric code. The first character is the letter designation of the comorbidity tier (A to D). The last four characters are the four-digit CMG. Therefore, the HIPPS code for a patient with a tier 1 comorbidity and a CMG of 0109 is B0109.

A **standardized payment** conversion factor (CF) formerly known as budget-neutral conversion factor, converts the CMG weight into a payment. In 2002 and 2003, the CF was $11,838.00 and $12,193.00, respectively. In 2005, the CF was $12,958 (DHHS 2004c, 45766).

Table 6.18.   Excerpt from relative weights for case-mix groups and tiers

CMG	CMG Description (M = Motor, C = Cognitive, A = Age)	Tier 1	Tier 2	Tier 3	None
0101	Stroke; M = 69–84, C = 23–35	0.4778	0.4279	0.4078	0.3859
0102	Stroke; M = 59–68, C = 23–35	0.6506	0.5827	0.5553	0.5255
0103	Stroke; M = 59–84, C = 5–22	0.8296	0.7430	0.7080	0.6700
0104	Stroke; M = 53–58	0.9007	0.8067	0.7687	0.7275
0105	Stroke; M = 47–52	1.1339	1.0155	0.9677	0.9158
0106	Stroke; M = 42–46	1.3951	1.2494	1.1905	1.1267
0107	Stroke; M = 39–41	1.6159	1.4472	1.3790	1.3050
0108	Stroke; M = 34–38, A ≥ 83	1.7477	1.5653	1.4915	1.4115
0109	Stroke; M = 34–38, A ≤ 82	1.8901	1.6928	1.6130	1.5265
0110	Stroke; M = 12–33, A ≥ 89	2.0275	1.8159	1.7303	1.6375
0111	Stroke; M = 27–33, A = 82–88	2.0889	1.8709	1.7827	1.6871
0112	Stroke; M = 12–26, A = 82–88	2.4782	2.2195	2.1149	2.0015
0113	Stroke; M = 27–33, A ≤ 81	2.2375	2.0040	1.9095	1.8071
0114	Stroke; M = 12–26, A ≤ 81	2.7302	2.4452	2.3300	2.2050

Adapted source: Department of Health and Human Services. 2001 (August 7). *Federal Register.* Final rule. 66 (152): 41394–41396.

Generic Payment Formula

The generic payment formula is as follows:

CMG Weight × CF =
CMG Unadjusted Prospective Payment

Calculating the payment for a patient with a HIPPS code of B0109 demonstrates the use of the formula (table 6.19):

B0109 = CMG 0109 and Tier 1 comorbidity

CMG 0109 and Tier 1 comorbidity =
CMG relative weight of 2.1998

CF = $13,451

2.1998 × $13,451 = $29,589.51

Therefore, in 2008, the unadjusted federal prospective payment was $29,589.51

Wage-Related Adjustments

Wages vary among areas. This variation in wages is reflected in the wage index, specific to each area. The federal government adjusts the wage index each year. Another wage-related adjustment is the labor-related share (labor ratio). The labor-related share reflects facilities' costs related to wages and salaries, employee benefits, professional fees, and the labor-related share of capital costs. The labor-related share is standard across the U.S. and is also adjusted each year. For example, in 2002, the labor ratio was 0.72395 and in 2008, it was 0.75818; and the Greenville, North Carolina, wage index was 0.9402 and 0.9432, respectively. These differences, although small, matter when multiplied across thousands of dollars and many discharges, as illustrated by the following calculations:

2008 Area wage adjustment: labor ratio, 0.75818; nonlabor ratio, 0.24182; Greenville, North Carolina wage index, 0.9432

Calculating the adjusted federal prospective payment for the local wage index in the urban area of Greenville, North Carolina results in (table 6.19):

$29,589.51 × 0.75818 (labor ratio) × 0.9432 (local wage index) = $21,159.91 (wage-adjusted labor portion)

$29,589.51 × 0.24182 (nonlabor ratio) = $7,155.34 (nonlabor portion)

Adding the portions back together to create a whole:

$21,159.91 + $7,155.34 = $28,315.25

It should be noted that the adjusted federal prospective payment of $28,315.25 is less than the unadjusted payment. This lowered payment occurs because the local wage index (0.9432) is less than 1.00. However, in some geographic areas of the country, the wage index is greater than 1.00. In those geographic areas, the adjustment increases the federal payment.

Payments are also adjusted to account for characteristics of the facility, such as cost outlier cases, rural areas, teaching status, and percentage of low-income patients (LIP).

High-Cost Outliers

High-cost outliers are cases in which the costs exceed an adjusted threshold amount. In 2008, the threshold amount was $7,362, adjusted for the IRF's

wage adjustment, low-income patient adjustment, and rural adjustment, as applicable (DHHS 2007d, 44287). CMS changes the threshold amount periodically. The outlier payment is 80 percent of the difference between the estimated cost of the case and the outlier threshold (Trela 2002, 48D).

Rural Adjustment

CMS defines rural as being located outside a core-based statistical area formerly known as a metropolitan statistical area (MSA). To increase payments to rural IRFs, their payments are multiplied by a rural adjustment. In 2002 through 2005, the rural adjustment was 1.1914.

Teaching Hospital Adjustment

Teaching IRFs receive an adjustment for the additional indirect costs of providing graduate medical education. This adjustment is based on the number of full-time residents training in the IRF.

Adjustment for Low-Income Patients

The adjustment for the percentage of low-income patients (LIP) is:

[1 + the disproportionate share percentage] raised to the power of .6229 (DHHS 2007d, 44285).

Therefore, the calculation of the LIP for an IRF with a disproportionate share percentage of 5 percent is:

[1 + 5%] raised to .6229 power
[1 + .0500] raised to .6229 power
[1.0500] raised to .6229 power = 1.0309

Table 6.19.   Calculation of payment under Inpatient Rehabilitation Facility Prospective Payment Systems (2008)

HIPPS Code	CMG and Tier	Weight	Std Pymt CF (FY 2008)	Unadjusted Rate ($)	Labor-Related Ratio	Local Wage Index*	Adj Labor Portion (Unadj. Rate × Labor Ratio × Local Wage Index)	Nonlabor Related Ratio	Unadjusted Nonlabor Portion (Unadj. Rate × Nonlabor Ratio)	Wage Adj. Rate (Adj. Labor Portion + Unadj. Nonlabor Ratio) ($)
B0109	0109 Tier 1	2.1998	$13,451	$29,589.51	0.75818	0.9432	$21,159.91	0.24182	$7,155.34	$28,315.25

*Core-based statistical area 24780 (CBSA, Greenville, NC).

Special Payments

Special payment arrangements are made for **interrupted stays** and transfer cases. In interrupted stays, the patient is discharged from the IRF and returns within three calendar days. Only one payment based on the CMG from the initial assessment is made. Transfer cases are paid on a per diem. This per diem is the facility-adjusted federal prospective payment (weight $\times$ CF) divided by the average length of stay for the tier (table 6.20).

Common Reimbursement Groups

Hospital leaders and financial analysts often use reimbursement reports to discern the financial viability of the organization. A typical report would provide aggregate data on the most common reimbursement groups (tables 6.21 and 6.22).

A representative IRF's overall reimbursement for 2002 was:

$3,773,487 (weight, 318.7605 $\times$ CF, $11,838)

and for 2005 was:

$4,130,499 (weight, 318.7605 $\times$ CF, $12,958).

The increase in the conversion factor between 2002 and 2005 accounts for $356,012 of the difference. However, increases in the level of dependence (higher relative weight) of the patients also affect overall reimbursement. In table 6.22, the effects of a hypothetical shift of ten patients are calculated. If ten more patients were discharged in the higher weight HIPPS A0404 (Traumatic spinal cord injury; 2.6212) rather than in the lower HIPPS of A0204 (Traumatic brain injury; 1.3269), the total HIPPS relative weight is increased to 331.7075 from 318.7605. This increase in total HIPSS relative weight results in an increase of $167,767, solely due to the increased case mix. Healthcare leaders carefully monitor the mix of patients to ensure the viability of their organizations.

Electronic Data Submission

Facilities must submit the IRF PAI to CMS electronically. The data must be encoded using CMS's free program, the **Inpatient Rehabilitation Validation and Entry (IRVEN)** software. There are strict time frames for submission (table 6.23). Failure to follow time frames results in a 25 percent reduction of the payment.

Implementation

Accuracy in coding and reporting the items of the IRF PAI is essential to generate correct Medicare payments. Documentation in the patient record should support the IGC and the ICD-9-CM codes. The guidelines for reporting codes on the IRF PAI need careful review.

The IRF and its agents must ensure the confidentiality of the information collected in accordance with the Conditions of Participation and HIPAA requirements. Patients must be informed of their rights regarding the collection of patient assessment data and the release of patient identifiable information.

An IRF must maintain all patient assessment data sets completed on Medicare Part A fee-for-service patients within the previous five years. The IRF may maintain these sets either in a paper format in the patient's clinical record or in an electronic computer file format that the IRF can easily obtain.

Table 6.20. Excerpt from average length of stay in days for case-mix groups and tiers

CMG	CMG Description (M = Motor, C = Cognitive, A = Age)	Tier 1	Tier 2	Tier 3	None
0101	Stroke; M = 69–84, C = 23–35	10	9	6	8
0102	Stroke; M = 59–68, C = 23–35	11	12	10	10
0114	Stroke; M = 12–26, A ≤ 81	37	34	32	33

Adapted source: Department of Health and Human Services. 2001 (August 7). *Federal Register.* Final rule. 66 (152): 41394–41396.

Table 6.21. Case study with change in conversion factor only: Our Town Inpatient Rehabilitation Facility top 10 HIPPS codes (2002 versus 2005)

HIPPS Code	Description (M = Motor, C = Cognitive, A = Age) and Tier	Relative Weight	2002			2005		
			No. of Pts	% of Tot	TOT HIPPS Relative Weight	No. of Pts	% of Tot	TOT HIPPS Relative Weight
A0103	Stroke; M = 59–84, C = 5–22; None	0.6700	15	5.0%	10.0500	15	5.0%	10.0500
D0103	Stroke; M = 59–84, C = 5–22; Tier 3	0.7080	16	5.3%	11.3280	16	5.3%	11.3280
A0108	Stroke; M = 34–38, A > 83, None	1.4115	30	10.0%	42.3450	30	10.0%	42.3450
D0108	Stroke; M = 34–38, A > 83; Tier 3	1.4915	23	7.7%	34.3045	23	7.7%	34.3045
A0204	Traumatic brain injury; M = 30–39; None	1.3269	59	19.7%	78.2871	59	19.7%	78.2871
A0404	Traumatic spinal cord injury; M = 12–18; None	2.6216	15	5.0%	39.3240	15	5.0%	39.3240
D0701	Fracture of lower extremity; M = 52–84; Tier 3	0.6710	65	21.7%	43.6150	65	21.7%	43.6150
A1701	Major multiple trauma without brain or spinal cord injury; M = 46–84; None	0.7205	45	15.0%	32.4225	45	15.0%	32.4225
D1701	Major multiple trauma without brain or spinal cord injury; M = 46–84; Tier 3	0.8138	20	6.7%	16.2760	20	6.7%	16.2760
A1802	Major multiple trauma with brain or spinal cord injury; M = 45–84, C = 5–32; None	0.9007	12	4.0%	10.8084	12	4.0%	10.8084
	TOTAL	11.3355	300	100%	318.7605	300	100%	318.7605
	2002 CF $11,838	$3,773,487						
	2005 CF $12,958	$4,130,499						
	Difference 2002 and 2005 due to change in CF	$357,012						

Table 6.22. Case study with change in case mix: Our Town Inpatient Rehabilitation Facility top 10 HIPPS codes (2002 versus 2005)

HIPPS Code	Description (M = Motor, C = Cognitive, A = Age) and Tier	Relative Weight	2002			2005		
			No. of Pts	% of Tot	TOT HIPPS Relative Weight	No. of Pts	% of Tot	TOT HIPPS Relative Weight
A0103	Stroke; M = 59–84, C = 5–22; None	0.6700	15	5.0%	10.0500	15	5.0%	10.0500
D0103	Stroke; M = 59–84, C = 5–22; Tier 3	0.7080	16	5.3%	11.3280	16	5.3%	11.3280
A0108	Stroke; M = 34–38, A > 83, None	1.4115	30	10.0%	42.3450	30	10.0%	42.3450
D0108	Stroke; M = 34–38, A > 83; Tier 3	1.4915	23	7.7%	34.3045	23	7.7%	34.3045
A0204	Traumatic brain injury; M = 30–39; None	1.3269	59	19.7%	78.2871	49	16.3%	65.0181
A0404	Traumatic spinal cord injury; M = 12–18; None	2.6216	15	5.0%	39.3240	25	8.3%	65.5400
D0701	Fracture of lower extremity; M = 52–84; Tier 3	0.6710	65	21.7%	43.6150	65	21.7%	43.6150
A1701	Major multiple trauma without brain or spinal cord injury; M = 46–84; None	0.7205	45	15.0%	32.4225	45	15.0%	32.4225
D1701	Major multiple trauma without brain or spinal cord injury; M = 46–84; Tier 3	0.8138	20	6.7%	16.2760	20	6.7%	16.2760
A1802	Major multiple trauma with brain or spinal cord injury; M = 45–84, C = 5–32; None	0.9007	12	4.0%	10.8084	12	4.0%	10.8084
	TOTAL	11.3355	300	100%	318.7605	300	100%	331.7075
	2002 CF $11,838	$3,773,487	Portion of difference due to change in CF (see Table 6.21)		$357,012			
	2005 CF $12,958	$4,298,266	Portion of difference due to change in case mix		$167,767			
	Difference 2002 and 2005	$524,779						

Table 6.23.   Inpatient rehabilitation facility prospective payment system time frames

Event	Admission	Discharge
Observation period	Days 1–3	Date of discharge or end of Medicare Part A fee-for-service coverage
Assessment reference date	Day 3	Date of discharge or discontinuation of covered services
Completion date	Day 4	Day 5 following discharge or discontinuation of covered services
Encoded date	Day 10	Day 7 following completion date (count completion date as day 1)
Transmission date	with discharge assessment	Day 7 following the encoded date

Source: Trela P. 2002. Inpatient rehabilitation PPS presents new challenges, opportunities. *Journal of the American Health Information Management Association.* 73 (1): 48A–48D.

Summary

The key components of the prospective payment system for inpatient rehabilitation facilities are:

- Data collection through the inpatient rehabilitation facility patient assessment instrument

- Case mix grouping

- Per discharge unit of payment

- Electronic submission

Inpatient Psychiatric Facility Prospective Payment System

The Medicare Program provides benefits for inpatient psychiatric care provided to its beneficiaries. Psychiatric hospitals and psychiatric units in acute care hospitals referred to as **inpatient psychiatric facilities (IPFs)** for payment purposes were exempt from the inpatient prospective payment system from 1982 through 2004. Section 1886(ed)(1)(B) of the Social Security Act (the Act) created this exemption and established a reasonable cost payment scheme based on the Tax Equity and Fiscal Responsibility Act (TEFRA) payment methodology (DHHS 2004f, 66923).

The Balanced Budget Refinement Act of 1999 (BBRA) required the development of a per-diem prospective payment system (PPS) for inpatient psychiatric services provided in IPFs. Specifically, the BBRA charged CMS with developing a classification system that would reflect the resource consumption and, therefore, cost differences among various IPFs. The legislation gave CMS the authority to collect hospital data necessary for the development of the new PPS. The system was mandated to maintain budget neutrality and CMS instructed to submit a report of the proposed system to Congress. The initial implementation date was set to be October 1, 2002. (DHHS 2004f, 66923).

Prior to the BBRA, CMS had researched several PPS options for IPFs. However, its research focus was a by-discharge payment methodology similar to other established PPSs, such as the IPPS and HOPPS. The research showed that a per-discharge system did not adequately explain the cost variations among psychiatric encounters (DHHS 2004f, 66923). Therefore, a new approach was necessary. The BBRA gave CMS a three-year period to research and develop a per-diem system (DHHS 2004f, 66923).

More than a year after the initial implementation date of October 1, 2002, the proposed rule for the IPF PPS was released on November 28, 2003 (DHHS 2004f, 66920). The proposed rule outlined the new PPS based on a per-diem rate with several add-on payments to provide reimbursement for cost variations. The new PPS called for major changes in the way an IPF would be reimbursed for Medicare services and discussed complex cost issues. CMS received many comments on the proposed rule, and the public requested an extended period of time to review the proposed PPS. Therefore, the comment period was extended. On November 15, 2004, the final rule for the IPF PPS was released (DHHS 2004f, 66922).The final rule established a new implementation date of April 1, 2005.

The IPF PPS is based on a federal per-diem amount that represents the average daily operational, ancillary, and capital costs expended to care for Medicare beneficiaries. For rate year 2008, the federal per-diem amount is $614.99. Adjustments to the payment are made at the facility and patient levels, as described in table 6.24. Although the large number of payment modifications creates a complex system, the payment methodology is designed to adequately reimburse facilities for the services provided to Medicare beneficiaries.

CMS used a regression analysis model to determine the types and levels of adjustments that were necessary to create a payment system that would explain cost variation among IPFs. Regression analysis is a statistical methodology that uses an independent variable to predict the value of a dependent variable. In this case, patient demographics and length of stay (independent variables) were used to predict cost (dependent variable). The regression analysis performed for the IPF PPS proposed rule (2003) used data from the FY 1999 MedPAR file and the FY 1999 healthcare cost reporting information system (HCRIS). A revised regression analysis was performed for the Final Rule and used updated MedPAR data from 2002 and updated HCRIS data from 2001 and 2002.

Table 6.24.   Facility and patient level adjustments

Facility-Level Adjustments	Patient-Level Adjustments
Wage index	Length of stay
Cost of living adjustment	DRG with principal diagnosis of mental disorder
Rural location	Comorbidity
Teaching status	Age of patient
Full service emergency department	Electroconvulsive therapy

Patient-Level Adjustments

Patient-level adjustments are made for length of stay, DRGs that contain a psychiatric ICD-9-CM code, comorbidity conditions, treatment of older patients, and encounters that include electroconvulsive therapy.

Length of Stay Adjustment
Cost regression, first based on 1999 claims data and then updated with 2002 data, showed that the per-diem cost for psychiatric cases decreased as the length of stay increased (DHHS 2004f, 66949). Therefore, the IPF PPS provides a length-of-stay adjustment factor for each day of the patient encounter. Table 6.25 shows the adjustment schedule by day.

DRG Adjustment
The IPF PPS will provide reimbursement for DRGs that contain a psychiatric ICD-9-CM code as identified in chapter five of the code book as principal diagnosis. However, a payment adjustment will be made only for fifteen designated psychiatric DRGs. Table 6.26 provides a listing of the fifteen psychiatric DRGs.

Comorbidity Conditions
The regression analysis of 2002 cost data identified a need to provide a payment adjustment for some comorbidity conditions. Table 6.27 provides a listing of the comorbidity groupings that warrant a payment adjustment in the IPF PPS system. This is not a complete list of comorbidities as used in the IPPS; rather, it is a listing of the conditions that were found to be more costly to treat for psychiatric patients in IPFs.

Older Patients
Reimbursement rates are altered to account for the additional costs incurred for treating older patients. Regression analysis showed that the cost per day increased with increasing patient age. Table 6.28 provides the age categories and the adjustment factors used for the IPF PPS.

Table 6.25. Length-of-stay adjustment schedule

Day of Stay	Variable Per-Diem Payment Adjustment
Day 1	1.31/1.19*
Day 2	1.12
Day 3	1.08
Day 4	1.05
Day 5	1.04
Day 6	1.02
Day 7	1.01
Day 8	1.01
Day 9	1.00
Day 10	1.00
Day 11	0.99
Day 12	0.99
Day 13	0.99
Day 14	0.99
Day 15	0.98
Day 16	0.97
Day 17	0.97
Day 18	0.96
Day 19	0.95
Day 20	0.95
Day 21	0.95
Over 21	0.92

*The adjustment for day 1 would be 1.31 or 1.19, depending on whether the IPF has or is a psychiatric unit in an acute care hospital with a qualifying emergency department.

Source: Department of Health and Human Services. 2004 (November 15). *Federal Register.* 69 (219): 66949.

Table 6.26. Psychiatric DRGs that qualify for payment adjustment

DRG Title	DRG Code	Adjustment Factor
Procedure with principal diagnosis of mental illness	DRG 424	1.22
Acute adjustment reaction	DRG 425	1.05
Depressive neurosis	DRG 426	0.99
Neurosis, except depressive	DRG 427	1.02
Disorders of personality	DRG 428	1.02
Organic disturbances	DRG 429	1.03
Psychosis	DRG 430	1.00
Childhood disorders	DRG 431	0.99
Other mental disorders	DRG 432	0.92
Alcohol/drug use, LAMA	DRG 433	0.97
Alcohol/drug, with CC	DRG 521	1.02
Alcohol/drug without CC	DRG 522	0.98
Alcohol/drug use, without rehab	DRG 523	0.88
Degenerative nervous system disorders	DRG 012	1.05
Nontraumatic stupor and coma	DRG 023	1.07

Source: Department of Health and Human Services. 2004 (November 15). *Federal Register.* 69 (219): 66938.

Table 6.27.   Comorbidity adjustment categories

Comorbidity Category	Applicable ICD-9-CM Codes	Adjustment Factor
Developmental disabilities	317, 318.0, 318.1, 318.2 and 319	1.04
Coagulation factor deficits	286.0 through 286.4	1.13
Tracheotomy	519.00 through 519.09 and V44.0	1.06
Renal failure, acute	584.5 through 584.9, 636.3, 637.3, 638.3, 639.3, 669.32, 669.34 and 958.5	1.11
Renal failure, chronic	403.01, 403.11, 403.91, 404.02, 404.03, 404.12, 404.13, 404.92, 404.93, 585, 586, V45.1, V56.0, V56.1 and V56.2	1.11
Oncology treatment	140.0 through 239.9 with either 92.21 through 92.29 or 99.25	1.07
Uncontrolled type I and type II diabetes mellitus with or without complications	250.02, 250.03, 250.12, 250.13, 250.22, 250.23, 250.32, 250.33, 250.42, 250.43, 250.52, 250.53, 250.62, 250.63, 250.72, 250.73, 250.82, 250.83, 250.92 and 250.93	1.05
Severe protein calorie malnutrition	260 through 262	1.13
Eating and conduct disorders	307.1, 307.50, 312.03, 312.33 and 312.34	1.12
Infectious disease	010.00 through 041.10, 042, 045.00 through 053.19, 054.40 through 054.49, 055.0 through 077.0, 078.2 through 078.89 and 079.50 through 079.59	1.07
Drug and/or alcohol induced mental disorders	291.0, 292.0, 292.2, 303.00 and 304.00	1.03
Cardiac conditions	391.0, 391.1, 391.2, 402.01, 404.03, 416.0, 421.0, 421.1 and 421.9	1.11
Gangrene	440.24 and 785.4	1.10
Chronic obstructive pulmonary disease	491.21, 494.1, 510.0, 518.83, 518.84, V46.11 and V46.12	1.12
Artificial openings—digestive and urinary	569.60 through 569.69, 997.5 and V44.1 through V44.6	1.08
Severe musculoskeletal and connective tissue diseases	696.0, 710.0, 730.00 through 730.09, 730.10 through 730.19 and 730.20 through 730.29	1.09
Poisoning	965.00 through 965.09, 965.4, 967.0 through 969.9, 977.0, 980.0 through 980.9, 983.0 through 983.9, 986 and 989.0 through 989.7	1.11

Source: Department of Health and Human Services. 2004 (November 15). *Federal Register.* 69 (219): 66944.

Table 6.28. Age adjustment categories

Age	Adjustment Factor
Under 45	1.00
45 and under 50	1.01
50 and under 55	1.02
55 and under 60	1.04
60 and under 65	1.07
65 and under 70	1.10
70 and under 75	1.13
75 and under 80	1.15
80 and over	1.17

Source: Department of Health and Human Services. 2004 (November 15). *Federal Register.* 69 (219): 66947.

Electroconvulsive Therapy

Providing electroconvulsive therapy (ECT) to Medicare beneficiaries is costly. Regression analysis showed that an encounter that included ECT was twice as expensive as an encounter that did not include ECT. The cost is mostly associated with the increased length of stay but is also a result of increased ancillary services (DHHS 2004f, 66951). The IPF PPS provides a patient-level adjustment for this service. Facilities will receive additional payment for each ECT session performed. For rate year (RY) 2008 (July 2007–June 2008) the additional reimbursement equals $264.77. The ECT amount is subject to cost of living (COLA) and wage index adjustments. ECT services should be reported with the CPT code 90870 and revenue code 901. The units of service must also be reported. ECT payments and charges are taken into account when fiscal intermediaries calculate the outlier threshold and outlier payment.

Facility-Level Adjustments

Payments are adjusted at the facility level to account for geographic variations such as wage differences, cost of living, and rural location. Adjustments are also made for teaching hospitals and facilities that provide emergency medical services. These adjustments are addressed in the following sections.

Wage Index Adjustment

A facility level adjustment is provided to account for wage differences among geographical areas. The labor portion of the federal per-diem base rate is 75.788 percent. The unadjusted, prereclassified IPPS hospital wage index using core-based statistical area (CBSA) definitions is used to make the adjustment. Figure 6.6 provides the IPF wage index adjustment formula. Please note that at implementation the IPF-PPS wage index adjustment was not based on the newly reclassified CBSA values that are being used in the IPPS and HOPPS. CMS will review claims data in the future to determine if a conversion to the CBSA methodology is warranted under this system.

Cost-of-Living Adjustment

In addition to the wage index adjustment, a cost-of-living adjustment (COLA) will be made for IPFs in the states of Hawaii and Alaska. The **nonlabor share** portion (2.212 percent) of the federal per diem base rate will be adjusted by the adjustment factor provided for the county in which the facility is located. Figure 6.6 provides the COLA formula. Table 6.29 provides a listing of the COLA adjustments.

Rural Location Adjustment

Regression analysis showed that IPFs incurred costs 17 percent greater when treating patients in rural locations than treating patients in urban locations. Many rural IPFs are small facilities that do not have the economy-of-scale advantages that larger facilities experience. Further, providing psychiatric services requires a set of minimum fixed costs that cannot be avoided or decreased. (DHHS 2004f, 66954). Therefore, the IPF PPS is providing a rural location adjustment of 1.17.

Figure 6.6. Wage index adjustment formula

(Federal per diem base rate × Labor percent × Wage index) + (Federal per diem base rate × Nonlabor percentage)

Table 6.29. COLA areas

State	Location	COLA
Alaska	Anchorage	1.24
Alaska	Fairbanks	1.24
Alaska	Juneau	1.24
Alaska	All other areas	1.25
Hawaii	Honolulu County	1.25
Hawaii	Hawaii County	1.17
Hawaii	Kauai County	1.25
Hawaii	Maui County	1.25
Hawaii	Kalawao County	1.25

Source: Department of Health and Human Services 2007 (May 4). *Federal Register.* 72 (86): 25617.

Teaching Hospital Adjustment

IPFs are granted a teaching hospital adjustment similar to the adjustment made for IPPS facilities. The adjustment is based on the number of full-time residents at the facility. The coefficient value of .5150 will be used for RY 2008 in the teaching status adjustment.

Emergency Facility Adjustment

Patients who receive emergency department (ED) care prior to admission are more costly to treat than patients who do not receive such care. Therefore, CMS provides an adjustment to adequately reimburse facilities for this greater cost without creating an incentive to provide ED care when it is not medically necessary in order to receive additional payments. A facility-level adjustment is made for IPFs with full-service EDs. IPFs with qualifying EDs receive a greater per-diem adjustment for the first day of each stay for all patients. (See table 6.25, Day 1.)

Provisions of the Inpatient Psychiatric Facility Prospective Payment System

The IPF PPS uses provisions to provide additional payments for unusual admissions that historically have added significant cost to patient care. Without the additional payments associated with these provisions, it may not be feasible for inpatient psychiatric facilities to provide all services to Medicare beneficiaries.

Outlier Payment Provision

The IPF PPS provides outlier payments for high cost encounters. Outlier payments are projected to account for 2 percent of the total payment for implementation year. In order to qualify for an outlier payment, the costs of an encounter must exceed the adjusted threshold amount. Cost is determined by converting charges to cost using cost-to-charge ratios (CCRs) from the facility's most recent settled or tentatively settled Medicare cost report. Facilities that have CCRs outside of the designated **trim points** will be required to use national rural/urban CCRs. The adjusted threshold amount is calculated by applying wage index, rural location, and teaching status adjustment to the national amount. The unadjusted threshold amount for RY 2008 is $6,488. In addition to reimbursement for the encounter, facilities will receive 80 percent of the difference between the IPF's estimated cost and the adjusted threshold amount for days 1 through 9, and 60 percent for days thereafter (DHHS 2004f, 66960).

Stop-Loss Provision

A stop-loss provision is a form of hold-harmless policy. A stop-loss schedule has been included in the implementation of the IPF PPS to assist facilities with changes in reimbursement levels that may occur. Multiple stop-loss levels were researched, but the 70 percent policy was adopted. IPF PPS payment can equal no less than 70 percent of the TEFRA payment had the IPF PPS not been implemented. In order to achieve the 70 percent policy, a four-year phase-in schedule was developed, as outlined in table 6.30.

Initial Stay and Readmission Provisions

The IPF PPS is designed to provide higher payment for initial days of a stay in order to adequately

Table 6.30.   Stop-loss schedule

Year	TEFRA Payment	IPF PPS Payment
Year one (4/1/2005–6/30/2006)	75%	25%
Year two (7/1/2006–6/30/2007)	50%	50%
Year three (7/1/2007–6/30/2008)	25%	75%
Year four (7/1/2008–6/30/2009)	0%	100%

reimburse facilities for the higher costs associated with a new admission. CMS has expressed concern that this adjustment could provide an incentive for facilities to prematurely discharge patients and then subsequently readmit them in order to again receive the higher per-diem rates associated with the first days of a stay. Therefore, an interrupted stay provision was created. Patients discharged from an IPF who are then admitted to the same or another IPF within three consecutive days (before midnight on the third day) of the discharge from the original facility stay would be treated as continuous for purposes of the variable per-diem adjustment and outlier calculation (DHHS 2004f, 66963).

Example:

A patient is admitted to IPF A on March 1. The patient is discharged on March 5 (length of stay is four). The patient is then admitted to IPF B on March 7 and continues the hospital stay until March 10 (length of stay = three). The admission to IPF B is considered a continuation of the initial stay at IPF A. Therefore, day one of the readmission will be considered day 5 of the combined stay for the purposes of the length of stay adjustment and outlier calculation (see table 6.25).

Medical Necessity Provision

Medical necessity must be established for each patient upon admission to the IPF. Physician recertification to establish continued need for inpatient psychiatric care is required on the eighteenth day

following admission. Inpatient care requires more intense service than outpatient. Inpatient admissions or continued stays are necessary when care requires intensive comprehensive multimodal treatments such as twenty-four hour supervision, safety concerns, diagnostic evaluations, monitoring for side effects of psychotropic medications, and evaluation of behaviors.

Payment Steps

Step One: Wage index adjust the labor portion of the per-diem rate.

Step Two: Apply COLA to the nonlabor portion of the per-diem rate if applicable.

Step Three: Add the results of step one and step two together to determine the wage adjusted per-diem rate.

Step Four: Apply the following patient-level and facility-level adjustments:
- Rural location
- Teaching
- Full-service ED
- DRG
- Comorbidity
- Age

Determine each level of adjustment for the case. Multiply the individual adjustments to determine the PPS adjustment factor.

Step Five: Multiply the PPS adjustment factor by the wage adjusted per-diem rate determined in step three to calculate the adjusted per diem.

Step Six: Identify whether the facility has a qualifying ED. If so, choose the appropriate (higher) adjustment factor for the first day of stay. Determine the patient's length of stay and LOS adjustment factor for each day.

Step Seven: Multiply the adjusted per-diem rate (step five) by the LOS adjustment factor for each day of the stay to calculate the per-diem payment amount.

Step Eight: Sum the per-diem payment amounts calculated for each day of the stay.

Step Nine: Calculate the adjusted ECT amount for the encounter if applicable. Multiply the national payment amount by the labor share and the area wage index. Then multiply the national payment amount by the nonlabor share and the applicable COLA. Sum these two products to calculate the adjusted ECT amount. Multiply the adjusted ECT amount by the units of service. Add the total ECT payment to the total per-diem payment amount (step eight).

Summary

With the implementation of a prospective payment system for inpatient psychiatric facilities and units, CMS projected that Medicare will save at least $7.5 million during the first five years with implementation of the IPF PPS (DHHS 2004f, 66974). Even though one of the primary objectives of implementing prospective payment systems is to control costs, CMS is dedicated to maintaining a PPS that not only focuses on cost and payment but also incorporates variables, such as quality and outcome measures, that influence cost and payment levels (DHHS 2004f, 66968). CMS will continue to research various payment methods as it makes future refinements to the system.

Check Your Understanding 6.2

1. What cost-sharing applies to beneficiaries residing in a LTCH for ninety days?

2. Even though long-term care diagnosis related groups (MS-LTC-DRGs) are based on the same general factors as the acute care MS-DRGs for the IPPS, MS-LTC-DRGs differ from acute care MS-DRGs because MS-LTC-DRGs have higher weights, use quintiles for low volumes, and employ short-stay outliers. True or false?

3. The budget-neutral conversion factor (CF) that converts the MS-LTC-DRG into a payment amount is the _____.

4. To collect information about Medicare patients that drives payment in the IRF PPS, the _____ is used.

5. IRF staff members record RICs on patients' PAIs to classify their impairment categories. True or false?

Summary

The Medicare prospective payment system (PPS) was introduced by the federal government in October 1983, as a way to change hospital behavior through financial incentives that encourage more cost-efficient management of medical care. Since that time, PPS has revolutionized healthcare reimbursement in settings across the continuum of care. Four more prospective payment systems for hospital settings in skilled nursing, long-term care, rehabilitation, and psychiatric facilities were designed and implemented between 1998 and 2005. As updates and revisions are required and/or warranted, CMS publishes proposed and final rules via the *Federal Register* to discuss and release updated information. Students and professionals should review final rules in order to obtain the most current payment values and provision specifications.

Chapter 6 Review Quiz

1. List at least two major reasons that Medicare administrators turned to the prospective payment concept for Medicare beneficiaries.

2. How do DRGs encourage inpatient facilities to practice cost management?

3. How are per-diem rates for SNF PPS patients determined for various cases?

4. How are MS-LTC-DRGs determined?

5. On the IRF PAI the patient's ability to perform activities of daily living, or _____ is recorded on the _____.

6. Why does the IPF PPS length-of-stay adjustment factor grow smaller during the patient encounter?

7. Describe at least two of the patient-level adjustments for IPF PPS claims and why they are used.

8. For inpatient rehabilitation facility patients, codes on the IRF PAI should follow the UHDDS and the UB-04 guidelines. True or false?

9. Facilities transmit IRF PAIs to the Centers for Medicare and Medicaid Services using CMS's free IRVEN software. True or false?

References and Bibliography

Averill, R. F., N. I. Goldfield, J. Eisenhandler, J. S. Hughes, and J. Muldoon. 2001. Clinical risk groups and the future of healthcare reimbursement. In *Reimbursement Methodologies for Healthcare Services* [CD-ROM], edited by L. M. Jones. Chicago: American Health Information Management Association.

Centers for Medicare and Medicaid Services. 2005. www.cms.hhs.gov.

Centers for Medicare and Medicaid Services. 2002a. Inpatient rehabilitation facility prospective payment system. Available online from www.cms.hhs.gov/medlearn/inpatref.asp.

Centers for Medicare and Medicaid Services. 2002b. LTCH PPS contractor training guide for providers. Available online from www.cms.hhs.gov/medlearn/trainguide.asp.

Centers for Medicare and Medicaid Services. 2003. Medicare Prescription Drug, Improvement, and Modernization Act of 2003. Section 626 (2)(B). Available online from www.cms.hhs.gov/medicarereform.

Centers for Medicare and Medicaid Services. 2004. *Expansion of Transfer Policy under Inpatient Prospective Payment System*. MedLearn Matters (MM2934), Medicare Learning Network. Available online from www.cms.hhs.gov/medlearn/matters/.

Centers for Medicare and Medicaid Services. 2005 (April 29). CMS Manual System, Pub 100-04 Medicare Claims Processing, Transmittal 540, Change Request 3774. Accessed at https://www.cms.hhs.gov/transmittals/downloads/R540CP.pdf. Accessed on 27 September 2007.

Department of Health and Human Services. 1999 (July 30). Medicare Program; Prospective Payment System and Consolidated Billing for Skilled Nursing Facilities—Update; Notices. *Federal Register* 64 (146). 41684–41701.

Department of Health and Human Services. 2001 (August 7). Medicare Program; Prospective Payment System for Inpatient Rehabilitation Facilities; Final Rule. *Federal Register* 66 (152): 41316–41427.

Department of Health and Human Services. 2002 (August 30). Medicare Program; Prospective Payment System for Long-Term Care Hospitals: Implementation and FY 2003 Rates; Final Rule. *Federal Register* 67 (169): 55953–56090.

Department of Health and Human Services. 2003a (June 6). Medicare Program; Prospective Payment System for Long-Term Care Hospitals: Annual Payment Rate Updates and Policy Changes; Final Rule. *Federal Register* 68 (109): 34122–34190.

Department of Health and Human Services. 2003b (November 28). Medicare Program; Prospective Payment System for Inpatient Psychiatric Facilities; Proposed Rule. *Federal Register* 68 (229): 66919–66978.

Department of Health and Human Services. 2004a (May 7). Medicare Program; Changes to the Criteria for Being Classified as an Inpatient Rehabilitation Facility; Final Rule. *Federal Register* 69 (89): 25751–25776.

Department of Health and Human Services. 2004b (May 7). Medicare Program; Prospective Payment System for Long-Term Care Hospitals: Annual Payment Rate Updates and Policy Changes; Final Rule. *Federal Register* 69 (89): 25674–25749.

Department of Health and Human Services 2004c (July 30). Medicare Program; Inpatient Rehabilitation Facility Prospective Payment System for Fiscal Year 2005; Notice. *Federal Register* 69 (146): 45721–45775.

Department of Health and Human Services 2004d (July 30). Medicare Program; Prospective Payment System and Consolidated Billing for Skilled Nursing Facilities—Update; Notice. *Federal Register* 69 (146): 45775–45822.

Department of Health and Human Services. 2004e (August 11). Medicare Program; Changes to the Hospital Inpatient Prospective Payment Systems and Fiscal Year 2005 Rates; Final Rule. *Federal Register* 69 (154): 48915–48964.

Department of Health and Human Services. 2004f (November 15). Medicare Program; Prospective Payment System for Inpatient Psychiatric Facilities; Final Rule. *Federal Register* 69 (219): 66921–67015.

Department of Health and Human Services. 2004g (December 30). Medicare Program; Prospective Payment System and Consolidated Billing for Skilled Nursing Facilities; Corrections; Notices. *Federal Register* 69 (250): 78445–78464.

Department of Health and Human Services. 2005a (May 6). Medicare Program; Prospective Payment System for Long-Term Care Hospitals: Annual Payment Rate Updates, Policy Changes, and Clarification; Final Rule. *Federal Register* 70 (87): 24168–24261.

Department of Health and Human Service. 2005b (August 4). Medicare Program; Prospective Payment System and Consolidated Billing for Skilled Nursing Facilities for FY 2006; Final Rule. *Federal Register* 70(149):45026–45127.

Department of Health and Human Services. 2007a (August 3). Medicare Program; Prospective Payment System and Consolidated Billing for Skilled Nursing Facilities for FY 2008; Final Rule. *Federal Register* 72 (149):43411–43463.

Department of Health and Human Services. 2007 (May 4). Medicare Program Inpatient Psychiatric Facilities Prospective Payment System Payment Update for Rate Year beginning July 1, 2007 (RY 2008); Notice. *Federal Register* 72 (86): 25602–25673.

Department of Health and Human Services. 2007b (May 11). Medicare Program; Prospective Payment System for Long-Term Care Hospitals RY 2008: Annual Payment Rate Updates, and Policy Changes; and Hospital Direct and Indirect Graduate Medical Education Policy Changes; Final Rule. *Federal Register* 72(91):26869–27029.

Department of Health and Human Services. 2007c (August 22). Medicare Program; Changes to the Hospital Inpatient Prospective Payment Systems and Fiscal Year 2008 Rates; Final Rule. *Federal Register* 72(162):45768–48175.

Department of Health and Human Services. 2007d (August 7). Medicare Program; Inpatient Rehabilitation Facility Prospective Payment System for Federal Fiscal Year 2008; Final Rule. *Federal Register* 72(151):44284–44335.

Gottlober, P., T. Brady, B. Robinson, T. Davis, S. Phillips, and A. Gruber. 2001 (August).. *Medicare Hospital Prospective Payment System: How DRG Rates are Calculated and Updated.* Publication No. OEI-09-00-00200. Office of Inspector General, Office of Evaluation and Inspections, Region IX. Available online from www.oig.hhs.gov/oei/reports/oei-09-00-00200.pdf.

Johns, Merida., ed. 2006. *Health Information Management Technology: An Applied Approach,* Second Edition. Chicago: American Health Information Management Association.

LaTour, K., and S. Eichenwald, eds. 2006. *Health Information Management: Concepts, Principles, and Practice,* Second Edition. Chicago: American Health Information Management Association.

Lave, J. R. 1989. The effect of the Medicare prospective payment system. *Annual Review of Public Health* 10:141–161.

Medicare Payment Advisory Commission. 2007 (March). Chapter 3D, Long-term care hospital services. 219-236. Accessed at http://www.medpac.gov/chapters/Mar07_Ch03d.pdf. Accessed on 28 September 2007.

Schraffenberger, L. 2005. *Basic ICD-9-CM Coding.* Chicago: American Health Information Management Association.

Trela, Patricia. 2002. Inpatient rehabilitation PPS presents new challenges, opportunities. *Journal of American Health Information Management Association.* 73 (January) (1): 48A–48D.

Chapter 7
Ambulatory and Other Medicare-Medicaid Reimbursement Systems

Objectives

- To differentiate major types of Medicare and Medicaid reimbursement systems for beneficiaries

- To define basic language associated with reimbursement under Medicare and Medicaid healthcare payment systems

- To explain common models and policies of payment for Medicare and Medicaid healthcare payment systems for physicians and outpatient settings

Key Terms

Ambulatory payment classifications (APCs)
Ambulatory surgical centers (ASCs)
Ancillary services
Ambulatory surgery center list of covered procedures (ASC list)
Budget neutrality (budget-neutral)
Budget neutrality adjustor (BN adjustor)
Bundling
Calendar year (CY)
Carrier
Case-mix diagnoses
Conversion factor (CF)
Core-based statistical area (CBSA)
Critical access hospitals (CAHs)
Critical care services
Discounted
Episode of care
Geographic practice cost index (GPCI)
Health insurance prospective payment system (HIPPS)
Hold-harmless status
Home assistance validation and entry (HAVEN)

Home health agencies (HHAs)
Home health resource group (HHRG)
Low-utilization payment adjustment (LUPA)
Market basket
Medicare Administrative Contractor (MAC)
Metropolitan statistical area (MSA)
National standard episode amount
National unadjusted copayment amount
National unadjusted payment amount
Nonroutine medical supplies (NRS)
Observation
Outcome Assessment Information Set (OASIS)
Outpatient Code Editor (OCE)
Packaging
Partial hospitalization
Pass-through
Payment status indicator (PSI)
Relative value scale
Relative value units (RVUs)
Resource-based relative value scale (RBRVS)
Rural area

Introduction to Reimbursement Systems for Physicians and Ambulatory Settings

The first prospective payment system (PPS), the acute care PPS, was a successful initiative for Medicare reimbursement reform. However, as the rate of growth of Medicare inpatient payments was effectively curbed, the rate of growth of Medicare payments for ambulatory patients and to physicians escalated sharply. For example, in the 1980s, the average rate of growth for Medicare spending on physicians grew at an average rate of more than 12 percent (Scanlon 2002, 2). Therefore, Congress authorized the Department of Health and Human Services (DHHS) to develop and implement reformed fee systems and prospective payment systems across the continuum of care for Medicare beneficiaries. These payment systems include the **resource-based relative value scale (RBRVS)** for physician services, the ambulance fee schedule, the ambulatory surgical center payment system, the hospital outpatient payment system, and the home health payment system.

Resource-Based Relative Value Scale for Physician Payments

A resource-based relative value scale (RBRVS) is a system of classifying health services based on the cost of furnishing physician services in different settings, the skill and training levels required to perform the services, and the time and risk involved. The RBRVS is the federal government's payment system for physicians.

Background

The concept of a **relative value scale** has existed since the mid-1940s. Such a system permits comparisons of the resources needed or appropriate prices for various units of service. It takes into account labor, skill, supplies, equipment, space, and other costs for each procedure or service.

In the 1940s, the Casualty Actuarial Society created a relative value scale for commercial insurance. In 1956, the California Medical Society devised one. Since 1956, medical societies of forty other states and six physician specialty groups have devised such scales. Antitrust actions in the 1970s slowed the adoption of relative value scales by professional groups. However, payers' interest in relative value scales continued.

Relative value scales attempt to represent the worth of healthcare services. Experts have used various ways to represent the worth of services. The different ways focus on the different qualities that people deem important. Some of the bases of these proposed ways have been:

- Historical charges for physician services (most popular and least difficult)

- Prices patients are willing to pay (consumerism)

- Physicians' assessments of the worth of different services and procedures

- Monetized benefits to society

- Consensus or negotiation process

- Estimates of the charges that would occur in a competitive market

- Micro-costing of physician services with time-and-motion studies or Delphi studies

The approach that eventually was adopted focused on the cost of furnishing physician services in different settings, the skill and training levels required to perform the services, and the time and risk involved.

History

In 1985, the Consolidated Omnibus Reconciliation Act (COBRA) directed the Department of Health and Human Services (DHHS) to develop a relative value scale for physician services. As a result of

COBRA, in 1985, the Centers for Medicare and Medicaid Services (CMS; formerly the Health Care Financing Administration, [HCFA]) awarded a grant to Dr. William Hsaio of Harvard University to devise a system of classifying services using resource-based relative values. The purpose of this research was twofold. Primarily, the intent of the research was to address the issue of income disparity between physician specialists and general practitioners. Because specialists were higher paid than general practitioners, more medical students were entering specialty fields. The nation as a result had fewer family doctors; this shortage was especially severe in **rural areas.** To resolve this shortage, the federal government decided to increase the rate of reimbursement for services typical of general practitioners to rates comparable to those for services of specialists. Thus, services such as office visits and consultations were to be weighted more heavily than in the past. The additional purpose and side benefit of this new system of classification was to save the government Medicare funds.

In the 1989 Omnibus Budget Reconciliation Act, Congress required the government to reform the physician payment system. Effective January 1, 1992, under section 1848 of the Social Security Act, "Payment for Physicians' Services," the federal government instituted RBRVS for reimbursement of physicians. RBRVS was phased in between 1992 and 1996. Although RBRVS is still a fee-for-service system of payment, the reimbursement is based on CMS's estimation of the value of a physician's service.

Structure of Relative Value Units

Relative value units (RVUs) exist for over 4,000 types of health services, accounting for 85 percent of Medicare payments to physicians. The system assigns each service a value representing the true resources involved in producing it, including the time and intensity of work, the expenses of practice, and the risk of malpractice. Under section 1848 of the Act, CMS analysts must review the RVUs at least every five years. The purpose of this review is to refine the RVUs. Five-year reviews have been finalized in 1997, 2002, and 2007. Annually, as new health services are implemented or existing health services are revised, the Relative Value Scale Update Committee (RUC) of the American Medical Association makes recommendations to the CMS on appropriate RVUs for these health services.

The RBRVS system applies to physician services, such as medical/surgical, diagnostic, and radiologic services. Physical and occupational therapy are also included. Laboratory tests are excluded. In addition, payments for the services of physician assistants, nurse practitioners, and nurse midwives are tied to the RBRVS payment amounts.

RBRVS is based on CPT coding. Each CPT code has been assigned a relative value unit (RVU). An RVU is a unit of measure designed to permit comparison of the amount of resources required to perform various provider services by assigning weights to such factors as personnel time, level of skill, and sophistication of equipment required to render service. In the RBRVS, the RVU reflects national averages and is the sum of the physician work, practice expenses, and malpractice costs. RVUs are adjusted to local costs through the **geographic practice cost indexes (GPCIs).**

Each RVU comprises three elements, each of which is a national average available in the *Federal Register:*

- Physician work (WORK)

- Physician practice expenses (PE)

- Malpractice (MP)

WORK is the element that covers the physician's salary. This work is the time the physician spends providing a service and the intensity with which that time is spent. The four aspects of intensity are:

- Mental effort and judgment

- Technical skill

- Physical effort
- Psychological stress

PE is the overhead costs of the practice, such as office rent, wages of nonphysician personnel, and supplies and equipment. PE is categorized as either facility or nonfacility. According to CMS experts, practice expenses differ for physicians when they perform services in facilities, such as hospitals, as opposed to nonfacilities, such as their own offices and clinics. In facilities, the organization incurs the overhead costs of personnel, supplies, equipment, and other costs, while in nonfacilities, the physician incurs the overhead expenses for such costs. Therefore, the PE is higher for nonfacilities. Some procedural codes do not have separate facility and nonfacility PEs. In these procedural codes, the description includes the setting (evaluation and management, initial hospital care) or the nature of the procedure restricts it to a particular site (major surgical procedures in hospitals).

Facilities include:

- Inpatient or outpatient hospital settings
- Emergency rooms
- Skilled nursing facilities
- Ambulatory surgical centers
- Inpatient psychiatric facilities
- Comprehensive inpatient rehabilitation facilities
- Community mental health centers
- Military treatment facilities
- Ambulance (land, air, or water)
- Psychiatric facility partial hospital
- Psychiatric resort treatment centers.

Nonfacilities include:

- Physicians' offices
- Clinics

- Dialysis centers
- Independent laboratories
- Nonskilled nursing facilities
- Patients' homes
- All other settings

Physicians can provide services in these multiple settings. Factors in choice of setting include:

- Patient's medical condition
- Type of procedure
- Patient's preference
- Geographic location
- Technology
- Regulation or healthcare insurance policies (Medicare Payment Advisory Commission 2004, 19)

The final decision of setting is a blend of the factors.

MP is the cost of the premiums for the professional liability insurance.

Payment Structure

Payments under the RBRVS system consist of three components. These three components are:

- The RVU
- A geographic adjustment
- A constant that converts a relative value into a payment

A payment amount results when the RVUs are adjusted for geographic variations, summed, and multiplied by the constant.

The elements of the RVU are national averages. A geographic adjustment is necessary because costs vary in different areas of the country. Therefore, each element of an RVU is adjusted for these differences. The adjustment component is called the geographic practice cost index (GPCI). This index is based on relative differences in the cost of a **market basket** of goods across geographic areas. GPCIs reflect local costs. Each element of the RVU—WORK, PE, and MP—has its own unique GPCI. The GPCIs can be found in the *Federal Register*.

The across-the-board multiplier is the **conversion factor (CF).** Unlike the GPCIs, the conversion factor is a constant that applies to the entire RVU. The conversion factor transforms the geographic-adjusted RVU into a national allowance for a Medicare payment. The conversion factor, as updated annually, can be found in the *Federal Register*.

The conversion factor is the government's most direct control on Medicare payments to physicians. CMS raises or lowers the conversion factor to raise or lower physician payments. For example, in 2001, CMS set the conversion factor at $38.2581. In 2002, in an effort to reduce costs, CMS set the conversion factor at $36.1992. In 2003 and 2005, Congress set the conversion factors at $36.7856 and $37.8975, respectively, to give physicians slight increases. In 2007, the conversion factor was held at $37.8975. Therefore, by altering one number, the CF, Congress can increase and decrease overall Medicare payments to physicians.

Payment Calculation

To calculate the national allowance for payments for various services, the following formula is used:

[(WORK RVU) (WORK GPCI) +
(PE RVU) (PE GPCI) + (MP RVU) (MP GPCI)] =
(SUM) $\times$ CF = National allowance

Table 7.1 dissects the general RBRVS formula, and table 7.2 shows the formula in action for a sample CPT code.

Sometimes, an extra adjustment must be made to the generic formula to maintain **budget neutrality.** This adjustment occurs because a provision of section 1848 requires that refinements to RVUs must maintain budget neutrality. Budget neutrality demands that refinements to federal payment systems do not result in significant differences in expenditures. Generally, upcoming expenditures must equal past expenditures. Specifically, for refinements to the RVUs, payments for physicians' services cannot differ by more than $20 million (DHHS 2006a, 69628).

In 2007, the refinement from the five-year review required that an extra adjustment be applied to the generic formula. This extra adjustment is known as the **budget neutrality adjustor** (BN adjustor). The BN adjustor altered the generic formula as follows:

[(WORK RVU) (BN ADJUSTOR
with product rounded to two decimal places)
(WORK GPCI) + (PE RVU) (PE GPCI)
+ (MP RVU) (MP GPCI)]
= (SUM) $\times$ CF
= National allowance

In 2007, the BN adjustor was 0.8994 (CMS 2007a). Applying the BN adjustor to the calculation of the nonfacility payment in Table 7.2 results in the following:

(0.88) (.8994) = .79
[(.79) (1.00) + (.84) (.922) + (.05) (.63) =
.79 + .77448 + .0315 = 1.59598
1.59598 $\times$ $37.8975 = $60.48

Table 7.1.   Generic formula: Resource-based relative value scale

General RBRVS Formula		
Relative value (RVU) of service = sum of work value, practice expenses, malpractice, each adjusted for geographic practice cost index (GPCI)	$\times$ Conversion factor (Conv. Fact.)	= National allowance

Table 7.2.   Calculation of nonfacility payment under resource-based relative value scale

Specific Example of RBRVS Allowance Calculation in 2007*				
CPT code = 99202 (Office visit, new patient, expanded problem-focused)				
Element	RVU	GPCI	Geographic Adjustment (RVU × GPCI***)	Adjusted Payment [Adjusted RVU × Conv. Fact. ($37.8975)]
Work value (WORK)**	.88	1.00	.88	
Practice expense (PE)	.84	0.922	.77448	
Malpractice (MP)	.05	0.63	.0315	
Sum			1.68598	
Adjusted allowance				$63.89

*Data source: Centers for Medicare and Medicaid Services. 2007b (January 12). Physician Fee Schedule Search. http://www.cms.hhs.gov/pfslookup/.
**2007 budget neutrality adjustor not applied.
***North Carolina payment locality (0553500).

These adjustors are only occasionally applied. Therefore, reimbursement specialists should understand the generic formula. However, they should be aware of adjustors, familiar with their functioning, and recognize the importance of monitoring the *Federal Register,* in the event, that they are required for the fiscal year.

Anesthesia services have a separate payment method. The following elements are used to calculate a payment for anesthesia services:

- Base units for anesthesia services from a uniform relative value guide based on anesthesia CPT codes (RVUs)

- Base units for CPT anesthesia codes range from 3 (anesthesia services for needle biopsy of thyroid) to 30 (anesthesia services for liver transplant)

- Time units in 15 minute intervals (personal performance of anesthesia services) or in 30 minute intervals (medically directing the performance of others, such as certified nurse anesthetists) and

reduced for the number of concurrent procedures

- Separate conversion factor adjusted for locality (because there is no GPCI).

In 2001, the anesthesia conversion factor was $17.2600. In 2007, the conversion factors for anesthesia by locality range from $14.40 (Puerto Rico) to $18.61 (New York City suburbs, Long Island)

The generic formula:

[Base Unit + Time (in units)] × CF = Allowance

Finally, the actual Medicare payment is 80 percent of the national allowance. Medicare beneficiaries are responsible for 20 percent coinsurance and $100 Medicare Part B deductible.

Operational Issues

Poor coding and inadequate documentation negatively affect RBRVS reimbursement. For example, overlooking the removal of a polyp or lesion during an esophagoscopy can significantly reduce payment (table 7.3). Other examples illustrate the difference documentation and accurate coding make (tables 7.4 and 7.5).

Table 7.3.   Impact of coding on nonfacility reimbursement under resource-based relative value scale

Comparison of Nonfacility Payment Based on Coding (2007)*						
	CPT 43200, Esophagoscopy			CPT 43217, Esophagoscopy, with removal of tumor(s), polyp(s), or other lesion(s) by snare technique		
	RVU ×	GPCI***	=	RVU ×	GPCI	=
Work value (WORK)**	1.59	1.000	1.59	2.9	1.000	2.9
Practice expense (PE)	3.54	0.922	3.26388	6.55	0.922	6.0391
Malpractice (MP)	0.13	0.63	.0819	0.26	0.63	0.1638
Sum			4.93578			9.1029
× Conversion factor			$37.8975			$37.8975
Total			$187.05			$344.98
Loss due to incomplete coding			$157.92			

*Data source: CMS. 2007a (January 12). Physician Fee Schedule Search. Medicare physician fee schedule. Available online http://www.cms.hhs.gov/pfslookup/.

**2007 budget neutrality adjustor not applied.

***North Carolina payment locality (0553500).

Table 7.4.   Effect of code selection on nonfacility revenue under resource-based relative value scale

Examples of Lost Nonfacility Revenue** from Poor Coding or Inadequate Documentation						Lost Payment
Careless Coding or Incomplete Documentation			Accurate Coding with Complete Documentation			
Code	Description	$	Code	Description	$	
10060	Incision and drainage of abscess; simple or single	$100.72	10061	Incision and drainage of abscess; complicated or multiple	$170.94	$70.22
11400	Excision benign lesion; excised diameter 0.5 cm or less	$100.09	11406	Excision benign lesion; excised diameter over 4.0 cm	$261.44	$161.35
19100	Biopsy of breast; percutaneous, needle core, not using imaging guidance	$123.58	19101	Biopsy of breast; open, incisional	$280.13	$156.55
45378	Colonoscopy	$369.58	45382	Colonoscopy with control of bleeding	$586.34	$216.76

*Data source: CMS. 2007a (January 12). Physician Fee Schedule Search. Medicare physician fee schedule. Available online http://www.cms.hhs.gov/pfslookup/.

**2007 budget neutrality adjustor not applied.

***North Carolina payment locality (0553500).

Table 7.5.   Comparison of sample Medicare fees by code: Nonfacility versus facility

2005 Medicare Allowables* for Selected Codes			
Code	Description	Nonfacility Fee**	Facility Fee**
99202	Office/outpatient visit, new patient	$62.26	$45.43
99211	Office/outpatient visit, established patient	20.36	8.79
99213	Office/outpatient visit, established patient	50.13	34.53
99243	Office consultation	117.06	90.42
33533	Coronary artery bypass, using arterial graft; single	NA	1,817.44
43239	Upper gastrointestinal endoscopy, biopsy	314.27	155.28
66984	Extracapsular cataract removal with insertion of intraocular lens prosthesis (one stage procedure)	NA	657.23
71020	Chest x-ray	33.74	NA
93000	Electrocardiogram, routine ECG with at last 12 leads; with interpretation and report	25.05	NA

*Data source: CMS. 2007a (January 12). Physician Fee Schedule Search. Medicare physician fee schedule. Available online http://www.cms.hhs.gov/pfslookup/.

**North Carolina payment locality (0553500).

Ambulance Fee Schedule

Section 1861(s)(7) of the Social Security Act (the Act) Medicare Part B provides beneficiary coverage for ambulance services. The benefit is intended to provide transportation services only if other means are inadvisable based on the beneficiary's medical condition. Transportation services are provided to the nearest facility that is able to provide services for the patient's condition. Beneficiaries may be transported from one hospital to another, to home, or to an extended care facility (DHHS 2002, 9100).

History

Prior to the prospective payment system implementation for ambulance services, providers and suppliers were reimbursed on a reasonable cost or charge methodology based on entity type. Providers were those ambulance service entities associated with a medical facility such as hospital, critical access hospital, skilled nursing facility, or home health agency, and were reimbursed based on retrospective reasonable cost payment. Providers used Health Care Common Procedure Coding System (HCPCS) Level II ambulance codes (A0030–A0999, excluding A0888) to report the type of service provided, and additional HCPCS Level II ambulance codes to report the type of mileage used. The charges associated with the HCPCS Level II codes selected for the case were converted to cost using the previous year's cost-to-charge ratio (CCR) for that entity.

Suppliers were those ambulance service entities not associated with any medical facility. They were reimbursed on a reasonable charge payment mechanism. The supplier could choose to report ambulance services one of four ways, as described in table 7.6. Services, mileage, and supplies were reported with HCPCS Level II ambulance codes (A0030–A0999, excluding A0888), HCPCS Level I codes 93005 and 93041, and other applicable HCPCS Level II Codes (A0000–Z9999). Suppliers reported a charge with each service, mileage,

Table 7.6.   Reporting methods for ambulance suppliers

Method	Reporting Requirements
1	A single, all-inclusive charge reflecting all services, supplies, and mileage
2	One charge reflecting all services and supplies (base rate) with a separate charge for mileage
3	One charge for all services and mileage, with a separate charge for supplies
4	Separate charges for services, mileage, and supplies

or supply code selected for that case. Payment for services was based on the lowest of the customary, prevailing, actual, or inflation index charge.

Development of the Ambulance Fee Schedule

The Balanced Budget Act of 1997 (BBA) added a new section, 1834(l), to the Act. The section required the creation of a fee schedule to establish prospective payment rates for ambulance services. The fee schedule was to be devised through negotiated rulemaking, as delineated in the Negotiated Rulemaking Act of 1990. The Negotiated Rulemaking Committee on Medicare Ambulance Services Fee Schedule (the Committee) was instructed to:

- Control Medicare expenditures for ambulance services through a prospective payment system

- Establish service definitions to link payment to the type of service

- Consider regional and operational differences in setting payment rates

- Consider inflation in setting payment rates

- Construct a phase-in period for the implementation of the fee schedule

- Require ambulance providers and suppliers to accept Medicare assignment

- Reimburse providers and suppliers at the lower of the fee schedule amount or billed charges (DHHS 2002, 9103)

During the first year of the fee schedule, payment for services could be no more than payments under the current (reasonable cost/charge) system. Additionally, BBA established the paramedic intercept service type (discussed here under levels of service). The BBA set an implementation date of January 1, 2000 for the ambulance fee schedule and paramedic intercept services.

As with most Medicare payment systems, additional legislation influenced and modified the ambulance fee schedule. The Balanced Budget Refinement Act of 1999 (BBRA) and the Benefits Improvement and Protection Act of 2000 (BIPA) were enacted to provide protections in the Medicare and Medicaid programs and the State Child Health Insurance Program (SCHIP). The BBRA modified the definition of rural for the paramedic intercept service type. The BIPA excluded **critical access hospitals (CAHs)** from the fee schedule payment methodology when the CAH is the only supplier or provider of ambulance services within a 35-mile drive. This modification called for the creation of an application process for this exemption. A qualifying CAH would be reimbursed on a reasonable cost basis. BIPA added a provision to increase payment rates for rural ambulance mileage. The proviso called for at least one-half additional payment per mile for the first seventeen miles of a rural trip and specified that an add-on percent be considered for miles seventeen through fifty. Additionally, BIPA modified the inflation factor for services provided from July 1, 2001 through December 31, 2001. The inflation factor was increased by two percentage points and set at 4.7 percent. Lastly, BIPA eliminated the blended payment rate for mileage phase-in provision for suppliers. This elimination applied to any **carrier** in a state in which the carrier's payment to all suppliers did not include a separate payment for all in-county ambulance mileage prior to the fee schedule implementation (DHHS 2002, 9104).

Implementation of the Ambulance Fee Schedule

The effective date for the ambulance fee schedule was January 1, 2000. However, due to other CMS obligations, specifically the hospital outpatient prospective payment system, preparation for year 2000 (Y2K), and the large scope of this project, CMS delayed the implementation until April 1, 2002. Implementation methodology for the ambulance fee schedule includes a five-year phase-in plan for payment. Table 7.7 displays the implementation schedule.

Reimbursement for Ambulance Services

Reimbursement for ambulance services is based on the level of service provided to the beneficiary. The

fee schedule consists of seven levels of service as defined in table 7.8. Each level specifies the EMT skill set necessary to provide services and care. The EMT skill sets are based on the National Emergency Medical Services Education and Practice Blueprint. (See table 7.9.)

Table 7.7. Ambulance fee schedule phase-in plan

Year	Former payment	Fee schedule
Year one (4/2002–12/2002)	80%	20%
Year two (CY 2003)	60%	40%
Year three (CY 2004)	40%	60%
Year four (CY 2005)	20%	80%
Year five (CY 2006)	0%	100%

Source: Department of Health and Human Services. 2004a (February 27). *Federal Register.* 67 (39): 9106.

Table 7.8. Levels of ambulance services

Service	Acronym	Description
Basic Life Support	BLS	Service level of an Emergency Medical Technician (EMT)-Basic, including the establishment of a peripheral intravenous line.
Advanced Life Support, Level 1	ALS1	In emergency cases, an assessment provided by an EMT-Intermediate or Paramedic (ALS crew) to determine patient needs and the furnishing of one or more ALS interventions. An ALS intervention is a procedure beyond the scope of an EMT-Basic.
Advanced Life Support, Level 2	ALS2	The administration of at least three different medications or the provision of one or more ALS procedures.
Specialty Care Transport	SCT	For critically injured or ill patient, the level of interhospital service furnished is beyond the scope of a paramedic. Ongoing care must be furnished by one or more health professionals in an appropriate specialty area.
Paramedic ALS Intercept	PI	ALS services furnished by an entity that does not provide the ambulance transport.
Fixed Wing Air Ambulance	FW	Destination is inaccessible by land vehicle or great distances or other obstacles (heavy traffic) and the patient's condition is not appropriate for BLS or ALS ground transportation.
Rotary Wing Air Ambulance	RW	Helicopter transport. Destination is inaccessible by land vehicle or great distances or other obstacles (heavy traffic) and the patient's condition is not appropriate for BLS or ALS ground transportation.

Source: Department of Health and Human Services. 2004 (February 27). *Federal Register.* 67 (39): 9106.

Table 7.9.   National Emergency Medical Services (EMS) education and practice blueprint

EMS Provider	Skill Set
First Responder Level	Personnel use a limited amount of equipment to perform initial assessments and interventions.
EMT-Basic	Has the knowledge and skill of the First Responder, but is also qualified to function as the minimum staff for an ambulance.
EMT-Intermediate	Knowledge and skills identified at the First Responder and EMT-Basic levels, but is also qualified to perform essential advanced techniques and to administer a limited number of medications.
EMT-Paramedic	In addition to having competencies of an EMT-Intermediate, has enhanced skills and can administer additional interventions and medications.

Source: Department of Health and Human Services. 2004 (February 27). *Federal Register.* 67 (39): 9106.

Nonemergency Transport

Medical necessity must be established for non-emergency transport provided to Medicare beneficiaries. There are two categories of nonemergency transport: repetitive and nonrepetitive. For repetitive nonemergency transports, the ambulance provider or supplier may attain physician certification in advance for the transportation service. The certification should be obtained no earlier than sixty days prior to transport.

For reimbursement of nonrepetitive nonemergency transports, the ambulance provider or supplier must provide physician certification within twenty-one days after the service was provided. The physician certification is ideally collected from the attending physician. However, the certification may be provided by a physician assistant, nurse practitioner, clinical nurse specialist, registered nurse, or discharge planner who is employed by the facility, hospital, or physician. The service provider should

have personal knowledge of the beneficiary's case. If the certification cannot be obtained from the physician or other service provider, the ambulance supplier or provider may submit a claim with documentation (that is, a signed return receipt from the U.S. Postal Service or similar delivery service) that shows all the attempts by the ambulance service to obtain certification (DHHS 2002, 9111).

Immediate Response Payment

Additional payment is made to ambulance providers and suppliers who furnish immediate response services in emergency situations. An emergency response involves responding immediately at the basic life support (BLS) or advanced life support level 1 (ALS-1) level of service to a 911 or 911-type call. Immediate response is one in which the ambulance supplier/provider begins as quickly as possible to take the steps necessary to respond to a call (DHHS 2002, 9108). The additional payment is provided to compensate those providers/suppliers the extra overhead expenses that are incurred to stay prepared at all times for emergency services. Ambulance suppliers and providers indicate that an emergency response service was provided by selecting the appropriate HCPCS Level II ambulance code. (See table 7.10 for examples.)

Payment Adjustment for Regional Variations

The ambulance fee schedule provides a payment adjustment to account for regional variations. Based on the point of beneficiary pick-up (as indicated by zip code), a geographic adjustment factor is applied. The adjustment factor used for this payment system is equal to the practice expense portion of the geo-

Table 7.10.   Sample of emergency response HCPCS Level II ambulance codes

HCPCS Code	Description
A0427	Ambulance service, ALS, emergency transport, level 1 (ALS 1 – emergency)
A0429	Ambulance service, BLS, emergency transport, (BLS – emergency)

graphic practice cost index (GPCI) established and maintained for the Medicare physician fee schedule (MPFS). For ground transport services, 70 percent of the payment rate is adjusted by the GPCI. For air ambulance services, 50 percent of the payment rate is adjusted by the GPCI. Payments for mileage are not adjusted.

Rural Area Service Adjustment

A rural area service adjustment is made to the ambulance provider/supplier when the location at which the patient is picked up is a rural area. For purposes of this provision, a rural area is an area outside of a **core-based statistical area (CBSA)** (formerly known as a **metropolitan statistical area** [MSA]) or an area that is identified as rural (DHHS 2002, 9110). The patient pick-up location is established by reporting the zip code for that location. For ground transportation, a 50 percent add-on is applied to the mileage payment rate for the first seventeen loaded miles. A 25 percent add-on is applied to the mileage payment rate for miles eighteen through fifty. No adjustment is made to the base rate for the level of service provided. For air ambulance services, a 50 percent add-on is applied to the base rate and to all of the loaded mileage.

In order for the provider/supplier to appropriately bill for services, the ambulance community requested a listing of rural, super rural and urban areas by zip code. CMS responded to the community request and now provides the National Breakout of Geographic Area Definitions by Zip Code file for download. This file can be retrieved from the CMS Web site under the Ambulance Fee Schedule section of the Medicare Hospital Center category.

Multiple-Patient Transport

An ambulance supplier or provider may encounter a situation in which multiple patients must be transported (for example, in a traffic accident). In these situations, CMS prorates the payment rate for the ambulance service for each Medicare beneficiary. If two or more patients are transported, the payment rate for each Medicare beneficiary is 75 percent of the base rate for the level of service provided. If three or more patients are transported, the payment rate for each Medicare beneficiary equals 60 percent of the base rate for the level of service provided. A single payment is made for the mileage (DHHS 2002, 9113). HCPCS Level II modifier GM, multiple patients on one ambulance trip, must be reported with the ambulance level of service code.

Transport of Deceased Patients

There are specific rules for transport cases in which a Medicare beneficiary is pronounced dead. When a beneficiary is pronounced dead by an individual who is licensed to pronounce death in that state, the following rules apply:

- When a patient is pronounced dead prior to the ambulance being called, no payment is made to the ambulance supplier/ provider.

- When a patient is pronounced dead after the ambulance has been called but prior to the ambulance arrival, a BLS base rate (for ground transport) or air ambulance base rate payment will be paid. Mileage will not be reimbursed.

- When a patient is pronounced dead during the ambulance transport, payment rules are followed as if the patient were alive (DHHS 2002, 9113).

HCPCS Level II modifier QL, Patient pronounced dead after ambulance called, should be reported with the ambulance level of service code.

Use of HCPCS Level II Modifiers

Providers must report HCPCS level II modifiers for services provided to Medicare beneficiaries. An origin and destination modifier must be reported for each ambulance trip. A two-character alpha code is designated for each line item on the claim.

The first character of the modifier represents the origin of the trip. The second digit represents the destination of the trip. Table 7.11 provides a listing of the alpha characters. Additionally, a modifier must be reported to indicate whether the service was provided under arrangement by a provider of services (QM) or if the service was furnished directly by a provider of services (QN). Figure 7.1 displays example line items from an ambulance

Table 7.11. Ambulance-specific modifiers

Modifier	Definition
D	Diagnostic or therapeutic site other than "P" or "H" when these are used as origin codes
E	Residential, domiciliary, custodial facility (other than an 1819 facility, SNF)
H	Hospital
I	Site of transfer (e.g. airport or helicopter pad) between modes of ambulance transport
J	Nonhospital-based dialysis facility
N	Skilled nursing facility (1819 facility)
P	Physician's office (includes HMO nonhospital facility, clinic, etc.)
R	Residence
S	Scene of accident or acute event
X	Intermediate stop at physician's office en route to the hospital (includes HMO nonhospital facility, clinic, etc.) Destination code only

Source: Centers for Medicare and Medicaid Services. 2005a (January 21). *Revisions and Corrections to the Medicare Claims Processing Manual,* Chapter 6, Section 30 and Various Sections in Chapter 15. Pub 100-04 Medicare Claims Processing. CMS Transmittal 437.

claim with correct use of origin/destination modifiers and service modifiers.

Payment Steps

A seven step process is used to determine payment for ambulance services. The process takes into consideration patient service level, modifiers, zip codes, miles, and add-on payments.

Step One: Identify the level of service code for the transportation provided. Determine whether the case meets the emergency response criteria before selecting the final code.

Step Two: Determine whether multiple patients were transported. If so, append modifier GM to the level of service code. Payment levels are adjusted to the prorated amounts: 75 percent per patient for two patients and 60 percent per patient for three or more patients.

Step Three: Determine whether the Medicare beneficiary was pronounced dead after the ambulance service was called. If so, append modifier QL to the level of service code. Payment levels are adjusted as outlined by this provision.

Step Four: Apply the regional variation adjustment. Identify the zip code for the location at which the patient was placed on the ambulance. 70 percent of the service payment rate is adjusted for ground transportation and 50 percent of the service payment rate is adjusted for air ambulance.

Step Five: Identify the mileage code and number of miles for the transportation provided.

Step Six: Apply the rural area payment add-on. Determine whether the patient pick-up location is a rural area based on the CBSA methodology. If the area is rural, then add an additional 50 percent to

Figure 7.1. Ambulance origin and destination modifier example

Record Type	Revenue Code	HCPCS Code	Modifier #1	Modifier #2	Date of Service	Units	Total Charges
61	0540	A0428	RH	QN	082701	1 (trip)	100.00
61	0540	A0380	RH	QN	082701	4 (mileage)	8.00

miles one through seventeen and an additional 25 percent to miles eighteen through fifty for ground transportation. For air ambulance, add an additional 50 percent to the entire mileage for the trip.

Step Seven: Add together the level of service payment and the mileage payment to determine the total reimbursement for the ambulance service provided.

Office of Inspector General Report

In January 2006, the OIG released "Medicare Payments for Ambulance Transports" report. In this study, the OIG evaluated whether claims for ambulance transports met Medicare billing requirements and evaluated the effectiveness of safety measures used by fiscal intermediaries and carriers to identify improper payments (OEI 2006, i).

Prior OIG studies identified that the ambulance transport benefit was susceptible to fraud and abuse (OEI 2006, i).

- A 1994 report indicated that 70 percent of sampled dialysis-related ambulance transport claims did not meet CMS coverage requirements

- A 1998 report indicated that two-thirds of sampled ambulance transports did not meet CMS coverage requirements

The 2006 report included 720 ambulance transport claims from 2002. Interestingly enough, 2002 was the first year of the Ambulance Fee Schedule implementation. The study found that 25 percent of the ambulance transport claims did not meet CMS program requirements. These deficient claims resulted in $402 million of improper payments (OEI 2006, i). The breakout of error or deficient claims is as follows:

- 13% of transport claims did not meet coverage criteria based on the patient's condition ($220 million)

- 9% of transport claims did not meet level of service criteria and a lower level ambulance transport should have been reported ($31 million)

- 5% of transport claims were categorized as error claims because the supplier did not respond to the OIG request for documentation ($150 million).

Dialysis and nonemergency transport claims (27 and 20 percent respectively) were found to have larger error rates than emergency transport claims (7 percent). However, more disturbing than the error rates for ambulance transport claims is the finding regarding contractors' safeguards for fraud and abuse monitoring. The report identifies several areas of weakness:

- Contractors use few prepayment edits consistently

- Less than half of the contractors conducted post-payment reviews; of those contractors who did administer post-payment reviews, most conducted only one or two post-payment reviews in CYs 2001 and 2002

- CMS does not provide any uniform requirements regarding the kind of documentation contractors should review to determine the appropriateness of ambulance transports

- Contractors make minimal effort to educate health care providers regarding coverage and level of service criteria for ambulance transports (OEI 2006, ii).

The OIG provided CMS with three main recommendations in order to improve program integrity for the ambulance transport benefit. First, CMS should consider requiring all Medicare contractors including MACs and Part B Carriers to implement prepayment edits. The OIG specifically suggests that dialysis and nonemergency transport claims should be highlighted in the edit set. Establishing this safeguard would provide consistency in claims processing activities, similar to the **Outpatient Code Editor (OCE)** used under the Hospital Outpatient Prospective Payment System. Second, the OIG recommends that CMS provide instructions for post-payment reviews. Specifically, documentation should be obtained from the ambulance supplier and third-party providers before a determination regarding coverage is made. Third, the OIG stressed that education must be provided to the ambulance and third-party community regarding the appropriate use of the Medicare ambulance benefit. The education should focus attention on the coverage guidelines for nonemergency transports. Once education is provided, CMS should monitor progress and take administrative action where necessary.

Clearly the ambulance transport benefit needs greater attention from the MACs and Part B Carriers. However, increased education is necessary for the provider community as well. Recent improvements to the ambulance fee schedule area appear to be a move in the right direction.

Recent Adjustments to the System

The move to prospective payment has been challenging for ambulance suppliers and providers. CMS states that it is dedicated to making necessary adjustments to the system as new claims data are analyzed. Additionally, the "Medicare Payments for Ambulance Transports" OIG report has identified areas of deficiency in the ambulance fee schedule program. A major area of concern for many providers and suppliers has been the determination of level of service. Many providers and suppliers have called for the use of medical condition lists to aid in determining the level of service required to transport patients. The proposed medical condition lists were broad in topic and did not use the mandated ICD-9-CM coding system as required by the Health Insurance Portability and Accountability Act of 1996 (HIPAA). In response to the numerous requests for level of service guidance, CMS

provided an updated Medical Conditions List to be used in conjunction with the Ambulance Fee Schedule in February 2007 (CMS Transmittal R1185CP). The Medical Conditions List is intended to be an educational tool for providers, suppliers, and A/B **Medicare Administrative Contractors (MACs).** There are two parts to the Medical Conditions List. The first part is the Conditions List which provides ICD-9-CM codes for use with ambulance claims. The Conditions List provides one set of codes for novice coders or providers with little ICD-9-CM coding experience (ICD-9 Primary Code) and a second more specific set of codes for experienced coders (ICD-9 Alternative Specific Code). Figure 7.2 provides an extract from section one of the Medical Conditions List.

The provider/supplier is instructed to choose a code from the Conditions List that most accurately reflects the on-site condition of the patient and that is the reason for the transport. The ICD-9-CM code is reported on the claim form and should be used by the MAC to understand why the level of service reported was chosen by the provider/supplier. The MAC can then determine if a pre- or post- payment review is necessary. The ICD-9-CM codes on the conditions list to not guarantee that payment will be provided for the ambulance service reported; however, it is a guideline for providers and suppliers to use when determining the level of service for individual cases in conjunction with other documentation from the transport.

Part two of the conditions list provides a listing of Transportation Indicators. These indicators should be reported by the supplier/provider to communicate why it was necessary for the patient to be transported in a particular way. Figure 7.3 provides the transportation indicator list. The Medical Conditions List is provided by CMS to foster and improve communication between the provider/suppliers and the MACs. Additionally, this education tool should be used by MACs in their program integrity safeguards as a way to identify potentially fraudulent claims.

Figure 7.2   Excerpt of ambulance medical conditions list

ICD9 Primary Code	ICD9 Alternative Specific Code	Condition (General)	Condition (Specific)	Service Level	Comments and Examples (not all-inclusive)	HCPCS Crosswalk
		Emergency Conditions—Nontraumatic				
535.50	458.9 780.2 787.01 787.02 787.03 789.01 789.02 789.03 789.04 789.05 789.06 789.07 789.09 789.60 through 789.69 or 789.40 through 789.49 PLUS any other code from 780 through 799 except 793, 794, and 795.	Severe abdominal pain	With other signs or symptoms	ALS	Nausea, vomiting, fainting, pulsatile mass, distention, rigid tenderness on exam, guarding.	A0427 A0433

Taken from: CMS Transmittal 1185, **Subject Ambulance Fee Schedule—Medical Conditions List—Manualization Revisions, page 11.**

Hospital Outpatient Prospective Payment System

In 1983, Medicare moved to a PPS for hospital inpatient services to help control increasing healthcare costs and Medicare expenditures. As CMS experienced savings by reducing Medicare expenditures for inpatient care by $17 billion per year from the payment system change, the program's administrators made efforts to incorporate prospective payment concepts into other healthcare settings (Averill 2001, 108). After more than thirteen years, CMS implemented a hospital outpatient prospective payment system (HOPPS) on August 1, 2000.

Legislative Influence and Background

The Omnibus Reconciliation Act (OBRA) of 1986 mandated that CMS move to a prospective payment system for hospital outpatient services. Congress instructed the Secretary of Health and Human Services (DHHS) to include facility costs for services provided in ambulatory surgery units, emergency departments, and hospital clinics in the system. Professional services, such as physician fees, were not intended to be included in the hospital outpatient PPS. The legislation prescribed that the system was to be based on the HCPCS Levels I and II because that was the prevailing coding system in the outpatient setting. OBRA gave CMS five years to develop the system and projected implementation for 1991.

3M Information Systems

A grant was awarded to 3M Health Information Systems (3M HIS) in 1988 to develop a grouping system for the outpatient prospective payment system. In 1990, 3M HIS proposed version 1.0 ambulatory patient groups (APGs). The APG system is a visit-based classification that describes the amount and type of resources consumed during the visit. A visit is an encounter between a patient and any healthcare provider (Jones 2001, 64). In 1995, 3M HIS released an updated version of APG Version 2.0.

Figure 7.3. Ambulance transportation indicator list

Transportation Indicators					
Transportation Indicators Air and Ground	**Transport Category**	**Transportation Indicator Description**		**Service Level**	**Comments and Examples (not all-inclusive)**	**HCPCS Crosswalk**
C1	Interfacility transport	EMTALA-certified inter-facility transfer to a higher level of care	Beneficiary requires higher level of care	BLS, ALS, SCT, FW, RW	Excludes patient-requested EMTALA transfer	A0428 A0429 A0426 A0427 A0433 A0434
C2	Interfacility transport	Service not available at originating facility, and must meet one or more emergency or non-emergency conditions.		BLS, ALS, SCT, FW, RW		A0428 A0429 A0426 A0427 A0433 A0434
C3	Emergency trauma dispatch condition code	Major incident or mechanism of injury	Major incident—this transportation indicator is to be used ONLY as a secondary code when the on-scene encounter is BLS-level patient.	ALS	Trapped in machinery, close proximity to explosion, building fire with persons reported inside, major incident involving aircraft, bus, subway, metro, train and watercraft. Victim entrapped in vehicle.	A0427 A0433
C4	Medically necessary transport but not to the nearest facility	BLS or ALS response	Indicates to carrier/intermediary that an ambulance provided a medically necessary transport, but that the number of miles on the Medicare claim form may be excessive.	BLS/ALS	This should occur if the facility is on divert status or the particular service is not available at the time of transport only. In these instances the ambulance units should clearly document why the beneficiary was not transported to the nearest facility.	Based on transport level
C5	BLS transport of ALS-level patient	ALS-level condition treated and transported by a BLS-level ambulance	This transportation indicator is used for ALL situations where a BLS-level ambulance treats and transports a patient that presents an ALS-level condition. No ALS-level assessment or intervention occurs at all during the patient encounter.	BLS		A0429

Figure 7.3.   (Continued)

Transportation Indicators Air and Ground	Transport Category	Transportation Indicator Description		Service Level	Comments and Examples (not all-inclusive)	HCPCS Crosswalk
C6	ALS-level response to BLS-level patient	ALS response required based upon appropriate dispatch protocols—BLS-level patient transport	Indicates to carrier/intermediary that an ALS-level ambulance responded appropriately based upon the information received at the time the call was received in dispatch and after a clinically appropriate ALS-assessment was performed on scene, it was determined that the condition of the patient was at a BLS level. These claims, properly documented, should be reimbursed at an ALS-1 level based upon coverage guidelines under the Medicare Ambulance Fee Schedule.	ALS		A0427
C7		IV meds required en route	This transportation indicator is used for patients that require an ALS level transport in a non-emergent situation primarily because the patient requires monitoring of ongoing medications administered intravenously. Does not apply to self administered medications. Does not include administration of crystalloid intravenous fluids. The patient's conditions should also be reported on the claim with a code selected from the list.	ALS	Does not apply to self-administered IV medications	A0426
Air Ambulance Transportation Indicators						
Transportation Indicators Air and Ground	Transport Category	Transportation Indicator Description		Service Level	Comments and Examples (not all-inclusive)	HCPCS Crosswalk
D1		Long distance—patient's condition requires rapid transportation over a long distance		FW, RW	If the patient's condition warrants only.	A0431 A0430
D2		Under rare and exceptional circumstances, traffic patterns preclude ground transport at the time the response is required.		FW, RW		A0430 A0431
D3		Time to get to the closest appropriate hospital due to the patient's condition precludes transport by ground ambulance. Unstable patient with need to minimize out-of-hospital time to maximize clinical benefits for the patient.		FW, RW		A0430 A0431
D4		Pick-up point not accessible by ground ambulance.		FW, RW		A0430 A0431

Taken from: CMS Transmittal 1185, **Subject: Ambulance Fee Schedule—Medical Conditions List—Manualization Revisions, page 32.**

Even though the 1991 deadline had come and gone, CMS had yet to implement APGs as the outpatient PPS for Medicare. However, many states were using APGs for Medicaid reimbursement.

1997 Balanced Budget Act

In 1997, the Balanced Budget Act (BBA) set new dates for Medicare to move to a prospective payment system. The implementation deadline for hospitals was January 1, 1999, and was one year later for IPPS-exempt cancer centers. In September of 1998, CMS released the proposed rule for the outpatient prospective payment system. The grouping system introduced in the proposed rule was **ambulatory payment classifications (APCs).** APCs were developed by modifying the APG system (created by 3M HIS) using past claims data and clinical analysis.

1998 Balanced Budget Refinement Act

Prior to the implementation of the APC system proposed in 1998, the Balanced Budget Refinement Act (BBRA) of 1999 required several modifications to the system. The BBRA mandated that an annual review of groups, weights, and wage index adjustments should be made, similar to the review used in the inpatient prospective payment system (IPPS). CMS was instructed to develop a professional advisory panel to assist with maintenance of the system. The BBRA determined that the beneficiary coinsurance for any given procedure/service could not exceed the inpatient deductible for that year. Consequently, the **pass-through** APC category was developed for high-cost drugs, biologicals, and devices, and a high-cost outlier provision was added to the system. The BBRA also provided a phase-in financial assistance mechanism to facilitate hospitals' adjustment to the prospective payment system.

Implementation and Modification of the HOPPS

In April 2000, CMS released the final rule for APC implementation. The implementation date was set for August 1, 2000. Facilities worked feverishly to make system changes and provide education to prepare for APC changes. On August 1, 2000, CMS ended the cost-based reimbursement system and started HOPPS.

Shortly after the HOPPS system was implemented, the Medicare, Medicaid, and SCHIP Benefits Improvement Act (BIPA) of 2000 added supplementary modifications to the APC system. BIPA accelerated the reduction of beneficiary copayment amounts. The legislation granted children's hospitals **hold-harmless status,** and developed device categories for pass-through APCs.

The Medicare Prescription Drug, Improvement, and Modernization Act (MMA) of 2003 further modified the HOPPS system. MMA now allows payment for an initial preventive physical examination for beneficiaries whose coverage began after January 1, 2005. MMA changed the screening and diagnostic mammography payment from HOPPS to a fee schedule-based payment. MMA added radiopharmaceuticals to the drug and biological categories and reduced the threshold for establishment of separate APCs with respect to drugs and biologicals from $150 to $50 per administration. The high-cost outlier calculation was modified to exclude several separately payable drugs. Additionally, the legislation modified payment for brachytherapy devices (seeds) by instructing that these devices be paid on a reasonable cost basis from January 1, 2004, through January 1, 2007. Cost for brachytherapy seeds is calculated by adjusted hospital charges for each device to cost via ratio of cost to charge. Brachytherapy devices are also excluded from outlier calculations.

Hospital Outpatient Prospective Payment Methodology

Prior to HOPPS, Medicare payment for hospital outpatient services was cost-based. The cost of services was calculated by converting total charges for each encounter to cost by using department-specific cost-to-charge ratios (CCRs) developed from cost report statistics. However, as healthcare costs continued to rise, CMS moved toward a prospective payment system to help encourage a more efficient delivery of care for outpatient beneficiaries (DHHS 2004a, 50450).

Reimbursement for Hospital Outpatient Services

CMS uses a variety of models to reimburse facilities for hospital outpatient services. The system uses three reimbursement methods: fee schedules, prospective payment and cost-based. The primary standard that distinguishes a prospective payment system from a fee schedule system is that in the PPS the costs for certain items and secondary services associated with a primary procedure are packaged into the payment for that procedure. A fee schedule system establishes a separate payment amount for each item or service and no **packaging** occurs (DHHS 2004a, 50505). Certain items and services, such as acquisition of corneal tissue and influenza and pneumococcal pneumonia vaccines, continue to be paid on a reasonable cost basis.

Most procedures and services are reimbursed under APCs. Ambulance transportation, physical therapy, occupational therapy, and speech language pathology are reimbursed via various fee schedules. Physician and nonphysician practitioners are paid under the Medicare physician fee schedule. Laboratory services are paid via the clinical diagnostic laboratory fee schedule. End-stage renal disease services are reimbursed with a composite rate (DHHS 2004a, 50451).

Reporting of Services and Supplies under HOPPS

HOPPS uses Levels I and II HCPCS codes to report services/procedures performed and items/supplies provided for beneficiaries. Each code in HCPCS has been assigned a **payment status indicator.** The payment status indicator establishes how that service, procedure, or item is paid (that is, fee schedule, APC, reasonable cost, unpaid). Table 7.12 provides a listing of the payment status indicators and their definitions for **calendar year (CY)** 2008.

Because Level I HCPCS codes (CPT codes) were originally designed to report physician services, the system contains codes for inpatient and outpatient procedures. HOPPS only covers outpatient services. Each year the Secretary of Health and Human Services reviews claims data and determines which procedures are inpatient-only procedures and creates the "inpatient-only list" (payment status indicator C). In order to move off of the inpatient-only list, a procedure must be performed in noninpatient settings at least 60 percent of the time. In order to be reimbursed, procedures indicated as inpatient-only must be provided to Medicare beneficiaries in an inpatient setting and payment is made under the IPPS.

Excluded Facilities

Excluded from HOPPS are Maryland hospital services that are part of a cost containment waiver, critical access hospitals (CAH), hospitals outside of the fifty states, District of Columbia, and Puerto Rico, and the Indian Health Service.

Maintenance of the HOPPS System

CMS maintains the HOPPS system. As mandated by the BBRA, CMS must perform an annual review of the APC groups and relative weights. The wage index amounts adjusted for the current IPPS system must also be incorporated into the HOPPS system each year.

BBRA also established the APC Advisory Panel to assist with the maintenance of HOPPS. The APC Advisory Panel is composed of fifteen experts from various healthcare settings. The panel is technical in nature and provides analysis and recommendations to CMS. CMS considers and addresses all panel recommendations, but does not have to accept them. CMS makes the final ruling for updates and changes to HOPPS. The panel has three subcommittees that focus on data issues, observation issues, and packaging issues.

Additionally, the Medicare Payment Advisory Commission (MedPAC) provides Congress and CMS with recommendations to improve HOPPS.

Table 7.12.   Payment status indicators for calendar year 2008

Payment Status Indicator	Reimbursement Method	Procedure or Service Example
A	Fee schedule payment	Durable medical equipment, prosthetics, orthotics, and supplies (DMEPOS)
B	Not reimbursed under HOPPS	Service not appropriate for Part B claim
C	Not reimbursed under HOPPS	Inpatient only services
D	Not reimbursed under HOPPS	Code is discontinued
E	Not reimbursed under HOPPS	Service not covered by Medicare
F	Reasonable cost payment	Acquisition of corneal tissue, certain CRNA services and hepatitis B vaccines
G	Pass-through payment	Drugs and biologicals
H	Pass-through payment	Devices
K	APC payment	Drugs, biologicals (including blood and blood products), therapeutic radiopharmaceutical agents and brachytherapy sources
L	Reasonable cost payment with no copayment amount	Flu and pneumococcal immunizations
M	Services not billable to the fiscal intermediary and not payable under HOPPS	Pharmacy dispensing fee, chemo assessment of nausea, pain, fatigue, etc.
N	Not reimbursed under HOPPS	Packaged into APC payment
P	Only reimbursed in partial hospitalization programs	Partial hospitalization
Q	APC payment when criteria are met	Conditionally packaged services
S	APC payment	Significant procedures, multiple procedure reduction does not apply
T	APC payment	Surgical procedures, multiple procedure reduction applies
V	APC payment	Medical visits
X	APC payment	Ancillary services
Y	Not reimbursed under HOPPS	Nonimplantable durable medical equipment that must be billed directly to the DME regional carrier

Source: Department of Health and Human Services. 2007b (November 27). *Federal Register.* 72 (227) 66824–66825.

Again, CMS considers and responds to all Med-PAC recommendations, but does not have to accept or implement them. CMS has the final ruling for updates and changes to HOPPS. Revisions to HOPPS are released in the *Federal Register* within forty-five days of the start of the calendar year.

Ambulatory Payment Classification System

Each APC group comprises procedures or services that are clinically comparable with respect to resource use. All procedures and/or services assigned to an APC group must meet the "two-times rule," which establishes that the median cost of the most expensive item or service within a group cannot be more than two times greater than the median cost of the least expensive item or service within the same group (DHHS 2004a, 50454). CMS can propose exceptions to the two-times rule based on the following criteria (DHHS 2004a, 50463):

* Resource homogeneity

* Clinical homogeneity

* Hospital concentration

* Frequency of service (volume)

* Opportunity for upcoding and code fragments

Violations of the two-times rule are reviewed by the APC Advisory Panel. After analysis of each situation, the panel makes recommendations for each group that violated the rule. CMS uses the recommendations proposed by the panel and makes the final determination. For CY 2008, twenty-one APC groups violated the two-times rule. CMS granted exemption from the two-times rule for these APC groups.

Partially Packaged System Methodology

Packaging and **bundling** concepts are used in the OPPS as a way to combine payment for multiple

services. In the CY 2008 OPPS Final Rule, CMS defines packaging and bundling. Packaging occurs when reimbursement for minor **ancillary services** associated with a significant procedure are combined into a single payment for the procedure. Bundling occurs when payment for multiple significant procedures or multiple units of the same procedure related to an outpatient encounter or to an **episode of care** is combined into a single unit of payment. The logic of groupers in the ambulatory payment classification system includes ancillary packaging and bundling. By using packaging and bundling concepts CMS is providing incentives for healthcare facilities to improve their efficiency by avoiding unnecessary ancillary services, supplies, and pharmaceuticals and by substituting less expensive, but equally effective, options.

In ancillary packaging, many ancillary service APC groups will automatically combine into a significant procedure APC group or a surgical service APC group, if one is present. For CY 2008 packaging of ancillary and supportive services was expanded. CMS moved several procedures in the following seven categories to packaged or conditionally packaged status.

* Guidance services

* Image processing services

* Intraoperative services

* Imaging supervision and interpretation services

* Diagnostic radiopharmaceuticals

* Contrast media

* **Observation** services

The majority of services included in these categories are assigned payment status indicator N meaning that the service is always packaged and separate reimbursement is not provided. However, some of the services are assigned payment status indicator Q meaning that the services are conditionally packaged or packaged only when certain criteria are met. There are two types of conditionally packaged services. First are STVX-packaged codes. When an ancillary service with payment status indicator Q is performed on the same date of service as a service with an S, T, V or X payment status indicator, then the ancillary service is packaged and has a payment rate of $0.00. But if the ancillary service is performed without any S, T, V, or X services, then payment is provided for the ancillary service. The second type of conditionally packaged services are T-packaged codes. The concept is similar to the STVX-packaged codes, but only payment status indicator T effects whether the ancillary service is separately paid or not.

Example:

A patient is admitted to the ED for a possible hip dislocation. A hip x-ray is performed and shows that the hip is dislocated. Therefore, treatment is provided to return the hip to proper alignment. The hip x-ray is assigned to APC group 0275 and has a payment status indicator of Q. The dislocation treatment is assigned to APC group 0043, which has a payment status indicator of T. Since the hip x-ray is conditionally packaged and performed with a T procedure, payment is only made for APC group 0043.

Bundling combines supply and pharmaceutical costs or medical visits with associated procedures or services. APC systems have two methods of bundling:

- Supply and pharmaceutical cost bundling

- Medical visit bundling

Supply and pharmaceutical cost bundling involves supplies and drugs, except some expensive chemotherapy drugs. Medical visits may also be bundled in some situations. For example, if a simple laceration repair occurs during an encounter that also includes extensive medical and diagnostic services, the medical visit would be bundled into the laceration repair.

The APC system uses a partially packaged system methodology. Services or items, such as recovery room, anesthesia, and some pharmaceuticals, are packaged into the APC payment for the service or procedure with which they are associated. Bundled services that are reported with a HCPCS code have the payment status indicator N. Some services and items have not been assigned a HCPCS code and therefore are reported by revenue code. Table 7.13 provides a list of services that are bundled into APC payment by revenue code. Although some services are packaged, many others are not. Ancillary services, such as x-rays, and MRI and minor procedures, such as injections, are not packaged, but rather paid separately via APC groups. For the inpatient setting, it is easier to predict which resources a patient will consume for a given clinical issue. However, in the outpatient setting treatment pathways greatly vary from patient to patient, making it much more difficult to determine the resources that will be consumed for a clinical issue. Consequently, average cost for a "typical" outpatient encounter cannot be accurately forecasted. Therefore, a partially packaged system provides adequate reimbursement and allows the treatment flexibility that is needed to appropriately care for patients in the outpatient setting.

Partial Hospitalization

Partial hospitalization is an intensive outpatient program of psychiatric services provided to patients as an alternative to inpatient psychiatric care for patients who have an acute mental illness (DHHS 2004a, 50543). Partial hospitalization may be provided by hospital outpatient departments and Medicare-certified community mental health centers (CMHCs). Patients who receive psychiatric services and have a diagnosis of an acute mental health disorder are grouped to APC 0033, Partial hospitalization and APC 0034, Mental health services composite. The unit of service for partial

Table 7.13.   Packaged services by revenue code

Revenue Code	Description	Revenue Code	Description
250	Pharmacy	621	Supplies incident to radiology
251	Generic pharmacy	622	Supplies incident to other diagnostic
252	Nongeneric pharmacy	624	Investigational device (IDE)
254	Pharmacy incident to other diagnostic	630	Drugs requiring specific identification, general class
255	Pharmacy incident to radiology	631	Single source drugs
257	Nonprescription drugs	632	Multiple source drugs
258	IV solutions	633	Restrictive prescription
259	Other pharmacy	681	Trauma response, level I
260	IV therapy, general class	682	Trauma response, level II
262	IV therapy/pharmacy services	683	Trauma response, level III
263	Supply/delivery	684	Trauma response, level IV
264	IV therapy/supplies	689	Trauma response, other
269	Other IV therapy	700	Cast room
270	M&S supplies	709	Other cast room
271	Nonsterile supplies	710	Recovery room
272	Sterile supplies	719	Other recovery room
273	Take home supplies	720	Labor room
275	Pacemaker drug	721	Labor
276	Intraocular lens source drug	732	Telemetry
278	Other implants	762	Observation room
279	Other M&S supplies	801	Hemodialysis
280	Oncology	802	Peritoneal dialysis
289	Other oncology	803	CAPD
343	Diagnostic radiopharms	804	CCPD
344	Therapeutic radiopharms	809	Other inpatient dialysis
370	Anesthesia	810	Organ acquisition
371	Anesthesia incident to radiology	819	Other organ acquisition
372	Anesthesia incident to other diagnostic	821	Hemodialysis comp or other rate
379	Other anesthesia	824	Maintenance 100%
390	Blood storage and processing	825	Support services
399	Other blood storage and processing	829	Other hemo outpatient
560	Medical social services	942	Education/training
569	Other medical social services		

Source: Department of Health and Human Services. 2007 (November 27). *Federal Register.* 72 (227) 66608–66609.

hospitalization is one day. Therefore, the APC payment for APC 0033 is based on a per-diem amount. For CY 2008, the APC payment rate for APCs 0033 and 0034 is $205.16, of which $41.03 is the beneficiary copayment amount.

Structure of the APC System

In the APC system there are ten classification types that represent the various services procedures and supplies used in the hospital outpatient setting. The classification type for any APC can be identified by the payment status indicator assigned to the procedures and/or services in the group. All procedures or services in an APC have the same payment status indicator. The ten classification types are:

- Clinic or emergency department visit (payment status indicator V)

- Surgical procedure, multiple procedure payment reduction applies (payment status indicator T)

- Significant procedure (payment status indicator S)

- Ancillary service (payment status indicator X)

- Separately payable drugs and biologicals (payment status indicator K)

- Pass-through drug or biological, and device (payment status indicator G)

- Pass-through device (payment status indicator H)

- Packaged items (payment status indicator N)

- Conditionally packaged items and services (payment status indicator Q)

- Partial hospitalization services (payment status indicator P)

Each HCPCS code is assigned to one and only one APC. The APC assignment for a procedure or

service does not change based on the patient's medical condition or the severity of illness. There may be an unlimited number of APCs per encounter for a single patient. The number of APC assignments is based on the number of reimbursable procedures or services provided for that patient.

Each APC contains the same components that drive the APC assignment (see figure 7.4):

- Title

- Payment status indicator

- Relative weight

- **National unadjusted payment amount**

- **National unadjusted copayment amount**

- Code range

The relative weight is a measure of the resource intensity of a particular procedure or service. The national unadjusted payment amount is the total amount a hospital will receive for a procedure or service in that APC. Hospital outpatient claims data from 1996 were used to determine the APC payment rates for implementation in 2000. The national unadjusted payment amount is divided into two components: Medicare facility amount and beneficiary copayment amount.

Figure 7.4.   APC components

APC 0609 Title: Level 1 Emergency Visits	
Payment Status Indicator	V
Relative Weight	0.7970
National Unadjusted Payment Amount	$50.76
National Unadjusted Copayment Amount	$12.70
Minimum Copayment Amount	$10.15
HCPCS Procedure Code(s) 99281 Emergency Department Visit	

Copayment

CMS wanted to move to a prospective payment system to ensure that the beneficiary copayment amount from hospital to hospital is consistent. Prior to PPS, beneficiaries were responsible for 20 percent of total charges and charges for procedures varied from hospital to hospital. Therefore, if hospital A charged $3,000 for a colonoscopy, the beneficiary amount would be $600, but if hospital B charged $3500 for the same colonoscopy, the beneficiary would be responsible for $700.

Again using 1996 data, CMS established the historical average copayment amount as the starting copayment amount in the APC system. However, the intent of the HOPPS is for all copayment amounts to be only 20 percent of the total APC payment amount. Section 1833(t)(8)(C)(ii) of the Social Security Act requires CMS to reduce the national unadjusted copayment amount to meet reduction requirements mandated in BIPA (DHHS 2004a, 50544). For CY 2008, the national unadjusted copayment amount cannot exceed 40 percent of the total APC payment. Any newly created APCs (those added to the system after August 1, 2000) must be added with a copayment amount equal to 20 percent of the total APC payment. The copayment amount may be collected from the beneficiary at the time of service or on a retrospective basis.

Both the Medicare facility component and the beneficiary copayment components are adjusted for differences in wage indexes. This is the only adjustment made to APC payment rates to account for differences among hospitals. Sixty percent of the facility amount is wage index adjusted. The wage index amount for the facility location based on CBSA is determined in the IPPS update for the corresponding federal fiscal year.

New Technology APCs

New technology APCs were created to allow new procedures and services to enter HOPPS quickly, even though their complete cost and payment information is not known. New technology APCs house modern procedures and services until enough data is collected to properly place the new procedure in an existing APC or to create a new APC for the service/procedure. A procedure/service can remain in a new technology APC for an indefinite amount of time.

The APC system contains eighty-two new technology APCs. Forty-one groups have payment status indicator S and are not subject to multiple procedure discounting. The remaining forty-one groups have payment status indicator T and are subject to the multiple-procedure discount provision. Placement into new technology APCs is based on cost bands. For example, APC 1491, New Technology–Level IA, contains procedures whose average cost is $0–$10. The payment for the group is $5.

Composite APCs

In CY 2008, CMS added the concept of composite APCs to HOPPS. In an effort to move towards an episode-of-payment-based payment system, the creation of composite APCs allows for multiple services that are typically performed together to be reimbursed by one APC rather than multiple APCs. CMS introduced five composite APCs in CY 2008:

- Mental health services composite APC 0034

- Cardiac electrophysiologic evaluation and ablation composite APC 8000

- Low dose rate prostate brachytherapy composite APC 8001

- Level I Extended assessment and management composite APC 8002

- Level II Extended assessment and management composite APC 8003

For each composite APC a code set is established. This code set represents the services that are almost always performed together. When the codes in this code set are reported together on the same date of service, the composite APC is activated and one reimbursement amount is released. It is important to note that these services are almost always performed together, but not always. Therefore, the payment will still be made if only one of the services is performed, but at a reduced regular APC rate. For example, composite APC 8001 is activated when transperineal placement of needles or catheters into prostate (55875) and the interstitial radiation source application procedures (77778) are performed together on the same date of service. However, if code 55875 is performed during a different admission than 77778, then only APC 0163 is reimbursed. Vice versa, if code 77778 is performed on a different date of service than code 55875, then only APC 651 is reimbursed. It is important to note that there is not a financial incentive to report these two procedures together or separately; the payments are almost identical either way. Therefore, hospitals should continue to follow correct coding guidelines and report these services as warranted by medical record documentation.

Obervation Services

With the inception of HOPPS, the APC system bundled costs for observation services into the APC payment for the procedure or visit with which the observation was associated. However, the CY 2002 revision added APC 0339 to pay separately for certain observation services associated with clinic visits, emergency department visits, or **critical care services.** Three clinical conditions qualified an observation service for APC 0339: chest pain, congestive heart failure, and asthma. As noted earlier, CMS moved to a composite APC payment for observation services in CY 2008. The clinical and ancillary requirements have been removed and separate observation services reimbursement is open to all cases that meet the new criteria. Two composite APCs are provided for observation services: Level I extended assessment and management composite

and Level II extended assessment and management composite. In order to activate the level I composite APC (8002) observation services (G0378) must be provided for at least eight hours and provided on the same date of service as a high level clinic visit (99205 or 99215) or a direct admission to the facility (G0379). Additionally, a surgical procedure (payment status indicator T) may not be performed on the same day or day before the observation services. The level II composite APC (8003) criteria are very similar. Observation services (G0378) must be provided for at least eight hours and provided on the same date of service as a high level emergency department visit (99284 or 99285) or a critical care service (99291). Additionally, a surgical procedure (payment status indicator T) may not be performed on the same day or day before the observation services. All observation services that do not meet the composite APC criteria are bundled and do not receive separate reimbursement.

Provisions of the APC System

The APC system uses provisions to provide additional payments for high-cost items and unusual admissions that historically have added significant cost to patient care. Without the additional payments associated with these provisions, it may not be feasible for hospital outpatient facilities to provide all services to Medicare beneficiaries.

Discounting

Multiple surgical procedures with payment status indicator T performed during the same operative session are **discounted.** The highest weighted procedure is fully reimbursed. All other procedures with payment status indicator T are reimbursed at 50 percent. (See figure 7.5.) This reduction is made to account for resource saving that hospitals experience by performing multiple procedures together. For example, OR surgical instruments are only prepped once, anesthesia is administered once, and recovery room is used once for all of the procedures performed.

Figure 7.5.   Discounting provision illustration for HOPPS

APC	Payment Status Indicator	Payment Rate
1	T	100%
2	T	50%
3	T	50%
4	S	100%
5	S	100%

Interruped Services

Interruped services are reported with modifiers. When modifiers are applied to the surgical codes a reduction in payment may be applied. Procedures reported with modifier 73, surgery discontinued for a patient who has been prepared for surgery (that requires anesthesia) and taken to the operating room but before the administration of anesthesia, will be reduced by 50 percent. A procedure reported with modifier 74, surgery discontinued after administration of anesthesia or initiation of the procedure, will be reimbursed at 100 percent of the APC rate. Procedures and services that do not require anesthesia but are reduced or discontinued at the physician's discretion should be reported with modifier 52. For these procedures the payment rate will be reduced by 50%.

High-Cost Outlier

Established by the BBRA, this provision is intended to provide financial assistance for unusually high cost services. The equations for case qualification and additional payment levels are adjusted each year. Medicare limits the percentage of total payments that can be attributed to outlier payments to 2 percent. For CY 2008, two requirements must be met to be eligible for outlier payment. The cost for a service must exceed 1.75 times the APC payment. The cost must also exceed the APC payment plus a fixed dollar threshold of $1,575. If these two conditions are met, the outlier payment is 50 percent of the cost that exceeds 1.75 the APC payment. Some

separately paid drugs and biologicals (payment status indicator G) are excluded from the outlier calculation.

Rural Adjustment

Public Law 108-173, better known as the Medicare Modernization Act of 2003, allowed for a rural adjustment to be applied if warranted after study. Therefore, CMS presented the results of their study in the CY 2006 update. Regression analysis showed that overall rural hospital costs were only 2.4 percent greater than urban hospital costs and did not warrant an adjustment. However, further analysis showed that rural sole community hospitals (SCH) cost was 7.1 percent greater than urban hospitals and therefore warranted an adjustment. Therefore beginning in CY 2006 OPPS, a rural adjustment of 7.1% was provided to SCH including essential access community hospitals (EACHs). For CY 2008 the adjustment of 7.1 percent continues to be provided to these select rural facilities.

Pass-Through Payments

Pass-throughs are exceptions to the Medicare prospective payment systems. These exceptions exist for high-cost services. Pass-throughs are not included in the packaging component of the prospective payment system and are passed through to other payment mechanisms that attempt to adjust for the high cost of pass-throughs. Therefore, pass-throughs minimize the negative financial impact of combining all services into one lump-sum payment. Pass-throughs occur in both the inpatient prospective payment system and the HOPPS.

Pass-through payments were established by the BBRA to provide hospitals with additional payment for high-cost drugs, biologicals, and devices. This specification was added to ensure the use of new and innovative drugs and supplies for Medicare beneficiaries when medically appropriate. Such drugs and supplies are often costly. If cost exceeds the payment for a new and innovative drug, a hospital might be motivated through cost containment practices to use a less expensive and potentially less effective drug for Medicare beneficiaries.

Pass-through payments cannot exceed 2 percent of the total payments for the year. CMS uses historical claims data to project whether pass-through payments will exceed this limit. If so, CMS can put a pro rata reduction in place for that calendar year. The pro rata reduction decreases all pass-through payments by a selected percentage so that the total pass-through payments will not exceed 2 percent for the year.

Drugs, biologicals, and devices qualify for pass-through status if they were not being paid for as a hospital outpatient drug as of December 31, 1996, and their cost is "not insignificant" in relation to the HOPPS payment for the procedures or services associated with their use (DHHS 2004a, 50502). An item can have pass-through status for at least two years, but not more than three years. After three years, the cost of the item will be bundled into the APC payment for the procedure in which the item is used or be transitioned into an individual APC group. The pass-through status application process is described on the CMS Web site (CMS 2005a).

Pass-through device APCs (payment status indicator H) are paid on a reasonable cost basis less the device offset amount. The device offset amount is the portion of the APC payment amount that CMS has determined is associated with the cost of the device (DHHS 2004a, 50501). This amount is deducted from the pass-through payment because it is already reimbursed as part of the surgical APC payment. Drug and biological pass-through APCs (payment status indicator G) are reimbursed by using an average sales price (ASP) methodology. The average sales price is equivalent to the dollar amount at which these drugs and biologicals would be reimbursed in the physician office setting (DHHS 2004a, 50503). From this amount the portion of the applicable fee schedule amount (APC payment rate) is subtracted. The result is the pass-through payment.

Transitional Corridor and Hold-Harmless Payments

The BBRA provided a mechanism for hospitals to decrease the financial burden of the implementation of HOPPS. This phase-in period provided the transitional corridor payments. Transitional corridor payments were provided beginning in 2000 and were discontinued December 31, 2003. However, hold-harmless payments are permanent for IPPS-exempt cancer centers and children's hospitals.

Eligible facilities receive a quarterly interim hold-harmless payment that provides additional reimbursement when the payment received under HOPPS is less than the payment the facility would have received for the same services under the prior reasonable cost-based system in 1996 (DHHS 2004a, 50530). The interim payment is based on ratios of cost to charge from their most recently closed Medicare cost report and their assigned pre-BBRA payment-to-cost ratio determined from their 1996 cost report. Payment-to-cost ratios average around 80 percent. Figure 7.6 displays the formula for hold-harmless payment calculation. The final hold-harmless amount is determined at the settlement of the cost report for that facility's fiscal year.

APC Assignment

The APC system is primarily based on the HCPCS code(s) assigned for each service or procedure per-

Figure 7.6.   Hold harmless formula for HOPPS

For specified quarter:

Department charges × Department-specific ratios
of cost-to-charge = Department cost

Sum department cost for all departments = Total cost

Total cost × Payment to cost ratio from 1996 =
Pre-HOPPS reimbursement

HOPPS reimbursement from current quarter −
Pre-HOPPS reimbursement = Hold-harmless payment

When current HOPPS exceeds pre-HOPPS reimbursement, no hold harmless payment is made.

formed and for devices, drugs, and reimbursable items provided to the patient. The first step in APC assignment is to code the encounter accurately and completely. The APC system is a partially packaged system and several items/services are separately reimbursed; therefore, failure to capture all reimbursable charges with HCPCS codes will result in lost revenue for the facility. Once all HCPCS codes have been assigned, the payment status indicator is identified for each code. Payment status indicators that are assigned to an APC and indicate APC payment are G, H, K, S, T, X, V, Q and P. There may be multiple APCs with the same or different payment status indicator per claim.

There is one exception to this process. For partial hospitalization services, the ICD-9-CM diagnosis code assignment is crucial. In partial hospitalizations (APCs 0033 and 0034), an acute mental health disorder diagnosis must be assigned with an ICD-9-CM code. If the appropriate ICD-9-CM diagnosis code is not assigned, the procedure/service will not group to the correct APC and may result in incorrect reimbursement.

Payment Determination

HOPPS payment for outpatient services is determined by using a seven-step methodology:

1. *APC assigned.* Hospitals submit a claim to Medicare for payment. Claims are sent electronically to the designated fiscal intermediary (FI) or Medicare administrative contractor (MAC). Each claim contains visit information, patient information, facility information, detailed charges by procedure code, and diagnosis codes. The Medicare contractor (FI or MAC) performs an audit of the claim to ensure that the claim contains complete and accurate information based on the edits found in the Outpatient Code Editor (OCE). During the editing process, APC(s) are assigned using grouper software as appropriate based on the HCPCS codes submitted.

2. *APC Payment rate established.* The payment rate is calculated by multiplying the relative weight for the assigned APC by the conversion factor for the current calendar year (CY). The conversion factor is the dollar amount that is equal to the relative weight of 1.000 and is updated each CY. For CY 2008, the conversion factor is $63.694.

3. *Wage index adjusted to national unadjusted facility component.* The facility component of the APC payment rate is wage-index adjusted. The formula for this adjustment is displayed in figure 7.7.

4. *Fee schedule amounts applied.* HCPCS codes with payment status indicator A are paid under a designated fee schedule. The fee schedule amounts for these procedures, services, and items are applied by the pricer software.

5. *Reasonable cost amounts applied.* HCPCS codes with payment status indicators F or L are reimbursed at a reasonable cost level. To calculate reasonable cost, the charge for the item or services is converted to cost by applying a department-specific ratio of cost to charge determined by historical cost report data for that hospital. These amounts are calculated and applied by the pricer software.

6. *Medicare payments summed.* All Medicare payments (APC, fee schedule, and

Figure 7.7.   Wage Index Adjustment Formula for HOPPS

[(National Unadjusted Payment Amount × 60%) × Wage index]
+ (National Unadjusted Payment Amount × 40%)
= Locality payment

reasonable cost) are summed for the claim.

7. *Outlier add-on applied.* The outlier calculation is completed in the pricer software for all eligible procedures and services. The amount is added to the total Medicare payments.

The pricer software completes steps two through seven. When the seven steps are completed, payment is made to the facility and the data from the encounter is included in the national claims history file. The outpatient standard analytical file and the hospital outpatient prospective payment system file, extracts from the national claims history file, are used for statistical analysis and research.

Summary

The hospital outpatient prospective payment system for hospital outpatient services provided to Medicare beneficiaries was successfully implemented in 2000. HOPPS has influenced hospitals to practice cost analysis and containment practices for their outpatient service areas. Additionally it has successfully lowered Medicare expenditures to hospitals for outpatient services. Hospitals continue to struggle with the intricacies of this complex reimbursement system and the numerous pieces of legislation that continue to modify the system.

Ambulatory Surgical Center Prospective Payment System

Designated surgical services may be provided to Medicare beneficiaries in the outpatient setting at **ambulatory surgical centers (ASCs)** under the Medicare supplementary medical insurance program (Part B). In an effort to control healthcare costs, CMS introduced a prospective payment system for ambulatory surgery centers in 1982. Section 934 of the Omnibus Budget Reconciliation Act of 1980 amended sections 1832(a)(2) and 1833 of

the Social Security Act (the Act) to specify procedures that would be covered under the prospective payment system, called the **ASC List of Covered Procedures (ASC list).** The ASC List was in effect from 1982 to 2007. In 2003, the Medicare Modernization Act (MMA) required that CMS revise the ASC prospective payment system and implement the modified system between 2006 and 2008. Therefore, on January 1, 2008, CMS implemented the Ambulatory Payment Classification system for use in the ASC PPS.

Medicare Certification Standards

ASCs that choose to treat Medicare beneficiaries must be state-licensed and Medicare-certified and are considered a supplier of services rather than a provider. In order to qualify as a Medicare-certified ASC, several standards must be met. The surgical center must (Jones 2001, 13):

- Be a separate entity distinguishable from any other entity or type of facility

- Have its own national identifier or supplier number under Medicare

- Maintain its own licensure, accreditation, governance, professional supervision, administrative functions, clinical services, record keeping, and financial and accounting systems

- Have a sole purpose of delivering services in connection with surgical procedures that do not require inpatient hospitalization

- Meet all conditions and requirements set forth in Section 1832(a)(2)(F)(i) of the Act, in 42 CFR 416, Subpart B and Subpart C in the *Federal Register*

Payment for ASC Services

As a Medicare-certified ASC, the facility must accept Medicare reimbursement as payment in full for the services supplied to Medicare beneficiaries.

The MMA established a lesser of provision for the revised ASC PPS. Therefore, beginning January 1, 2008, the Medicare program payment will equal 80 percent of the lesser of the actual charge for the services or the payment amount under APCs for the ASC PPS (FR Vol. 72, No. 148, 42473).

Medicare payment equals 80 percent of the total reimbursement for services provided. Beneficiaries are responsible for the 20 percent copayment of the total payment and any deductible that is required. There are two exceptions to the copayment percentage. Screening flexible sigmoidoscopy and screening colonoscopy procedures are subject to a 25 percent coinsurance rate. However, there is no deductible requirement for these two types of services under the ASC PPS. Additionally, beneficiaries are responsible for ASC charges associated with noncovered services furnished in the ASC setting (DHHS 2007, 42792).

Payment for the procedures allowed in the ASC setting is intended to reimburse ASCs for the facility resources extended to provide surgical services in that locality. The costs of the physician's professional services are excluded from the ASC payment. Professional services must be separately reported and are reimbursed via the Medicare physician fee schedule. The payment rate is wage index-adjusted to account for regional differences among providers. The labor portion for CY 2008 is 50 percent. The urban and rural wage index tables are used from the applicable year.

Criteria for ASC Procedures

With the adoption of APCs for the ASC setting, CMS moved from an inclusion methodology for approved ASC services to an exclusion methodology. Using a payment indicator system similar to the one used in OPPS, CMS identifies each year in the *Federal Register* which services can and cannot be performed for Medicare beneficiaries in the ASC setting. A listing of the CY 2008 payment indicators is found in table 7.14. Beginning in CY 2008, the scope of services dramatically increased

Table 7.14   ASC Payment Indicators— Addendum DD1—CY 2008

Addendum DD1—Illustrative ASC Payment Indicators	
Indicator	**Payment Indicator Definition**
A2	Surgical procedure on ASC list in CY 2007; payment based on OPPS relative payment weight.
F4	Corneal tissue acquisition; paid at reasonable cost.
G2	Non office-based surgical procedure added to ASC list in CY 2008 or later; payment based on OPPS relative payment weight.
H7	Brachytherapy source paid separately when provided integral to a surgical procedure on ASC list; payment contractor-priced.
H8	Device-intensive procedure on ASC list in CY 2007; paid at adjusted rate.
J7	OPPS pass-through device paid separately when provided integral to a surgical procedure on ASC list; payment contractor-priced.
J8	Device-intensive procedure added to ASC list in CY 2008 or later; paid at adjusted rate.
K2	Drugs and biologicals paid separately when provided integral to a surgical procedure on ASC list; payment based on OPPS rate.
K7	Unclassified drugs and biologicals; payment contractor-priced.
L6	New technology intraocular lens (NTIOL); special payment.
N1	Packaged procedure/item; no separate payment made.
P2	Office-based surgical procedure added to ASC list in CY 2008 or later with MPFS nonfacility PE RVUs; payment based on OPPS relative payment weight.
P3	Office-based surgical procedure added to ASC list in CY 2008 or later with MPFS nonfacility PE RVUs; payment based on MPFS nonfacility PE RVUs.
R2	Office-based surgical procedure added to ASC list in CY 2008 or later without MPFS nonfacility PE RVUs; payment based on OPPS relative payment weight.
Z2	Radiology service paid separately when provided integral to a surgical procedure on ASC list; payment based on OPPS relative payment weight.
Z3	Radiology service paid separately when provided integral to a surgical procedure on ASC list; payment based on MPFS nonfacility PE RVUs.

when CMS added over 800 procedures to the ASC scope of services.

By creating a list of appropriate outpatient surgery procedures, CMS influences the site of service for certain procedures. The ASC list of approved procedures creates a motivation for surgical procedures to migrate from the more expensive inpatient setting to the less expensive outpatient surgery setting without creating a motivation to shift procedures from the less expensive physician office setting to the more expensive outpatient surgery setting (DHHS 2004c, 69179). The procedures and services covered under the ASC PPS are reported using Levels I and II HCPCS codes. The ASC scope of services criteria was modified with the adoption of APCs as well. To identify procedures eligible for the revised ASC PPS, CMS excluded the following types of procedures:

Surgical procedures that are on the OPPS inpatient list

Procedures that are packaged under the OPPS

CPT unlisted surgical procedure codes

Surgical procedures that are not recognized for payment under the OPPS (DHHS 2007, 42778)

Additionally, CMS followed established criteria to determine if a procedure could pose a significant safety risk to beneficiaries when performed in the ASC setting. The criteria identified procedures that:

Generally result in extensive blood loss

Require major or prolonged invasion of body cavities

Directly involve major blood vessels

Are emergent or life-threatening in nature

Commonly require systemic thrombolytic therapy ((DHHS 2007, 42778)

The above criteria for evaluating surgical procedures are included in section 416.166(c) of the Act. These services are excluded from the ASC PPS.

APCs and Payment Rates

The APC system is updated yearly to account for changes in the HCPCS coding system. Each year codes are added, deleted, and modified to account for changes in healthcare delivery practices.

ASC PPS History

In 1987, CMS implemented selection criteria to assist with the ASC list maintenance. CMS used quantitative criteria to identify procedures to be added and deleted from the ASC list. If a procedure was performed on an inpatient basis 20 percent of the time or less, it would be excluded from the ASC list. Likewise, if a procedure was performed in a physician's office 50 percent of the time or more, it would be excluded from the ASC list. Applying these criteria resulted in the first major revision of the ASC list in 1987. (See table 7.15)

As the healthcare environment became ever more cost-conscious, a growing number of procedure types were shifted from the inpatient setting to the outpatient setting. This trend created the need for a major revision to the ASC list. In

Table 7.15.   Release dates of the ASC List of Covered Procedures

Date	Reference	Action
August 5, 1982	47 FR 34082	Creation
April 21, 1987	52 FR 13176	Revision
June 1, 1989	54 FR 23540	Revision
December 31, 1991	56 FR 67666	Revision
January 26, 1995	60 FR 5185	Revision
March 28, 2003	68 FR 15268	Revision
November 26, 2004	69 FR 69178	Revision, proposed rule

Source: Department of Health and Human Services. 2004 (November 26). *Federal Register.* 69 (227) 69179.

1995, CMS adopted a modified standard for ASC list maintenance that allowed for minor fluctuations in utilization across settings and accounted for site-of-service errors from the National Claims History File that was used to determine qualification for the list. Procedures that had a combined inpatient, outpatient, and ASC volume of less than 46 percent of the total procedure volume and were either performed 50 percent of the time or more in the physician office setting or 10 percent or less in the hospital inpatient setting would be deleted from the ASC list (DHHS 2004c, 69180). CMS retained the 20 percent inpatient/50 percent physician office criteria for additions to the ASC list.

First Attempt to Implement Ambulatory Payment Classifications

In 1997, the Balanced Budget Act (BBA) proposed a new prospective payment system (PPS) for hospital outpatient services based on ambulatory payment classifications (APCs). Included in the BBA was the requirement that a new rate-setting methodology, APCs, be used for the ASC PPS. The new payment rates would be calculated using 1994 ASC survey data.

Several pieces of legislation modified the hospital outpatient prospective payment system (HOPPS) and the requirement for the transition to APCs for ASCs. The Balanced Budget Refinement Act of 1999 (BBRA) required that a three-year phase-in period be used for the implementation of the new APC system for ASCs. However, one year later, the Medicare, Medicaid and SCHIP Benefits Improvement and Protection Act of 2000 (BIPA) delayed the implementation of APCs for ASCs to January 1, 2002 or after, and extended the phase-in period established by the BBRA to four years. Additionally, BIPA required that the payment rates for the ASC list be rebased with ASC survey data from 1999 or later by January 1, 2003 (DHHS 2003a, 15270).

Implementation of the APC system for ASCs and the rebasing of payment rates for the ASC list

did not occur. CMS was not able to focus on the ASC setting because the majority of the resources available were dedicated to the implementation of HOPPS. Further, preparation for Y2K changes tied up even more CMS resources.

Attempts to Resolve Rate-Setting Issues

In January of 2003, the Office of the Inspector General (OIG) issued results of the "Payments for Procedures in Outpatient Departments and Ambulatory Surgical Centers" study. The results showed that there was a need for greater similarity in payment rates between the hospital outpatient and ASC settings (DHHS 2004c, 69180). The study revealed that disparity in payments for the same services performed in the ASC setting versus the hospital outpatient setting resulted in additional costs of $1.1 billion to the Medicare system. The differences in reimbursement were not consistent. In 66 percent of the procedure codes examined, outpatient department rates were higher than ASC rates, with a median difference of $282.33. For the remaining 145 procedure codes, Medicare reimbursed ASCs more (DHHS 2003a, 15270).

The OIG recommended that CMS should:

- Seek authority to set rates that are consistent across sites and reflect only the costs necessary for the efficient delivery of health services

- Conduct and use timely ASC survey data to reevaluate ASC payment rates

- Remove procedure codes that meet deletion criteria (72 CPT codes were identified as meeting criteria for deletion)

CMS responded to the study in the March 28, 2003, ASC List of Covered Procedures Update Final Rule. CMS stated that it would consider assisting in the development of future legislation but expressed concerns with using survey data for rate setting. CMS administrators specifically responded that they wanted to be confident that the methodology used to rebase the payment rates would not inadvertently result in disproportional reimbursement rates across the different ambulatory care sites of service (DHHS 2003a, 15270). CMS administrators indicated that they would continue to study alternatives for rate setting methodologies.

The Medicare Prescription Drug, Improvement and Modernization Act of 2003 (MMA) repealed the survey requirement or the need to collect updated ASC cost data to utilize for rebasing ASC payment rates set forth in BIPA. More importantly, MMA requires CMS to implement a revised prospective payment system for ASC services between January 1, 2006, and January 1, 2008. Therefore, updates to the ASC List that took place before the implementation of the revised system were based on the 1986 survey of ASC costs.

On November 26, 2004, CMS released a proposed rule for the Update of Ambulatory Surgical Center List of Covered Procedures. In the proposed rule, payment rates were updated for inflation. Several procedures were removed from the ASC list prompted by the 2003 OIG report, and basic code updates were made based on the annual changes to the HCPCS Level I coding system (DHHS 2004c, 69178). On August 2, 2007, CMS released the final rule for the revised ASC payment system. The rule solidified that APCs would be implemented for ASC PPS on January 1, 2008. Additionally, the final rule established that the components of the ASC PPS would be updated annually as part of the HOPPS rule-making process.

ASC APC Payment

Reimbursement for the procedures performed in the ASC equals 65 percent of the OPPS APC payment rate for CY 2008, which results in a conversion factor of $41.401.

Separately Payable Services

Unlike the previous PPS utilized in the ASC PPS, APCs allow for separate payment of certain ancillary services and supplies.

Radiology Services

ASCs will receive separate payment for ancillary radiology procedures designated as separately payable under the OPPS when the services are integral to the performance of a covered surgical procedure provided on the same day. No separate payment will be made for radiology procedures that are packaged under OPPS (payment status indicator N).

Brachytherapy Sources

ASCs will receive separate payment for brachytherapy sources when they are implanted in conjunction with covered surgical procedures. The ASC brachytherapy source payment rate is the same as the OPPS payment rate for a given year. Brachytherapy sources are considered a supply and potentially cost the same if purchased by a hospital outpatient department facility or by an ASC; therefore, the payment rate is not reduced by 65 percent. If OPPS prospective payment rates are unavailable, ASC payments will be contractor-priced by the MAC or Part B Carrier in that region. Additionally, brachytherapy reimbursement is not subject to the geographic adjustment (wage index adjustment).

Drugs and Biologicals

Separate payment will be made when certain drugs and biologicals are provided integral to a covered surgical procedure. The ASC payment for these items is equal to the OPPS payment rates for the same year without application of the ASC budget neutrality adjustment. ASC payments for these items are not subject to the geographic adjustment.

Implantable Devices with Pass-Through Status under OPPS

Pass-through devices will be reimbursed at a contractor-priced rate. The device must be provided in the ASC immediately before, during, or immediately following the covered surgical procedure and is billed by the ASC on the same day as the covered surgical procedure. The only applicable pass-through device for CY 2008 is L8690, Auditory osseointegrated device, including all internal and external components. Pass-through devices are not subject to the geographic adjustment.

Corneal Tissue Acquisition

Corneal tissue acquisition is reported with HCPCS Level II code V2785 and reimbursement is based on invoice costs.

Device Intensive Procedures

Payment methodology is modified for certain device-intensive procedures. Each year a list of device-intensive procedures is published in the *Federal Register*. The list consists of those procedures for which the device offset percentage is greater than 50 percent of the median cost under HOPPS; meaning the cost of the device is a significant amount of the cost of providing the service. Then intent of the modified methodology is to ensure that ASCs are adequately reimbursed for the supply cost associated with these device intensive procedures.

The modified methodology divides the unadjusted HOPPS national payment rate into two portions: a device portion and a service portion. The ASC conversion factor is applied only to the service portion of the payment rate. The device portion is not modified by the conversion factor. Both portions are subject to the geographic adjustment. Figure 7.8 provides the device-intensive formula for the ASC PPS.

Multiple and Bilateral Procedures

When multiple procedures are performed during the same surgical session, a payment reduction is applied.

Each year services applicable for the discounting provision are identified in the *Federal Register*. The procedure in the highest weighted APC group is reimbursed at 100 percent and all remaining procedures eligible for discounting are reimbursed at 50 percent. Bilateral procedures are reimbursed at 150 percent of the payment rate for their group.

Interrupted Procedures

Procedures reported with modifier 73, surgery discontinued for a patient who has been prepared for surgery (that requires anesthesia) and taken to the operating room but before the administration of anesthesia, will be reduced by 50 percent. A procedure reported with modifier 74, surgery discontinued after administration of anesthesia or initiation of the procedure, will be reimbursed at 100 percent of the ASC rate. Procedures and services that do not require anesthesia but are reduced or discontinued at the physician's discretion should be reported with modifier 52. For these procedures the payment rate will be reduced by 50 percent.

Transition Period

A four-year transition phase has been established for the migration to APC payment for the ASC PPS. Although APC grouping and provisions will be used, the payment rate will be a blend of the 2007 ASC group rates and the CY 2008 APC-based payment rate. Table 7.16 provides the blended rate schedule. Since CMS is expanding the scope of services for the ASC PPS, several procedures do not have a 2007 ASC group rate. Therefore, these

Figure 7.8   Device-Intensive Formula for the ASC PPS

National unadjusted HOPPS payment rate × device offset percentage = device portion

National unadjusted HOPPS payment rate − device portion = service portion

Service portion × ASC CF = adjusted service portion

Adjusted service portion + unadjusted device portion = ASC payment rate for device-intensive APC

Table 7.16   Transition plan for ASC PPS move to APCs

Year	ASC Rate %	APC Rate %
2008	75%	25%
2009	50%	50%
2010	25%	75%
2011	0%	100%

services will not be included in the transition plan. The services excluded from the transition plan are:

- Payment Indicator G2: Non office-based surgical procedure added to ASC list in CY 2008 or later; payment based on OPPS relative payment weight.

- Payment Indicator J8: Device-intensive procedure added to ASC list in CY 2008 or later; paid at adjusted rate.

- Payment Indicator P2: Office-based surgical procedure added to ASC list in CY 2008 or later with MPFS nonfacility PE RVUs; payment based on OPPS relative payment weight.

- Payment Indicator P3: Office-based surgical procedure added to ASC list in CY 2008 or later with MPFS nonfacility PE RVUs; payment based on MPFS nonfacility PE RVUs.

- Payment Indicator R2: Office-based surgical procedure added to ASC list in CY 2008 or later without MPFS nonfacility PE RVUs; payment based on OPPS relative payment weight.

Payment Steps

Coding and billing personnel follow five steps in obtaining payment for the ASC facility:

1. The procedure or service is coded using the HCPCS coding system.

2. The APC group is identified based on the HCPCS code reported.

3. Multiple procedure and bilateral procedure provisions are applied when applicable.

4. The payment for the established group is wage indexed.

5. Payment is made to the ASC facility.

Summary

The MMA instructed CMS to implement a revised prospective payment system for the ASC setting by 2008. The intent of the move to APCs is that implementation will help bring parity to outpatient payments across the varying service locations. How the move to APCs will affect ASCs operations and profitability is unknown. What is known is that accurate coding and billing is essential for a facility to receive proper reimbursement under APCs. ASCs will undoubtedly strive to make enhancements to internal operations to ensure proper reimbursement is received.

Check Your Understanding 7.1

1. Claims for RBRVS physician payments are prepared using _____ that have associated RVUs.

2. What are the three elements of the RVU?

3. What are the bases for the seven levels of service used in the ambulance services fee schedule?

4. Medicare-certified ASCs may share record keeping and financial and accounting systems with hospitals in the same parent corporation. True or false?

5. CMS created a motivation for surgical procedures to migrate from the more expensive inpatient setting to the less expensive outpatient surgery setting without creating a motivation to shift procedures from the less expensive physician office setting to the more expensive outpatient surgery setting by creating _____.

Home Health Prospective Payment System

Since October 1, 2000, Medicare has reimbursed **home health agencies (HHAs)** under a PPS based on the **home health resource group (HHRG)** classification. The system is known as the home health prospective payment system (HHPPS). The legal authorization for the HHPPS comes from the Balanced Budget Act (BBA) of 1997 and the Omnibus Consolidated and Emergency Supplemental Appropriations Act (OCESAA) of 1999. Section 4603(a) of the BBA of 1997 amended the Social Security Act by adding Section 1895, entitled "Prospective Payment for Home Health Services." The OCESAA amended Section 1895 by making the effective date October 1, 2000, and by stating that all Medicare services under the Medicare home health benefit that previously had been covered and paid on the basis of reasonable cost would now be paid on the basis of a prospective payment amount. The final rule implementing the HHPPS was published in the *Federal Register* of July 3, 2000 (DHHS 2000).

Data Collection

The payment is based on data elements in the **Outcome Assessment Information Set (OASIS).** OASIS uses ICD-9-CM codes to represent the health status of patients. In addition, for tracking purposes, HCPCS codes may be used to report non-routine supplies. Medicare Program Memorandum, Transmittal A-00-71 (October 2, 2000; Change Request 1356) describes in detail the required data elements on CMS Form 485 (Youmans, Scichilone, and Dougherty 2001, 76).

One data element in addition to the OASIS is also collected: the number of therapy hours that the patient has received in the sixty-day episode that forms the basic unit of service under HHPPS.

CMS defines the principal (primary) diagnosis for the HHPPS as the diagnosis most related to the current plan of care. On the OASIS form, the principal diagnosis is entered in the field M0230. The diagnosis may or may not be related to the patient's most recent hospital stay, but must relate to the services rendered by the HHA. If more than one diagnosis is treated concurrently, the diagnosis that represents the most acute condition and requires the most intensive services should be entered (Youmans, Scichilone, and Dougherty 2001, 77). Specific V-codes may be reported as principal (primary) diagnoses. For guidance, reimbursement analysts are referred to the *ICD 9-CM Official Guidelines for Coding and Reporting* referenced by CMS (See http://www.cdc.gov/nchs/datawh/ftpserv/ftpicd9/ftpicd9.htm.) (National Center for Health Statistics 2007).

However, only certain codes are case-mix codes. **Case-mix diagnoses** are conditions from many diagnostic categories, as designated by CMS. For 2008, there were 22 diagnostic categories:

- Blindness and low vision
- Blood disorders
- Cancer and selected benign neoplasms
- Diabetes
- Dysphagia
- Gait abnormality
- Gastrointestinal disorders
- Heart disease
- Hypertension
- Neuro 1 (brain disorders and paralysis)
- Neuro 2 (peripheral neurological disorders)
- Neuro 3 (stroke)
- Neuro 4 (multiple sclerosis)
- Ortho 1 (leg disorders)
- Ortho 2 (other orthopedic disorders)
- Psych 1 (affective and other psychoses, depression)
- Psych 2 (degenerative and other organic psychiatric disorders)
- Pulmonary disorders
- Skin 1 (traumatic wounds, burns, and post-operative complications)
- Skin 2 (ulcers and other skin conditions)
- Tracheostomy care
- Urostomy or cystostomy care (DHHS 2007a, 49787–49817)

These case-mix codes, in the principal diagnosis field, are important because they feed into the home health case-mix grouper. Should a V-code that is a noncase-mix diagnosis, be entered in field M0230, the case-mix code should be entered in field M0246 (See example). The ICD-9-CM guidelines dictate that a certain specific diagnosis is only to be used when a specific secondary diagnosis is present.

Secondary (additional) diagnoses are all conditions that existed when the plan of care was established, subsequently developed, or affected the treatment or care. Secondary diagnoses are entered in OASIS field M0240. Examples of conditions or diagnoses that may affect treatment or care are those that affect patients' responsiveness to treatment or their rehabilitative prognosis. Moreover, some V-codes may not be listed as secondary codes. Again, reimbursement analysts are advised to reference the *ICD-9-CM Official Guidelines for Coding and Reporting.*

Example:

A Medicare beneficiary's right foot was amputated due to diabetic osteomyelitis (250.80, 731.8) with an admission to a home care agency for surgical wound care (V58.78). The patient is a Type II diabetic who also received gait training (V57.1). Coding guidelines require that the diabetes code (250.80) precede the osteomyelitis code (731.8) that occasioned the amputation. HHA field entries in OASIS:

M0230 V58.78, surgical aftercare

M0240 250.80, diabetes with specified manifestations

M0240 731.8, other bone involvement in diseases classified elsewhere

M0240 781.2, abnormality of gait

M0246 250.80, diabetes with specified manifestations

M0245 731.8, other bone involvement in diseases classified elsewhere

---

The OASIS data set is completed and submitted electronically. Special software called the **home assistance validation and entry (HAVEN)** system is used for the collection and submission of the OASIS data, with a new OASIS data set completed whenever an unexpected decline or improvement in the patient's situation occurs.

Episode-Based Payment

The unit of payment is the episode of care. The per-episode home health payment covers all home care services and all medical supplies, including nonroutine medical supplies delivered to the patient during a sixty-day period. Claims for episodes of care usually include more than one date of service.

The episode-based payment system consolidates payments. Types of services consolidated into the single payment include all therapy (speech, physical, and occupational), skilled nursing visits, home health aide visits, medical social services, and all medical supplies, including **nonroutine medical supplies.** Durable medical equipment (DME) is excluded from the per-episode payment and is reimbursed under another payment method (DME fee schedule).

There are three special circumstances for which CMS adjusts the episode-based payment:

- Minimal care

- Intervening events

- Excessive costs

One special adjustment in which an agency provides minimal care is termed a **low-utilization payment adjustment (LUPA).** The LUPA is applied when an agency provides four or fewer visits in an episode. Under LUPA, the agency is reimbursed for each visit rather than for the sixty-day episode (Dougherty 2000, 84).

Intervening events, such as a patient's elective transfer or a patient's discharge and then return to care, may initiate the partial episode payment (PEP) adjustment. The PEP adjustment is based on the span of days of the shortened episode. The proportion of the 60-day episode that the span of days represents is calculated. For example a 45-day span equals 75 percent of a 60-day episode. The original, potential payment, had the patient not left prior to the end of the 60-day episode is multiplied by this proportion, 75 percent (DHHS 2000, 41131).

For cases incurring excessive costs, an outlier payment is made. The outlier payment is in addition to the 60-day episode payment. Home health agencies receive outlier payments when cost thresholds are exceeded. CMS established thresholds for each case-mix group by estimating costs per visit and including a fixed-loss amount (DHHS 2000, 41132).

Grouping and Payment

The case-mix system for the HHPPS combines twenty data elements from the OASIS to measure the three domains of the case mix. These three domains are:

- Clinical severity (C)

- Functional status (F)

- Service utilization (S)

The HHPPS defines eighty HHRGs based on these three domains, which are derived from all possible combinations of the severity levels across the three domains. The grouper program reviews selected data to assign the HHRG. This Grouper program is embedded in the HAVEN software. This embedded grouper program is sometimes called the pricer.

The HHRG is a six-character alphanumeric code that represents a severity level in the three domains: C, F, and S (Dougherty 2000, 86). These domains form the core of the **health insurance prospective payment system (HIPPS)** codes (table 7.17). A patient with the lowest severity in all three domains would be C0F0S0. This score is the minimum score.

From the HHRG, the health insurance prospective payment system (HIPPS) code is derived (table 7.18). There are eight HIPPS codes for each

Table 7.17. Basics of health insurance prospective payment system code and home health resource group classification

Coding Scheme for Home Health Resource Group (HHRG) Classification				
(Clinical) Position #2	(Functional) Position #3	(Service) Position #4	Position #5	Domain Level
A (C0)	E (F0)	J (S0)	1 = all positions computed	= min
B(C1)	F (F1)	K (S1)	2 = 2nd position derived	= low
C (C2)	G (F2)	L (S2)	3 = 3rd position derived	= mod
D (C3)	H (F3)	M (S3)	4 = 4th position derived	= high
	I (F4)		5 = 2nd & 3rd positions derived	= max
			6 = 3rd & 4th positions derived	
			7 = 2nd and 4th positions derived	
			8 = 2nd, 3rd & 4th positions derived	
		N through Z	9, 0	expansion values

Health Care Financing Administration (HCFA). 2000b (July 27). Program Memorandum Intermediaries Transmittal A-00-41, Change Request 1264. p. 4. Available online from www.cms.hhs.gov/manuals/pm_trans/A0041.pdf.

Table 7.18.   Sample listing of home health resource groups (HHRGs), health insurance prospective payment system (HIPPS) codes, and weights

Excerpt from Listing of HHRGs, HIPPS Codes, and Weights			
HHRG Description	**Case Mix Description of Domains**	**HIPPS Code**	**Weight**
C0F0S0—all computed	Clinical = Min, Functional = Min, Services = Min	HAEJ1	0.5265
2nd position derived		HAEJ2	0.5265
3rd position derived		HAEJ3	0.5265
4th position derived		HAEJ4	0.5265
2nd & 3rd derived		HAEJ5	0.5265
3rd & 4th derived		HAEJ6	0.5265
2nd & 4th derived		HAEJ7	0.5265
All derived		HAEJ8	0.5265
C0F0S1—all computed	Clinical = Min, Functional = Min, Services = Low	HAEK1	0.6074
2nd position derived		HAEK2	0.6074
3rd position derived		HAEK3	0.6074
4th position derived		HAEK4	0.6074
2nd & 3rd derived		HAEK5	0.6074
3rd & 4th derived		HAEK6	0.6074
2nd & 4th derived		HAEK7	0.6074
All derived		HAEK8	0.6074
C3F4S3—all computed	Clinical = High, Functional = Max, Services = High	HDIM1	2.8113
2nd position derived		HDIM2	2.8113
3rd position derived		HDIM3	2.8113
4th position derived		HDIM4	2.8113
2nd & 3rd derived		HDIM5	2.8113
3rd & 4th derived		HDIM6	2.8113
2nd & 4th derived		HDIM7	2.8113
All derived		HDIM8	2.8113

Source: CMS. Available online from www.cms.hhs.gov/PCPricer/Downloads/HHCodesWeights.pdf.

HHRG. HIPPS codes are five-character alphanumeric codes:

- The first character is an H.

- The second, third, and fourth characters represent the HHRG.

- The fifth character indicates what elements were computed or derived. Computed elements are output from the grouper based on complete OASIS data. Derived elements are output from the grouper based on a system of defaults where OASIS data are incomplete.

Therefore, the HIPPS code for the HHRG, C0F0S0, would be HAEJ1.

- First character = H

- Second, third, and fourth characters are: C0 = A, F0 = E, S0 = J

- 1 = all positions are computed

The HIPPS code is submitted on the claim to the regional home health intermediary (RHHI). The weight of the applicable HIPPS code is multiplied by the **national standard episode amount,** or conversion factor (table 7.19). The national standard episode amount is an across-the-board multiplier or a constant. The national standard episode amount is changed from year to year. In 2000, the national standard episode rate was \$2,115.30 and in 2008, the national rate was \$2,270.32 (DHHS 2000a, 41190–41191; DHHS 2007a, 49865).

The product resulting from the multiplication of the weight by the national standard episode amount is also adjusted for geographic wage differences. Adjusting for geographic wage differences is a two-step process:

1. In order to calculate this adjustment, the labor and nonlabor portions must be computed. The labor and nonlabor portions are computed from ratios. These ratios also vary from year to year. For example, in 2000 the ratio for the labor portion was 0.77668 and the ratio for the nonlabor portion was 0.22332 (DHHS 2000a, 41191). In 2008, though, the ratio for the labor portion was 0.77082, and the ratio for the nonlabor portion was 0.22918 (DHHS 2007a, 49764).

2. The labor portion is then adjusted for the wage index of the geographic area. Urban geographic areas use the wage index of the corresponding core-based statistical area (CBSA) (similar to the former metropolitan statistical area [MSA]). Rural areas use the nonurban area wage index of the respective state (sometimes called nonMSA). Again, the wage indexes vary from year to year. For example, in 2000 the wage index for Greenville, North Carolina (MSA 3150) was 0.9501 (DHHS 2000a, 41176). In 2008, the wage index for Greenville, North Carolina was 0.9402 (DHHS, 2007a, 49000). To calculate this adjustment, the labor portion of the product is multiplied by the wage index of the CBSA (24780, Greenville, North Carolina). The product of the labor portion multiplied by the CBSA wage index is then added back to the nonlabor portion to produce the total possible episode payment (table 7.19).

Case Study of HHPPS Calculations

With key data and the formulae, readers can calculate the wage-adjusted episode payment for an HHA patient in Greenville, North Carolina. The patient is receiving home health services following discharge from an acute care hospital. The patient's HIPPS code (HDIM1) reflects the highest severity in all three domains.

Table 7.19.   Calculation of home health payments

Sample Calculation of Wage-Adjusted Federal Payment (2005)							
A	B	C	D	E	F	G	H
HIPPS Code	Weight	Nat'l. Stnd. Epi. Amt. (NSAE) ($)*	Unadj. Rate [Weight × NSEA] ($)	Local Wage Index**	Adjusted Labor Portion [Unadj. Rate × Labor Ratio (.76775) × Local Wage Index] ($)	Nonlabor Portion [Unadj. Rate × Nonlabor Ratio (.23225)] ($)	Wage-Adjusted Rate [Adj. Labor Portion + Nonlabor Portion]($)
HAEJ1	0.5265	2264.28	1192.14	0.9183	840.49	276.88	1117.37
HDIM1	2.8113	2264.28	6365.57	0.9183	4487.89	1478.40	5966.29

*National 60-day episode rate. Department of Health and Human Services. 2004b (October 22). *Federal Register.* 69 (204): 62133.

**Greenville, NC, is in the Metropolitan Statistical Area (MSA) 3150. Department of Health and Human Services. 2004d (November 30). *Federal Register.* 69 (229): 69699.

Key Data

HHRG = C3F4S3 and the OASIS is complete (all computed)

HIPPS = HDIM1

Weight = 2.8113

National standard episode amount = $2,270.32

Labor ratio = 0.77082

Nonlabor ratio = 0.22918

CBSA wage index = 0.9402

Generic Formula

Weight × constant = Unadjusted payment
2.8113 × $2,270.32 = $6,382.55

Geographic Wage Adjustment

Unadjusted payment × 0.77082 (labor ratio) = Labor portion

$6,382.55 × 0.77082 (labor ratio) = $4,919.80

Labor portion × 0.9402 (CBSA wage index)

$4,919.80 × 0.9402 (CBSA wage index)

$4,919.80 × 0.9402 = $4,625.59

Unadjusted payment × 0.22918 (nonlabor ratio) = Nonlabor portion

$6,382.55 × 0.22918 (nonlabor ratio) = $1,462.75

Wage-index adjusted labor portion + Nonlabor portion = Total possible episode payment

$4,625.59 + $1,462.75 = $6,088.35

Table 7.19 illustrates this process.

For calendar year 2008, CMS mandated extensive refinements to the HHPPS. CMS expanded the case-mix model with four equations that account for:

- Variation in resource consumption between earlier episodes of care (1st or 2nd) and later episodes of care (3rd and beyond) that are adjacent (contiguous and separated by no more than 60 days)

- Numbers of therapy visits (therapy being physical therapy, speech-language pathology, or occupational therapy; high being 14 or more and low being 13 or fewer) and operationalized as three thresholds of therapy visits (6, 14, and 20 visits) with graduated steps of 1 to 4 visits per grouping (DHHS 2007a, 49776) (See table 7.20).

- Case-mix weights are higher for 3rd and beyond episodes of care than for 1st and 2nd episodes of care (DHHS 2007a, 49779). CMS' analyses revealed that the later episodes reflected patients who tended to average higher consumption of resources and had extended stays of care under home health (See table 7.21).

CMS also included additional variables to account for the resource use of different conditions:

- Scores for certain wound and skin conditions, such as infected wounds, abscesses, chronic ulcers, and gangrene

- More diagnosis groups, such as pulmonary, cardiac, and cancer

- Certain secondary diagnoses

Case-mix scores were attached to groupings of these conditions (See table 7.22. Scores in multiple groupings are added. These scores are factored into the case weight.

CMS also inserted a six-group severity adjustment to the national standardized episode amount to account for nonroutine medical supplies (NRS). Nonroutine medical supplies are those that are not bundled into typical (routine) medical care. Examples include catheter bags, urinary and stool collection pouches, irrigation trays, and appliance cleaners. Since the implementation of the HHPPS in 2000, CMS has accounted for nonroutine medical supplies by attributing a set portion of the national standard episode amount to them ($49.62) (DHHS 2007a, 49852). CMS believes that six groups of severity better reflect the variations in costs across patients with different conditions than a single set amount.

Table 7.20 Four equation model with thresholds

Equation and Services Utilization Severity Level	Number of Therapy Visits
1st and 2nd Episodes, 6 to 13 Therapy Visits	
S3	7, 8, 9
S4	10
S5	11, 12, 13
1st and 2nd Episodes, 14 to 19 Therapy Visits	
S1	14, 15
S2	16, 17
S3	18, 19
3rd + Episodes, 6 to 13 Therapy Visits	
S3	7, 8, 9
S4	10
S5	11, 12, 13
3rd + Episodes, 14 to 19 Therapy Visits	
S1	14, 15
S2	16, 17
S3	18, 19

Adapted from DHHS. 2007a (August 29). Medicare Program; Home Health Prospective Payment System Refinement and Rate Update for Calendar Year 2008; Final Rule. *Federal Register* 72(167):49779.

Table 7.21 Case-mix adjustment variables and scores

	Episode number within sequence of adjacent episodes	1 or 2	1 or 2	3+	3+
	Therapy visits	0 to 13	14+	0 to 13	14+
	EQUATION:	1	2	3	4
CLINICAL DIMENSION					
1	Primary or Other Diagnosis = Blindness/Low Vision	3	3	3	3
4	Primary Diagnosis = Diabetes	5	12	1	8
17	Primary or Other Diagnosis = Neuro 3 – Stroke AND M0700 (Ambulation) = 3 or more	1	5		
FUNCTIONAL DIMENSION					
51	M0700 (Ambulation) = 3 or more	3	4	4	5

Excerpts from DHHS. 2007a (August 29). Medicare Program; Home Health Prospective Payment System Refinement and Rate Update for Calendar Year 2008; Final Rule. *Federal Register* 72(167):49782–49786.

Table 7.22   153 Case-mix groups, average cost, and case-mix weight

No.	Clinical	Functional	Service Utilization	Average Cost	Case-Mix Weight
1st and 2nd Episodes, 0 to 13 Therapy Visits					
1	C1	F1	S1	$1,322.84	0.5827
5	C1	F1	S5	$3,293.37	1.4506
12	C1	F3	S2	$2,322.56	1.0230
1st and 2nd Episodes, 14 to 19 Therapy Visits					
46	C1	F1	S1	$3,659.40	1.6118
3rd + Episodes, 0 to 13 Therapy Visits					
73	C1	F1	S1	$1,485.36	0.6543
3rd + Episodes, 14 to 19 Therapy Visits					
144	C3	F3	S3	$6,629.53	2.9201
All Episodes, 20+ Therapy Visits					
153	C3	F3	S1	$7,916.89	3.4872

Excerpts from DHHS. 2007a (August 29). Medicare Program; Home Health Prospective Payment System Refinement and Rate Update for Calendar Year 2008; Final Rule. *Federal Register* 72(167):49828–49832.

The result was 153 case-mix groups rather than the original 80 (DHHS 2007a, 49764). These case-mix groups will have corresponding Health Insurance Home Health Prospective Payment System (HIHH PPS) codes. The grouper software will produce the unique HIHH PPS code (DHHS 2007a, 49845). CMS plans that the HIHH PPS code will have five positions:

1st—Payment grouping step for episode

2nd, 3rd, and 4th—clinical, functional, and service domains

5th—NRS severity

The purpose of these refinements was to improve the performance of the case-mix model. These improvements reflect differences in consumption of resources. However, the refinements added layers of complexity to the payment system without fully-developed training materials.

Implementation

Implementation of HHPPS requires management of the process, accuracy and completeness of coding, and submission of quality data. All functions in the implementation of HHPPS demand attention to details.

Abraham (2001) provides the major steps of the payment process:

1. Complete OASIS within seven days of start of care (SOC), resumption of care (ROC), significant change in condition (SCIC), or end of care (EOC). A regulatory interpretation changed this reporting requirement to within forty-eight hours for discharges, transfers, or deaths.

2. Calculate the HHRG with grouper software.

3. Convert the HHRG into health insurance prospective payment system (HIPPS) code for payment.

4. Send request for anticipated payment (RAP), low-utilization payment adjustment (LUPA), or final claims to regional home health intermediary (RHHI).

5. Extract and transmit OASIS data to state survey agency once monthly.

6. Retrieve and analyze outcome-based quality improvement management (OBQM) reports to identify quality improvement opportunities.

Coding accuracy and completeness are critical. Some ICD-9-CM diagnosis codes affect payment (DHHS 2000a). CMS is tracking the HCPC codes used for the nonroutine supplies (Youmans, Scichilone, and Dougherty 2001, 76).

In calendar year 2007, CMS required that HHAs submit data on quality measures. In 2007, ten OASIS quality measures were identified (DHHS 2006b, 65888). For 2008, CMS increased the number of quality measures to twelve (DHHS 2007a, 49765) (See figure 7.9). HHAs that do not submit the quality data are subject to a 2 percent reduction in the next year's percentage increase in the home health market basket (mix of goods and services appropriate to home health services) (DHHS 2007a, 49764).

Figure 7.9.   Home health quality measures

Improvement in ambulation/locomotion
Improvement in bathing
Improvement in transferring
Improvement in management of oral medications
Improvement in pain interfering with activity
Acute care hospitalization
Emergent care
Improvement in dyspnea
Improvement in urinary incontinence
Discharge to community
Emergent care for wound infection, deteriorating wound status
Improvement in the status of surgical wounds

DHHS. 2006b (November 9). Medicare Program; Home Health Prospective Payment System Rate Update for Calendar Year 2007 and Deficit Reduction Act of 2005 Changes to Medicare Payment for Oxygen Equipment and Capped Rental Durable Medical Equipment; Final Rule. *Federal Register* 71(217):65888.

DHHS. 2007a (August 29). Medicare Program; Home Health Prospective Payment System Refinement and Rate Update for Calendar Year 2008; Final Rule. *Federal Register* 72(167):49765.

Check Your Understanding 7.2

1. Ambulatory payment classifications (APCs) were developed by modifying _____.

2. Name the two reimbursement methods used by HOPPS.

3. Procedures in HOPPS with a status indicator of C are indicated as inpatient-only; they must be provided to Medicare beneficiaries in an inpatient setting and are reimbursed under the IPPS. True or false?

4. When is LUPA used and how does it affect reimbursement?

5. Name the three domains of case mix measured using data elements from OASIS for the home health prospective payment system.

Summary

Reform of reimbursement systems for healthcare services provided to ambulatory patients began in 1992. Spurred by effective curbs in the acute care setting, Congress authorized the Department of Health and Human Services to design and implement reformed payment systems in many settings for ambulatory patients. These settings include physician offices, ambulance services, ambulatory surgery centers, hospital outpatient services, and home health agencies. To the credit of lawmakers and CMS analysts, these systems combine a focus on cost savings and an attention to quality outcomes. Updates and revisions for these payment systems are released each year in the *Federal Register* via proposed and final rules. Students and professionals should reference these documents to obtain yearly payment rates and to examine revised or new payment provisions and policies.

Review Quiz

1. How can physician payments be adjusted for the price differences among various parts of the country?

2. What is the control mechanism the government uses on Medicare payments to physicians, and how is it applied?

3. Describe at least two issues that delayed implementation of the APC system for ambulatory surgical centers.

4. What is the current status of the ASC PPS?

5. How is the "two-times rule" applied to APC groups?

6. In the HHPPS, the _____ software is used to collect and submit OASIS data.

7. How is durable medical equipment (DME) reimbursed in the HHPPS?

8. When a patient is pronounced dead during ambulance transport, Medicare payment rules are followed as if the patient were alive. True or false?

9. CMS, not the APC Advisory Panel or MedPAC, makes the final ruling for updates and changes to HOPPS. True or false?

10. The number of APCs per encounter for a single patient is limited to ten. True or false?

References and Bibliography

Abraham, P. 2001 (October). HIPPS table for pricer. Home health prospective payment systems (HHPPSs). AHIMA Convention Proceedings. Centers for Medicare and Medicaid Services. Available online from www.cms.hhs.gov/medlearn/addendc.pdf.

Averil, R. F., N. I. Goldfield, J. Eisenhandler, J. S. Hughes, and J. Muldoon, 2001. Clinical risk groups and the future of healthcare reimbursement. In *Reimbursement Methodologies for Healthcare Services* [CD-ROM], edited by L. M. Jones. Chicago: American Health Information Management Association.

Centers for Medicare and Medicaid Services. 2005a. Listing of HHRGs, HIPPS codes and weights. Available online from www.cms.hhs.gov/PCPricer/Downloads/HHCodesWeights.pdf.

Centers for Medicare and Medicaid Services. 2005b (January 21). *Revisions and Corrections to the Medicare Claims Processing Manual,* Chapter 6, Section 30 and Various Sections in Chapter 15. Pub 100-04 Medicare Claims Processing. CMS Transmittal 437.

Centers for Medicare and Medicaid Services. 2007a (February 2). Overview. Accessed at http://www.cms.hhs.gov/PhysicianFeeSched/25 September 2007.

Centers for Medicare and Medicaid Services. 2007b (January 12). Physician Fee Schedule Search. http://www.cms.hhs.gov/pfslookup/.

Department of Health and Human Services. 2000a (July 3). Medicare Program; Prospective Payment System for Home Health Agencies; Final Rule. *Federal Register* 65 (128): 41127–41214.

Health Care Financing Administration (HCFA). 2000b (July 27). Program Memorandum Intermediaries Transmittal A-00-41, Change Request 1264. p. 4. Available online from www.cms.hhs.gov/manuals/pm_trans/A0041.pdf.

Department of Health and Human Services. 2002 (February 27). Medicare Program; Fee Schedule for Payment of Ambulance Services and Revisions to the Physician Certification Requirements for Coverage of Nonemergency Ambulance Services; Final Rule. *Federal Register* 67 (39): 9099–9135.

Department of Health and Human Services. 2003a (March 28). Medicare Program; Update of Ambulatory Surgical Center List of Covered Procedures Effective July 1, 2003; Final Rule. *Federal Register* 68 (60): 15267–15312.

Department of Health and Human Services. 2003b. Payments for procedures in outpatient departments and ambulatory surgical centers. Report of a study from the Office of the Inspector General. Available online from oig.hhs.gov/oei/reports/oei-05-00-00340.pdf.

Department of Health and Human Services. 2004a (February 27). *Federal Register* 67 (39): 9106.

Department of Health and Human Services. 2004b (August 16). Medicare Program; Proposed Changes to the Hospital Outpatient Prospective Payment System and Calendar Year 2005 Payment Rates; Proposed Rule. *Federal Register* 69 (157): 50447–50546.

Department of Health and Human Services. 2004c (October 22). Medicare Program; Home Health Prospective Payment System Rate Update for Calendar Year 2005; Final Rule. *Federal Register* 69 (204): 62123–62162.

Department of Health and Human Services. 2004d (November 26). Medicare Program; Update of Ambulatory Surgical Center List of Covered Procedures; Proposed Rule. *Federal Register* 69 (227): 69178–69180.

Department of Health and Human Services. 2004e (November 30). Medicare Program; Home Health Prospective Payment System Rate Update for Calendar Year 2005; Correction; Final Rule. *Federal Register* 69 (229) 69685–69727.

Department of Health and Human Services. 2006 (January). Office of Inspector General; *Medicare Payments for Ambulance Transports.*

Department of Health and Human Services. 2006a (December 1). Medicare Program; Revision to Payment Policies, etc.; Final Rule. *Federal Register* 71(231):69623–70274.

Department of Health and Human Services. 2006b (November 9). Medicare Program; Home Health Prospective Payment

System. Rate Update Calendar Year 2007 and Deficit Reduction Act of 2005 Changes to Medicare Payment for Oxygen Equipment and Capped Rental Durable Medical Equipment; Final Rule. *Federal Register* 71(217):65884–66006.

Department of Health and Human Services. 2007a (August 29). Medicare Program; Home Health Prospective Payment System Refinement and Rate Update for Calendar Year CY 2008; Final Rule. *Federal Register* 72(167):49762–49945.

Department of Health and Human Services 2007 (August 2). Medicare Program; Revised Payment System Policies for Services Furnished in Ambulatory Surgical Centers (ASCs) Beginning in CY 2008; Final Rule. *Federal Register* 72 (148) 42470–42626.

Department of Health and Human Services 2007 (August 2). Medicare Program; Proposed Changes to the Hospital Outpatient Prospective Payment System and CY 2008 Payment Rates; Proposed Changes to the Ambulatory Surgical Center Payment System CY 2008 Payment Rates; Proposed Rule. *Federal Register* 72 (148) 42628–43129.

Department of Health and Human Services 2007 (November 27). Medicare Program; Changes to the Hospital Outpatient Prospective Payment System and CY 2008 payment Rates, the Ambulatory Surgical Center Payment System and CY 2008 Payment Rates, the Hospital Inpatient Prospective Payment System and FY 2008 payment Rates; and Payments for Graduate Medical Education for Affiliated Teaching Hospitals in Certain Emergency Situations Medicare and Medicaid Programs: Hospital Conditions of Participation; Necessary Provider Designations of Critical Access Hospitals; Interim and Final Rule. *Federal Register* Vol. 72 (227): 66580–67225.

Department of Health and Human Services. 2007b (November 27). *Federal Register.* 72 (227) 66824–66825.

Dougherty, Michelle. 2000. New home care PPS brings major changes. *Journal of the American Health Information Management Association* 71(9):84–86.

Health Care Financing Administration (HCFA; now the Centers for Medicare and Medicaid Services, CMS). 2000 (July 27). Program Memorandum Intermediaries Transmittal A-00-41. Change Request 1264, 4. Available online from www.cms.hhs.gov/ transmittals/downloads/A0041.pdf.

Jones, L. M. ed. 2001. Ambulatory payment classifications for freestanding ambulatory surgery centers. In *Reimbursement Methodologies for Healthcare Services* [CD-ROM]. Chicago: American Health Information Management Association.

Medicare Payment Advisory Commission. 2004 (December). *Report to the Congress: Growth in the Volume of Physician Services.* Available online from www.medpac.gov/publications/ congressional_reports/Dec04_PhysVolume.pdf.

National Center for Health Statistics. 2007 (October 1). *ICD-9-CM Official Guidelines for Coding and Reporting.* Available online from http://www.cdc.gov/nchs/datawh/ ftpserv/ftpicd9/ftpicd9.htm. 26 September 2007.

Office of the Inspector General. 2006 (January). Medicare payments for ambulance transports. Also available at http:// oig.hhs.gov/oei/reports/oei-05-02-00590.pdf.

Scanlon, W. J. 2002 (February). *Medicare Physician Payments: Spending Targets Encourage Fiscal Discipline, Modifications Could Stabilize Fees.* Publication No. GAO-02-441T. Government Accounting Office. Available online from www.gao.gov/cgi-bin/getrpt?GAO-02-441T.pdf.

Youmans, Karen, Rita Scichilone, and Michelle Dougherty. 2001. Another look at home care PPS. *Journal of American Health Information Management Association* 72(2):76–78.

Chapter 8
Revenue Cycle Management

Objectives

- To understand the components of the revenue cycle

- To define revenue cycle management

- To describe the importance of effective revenue cycle management in a provider's fiscal stability

Key Terms

Accounts receivable
Charge capture
Charge description master
Copayment
Deductible
Explanation of benefits
Fiscal intermediary (FI)
Hard coding
Key performance indicator
Medicare carrier
Medicare Summary Notice
Remittance advice
Revenue cycle
Revenue cycle management

Introduction to Revenue Cycle Management

Prospective payment systems have been implemented in virtually every service area in the healthcare arena. In order to maintain profitability under the prospective payment systems, healthcare facilities must constantly examine and implement methods to either increase reimbursement or decrease costs. Managers of many facilities understand the importance of decreasing payment delays and lost revenue through **revenue cycle management (RCM).** RCM is the supervision of all administrative and clinical functions that contribute to the capture, management, and collection of patient service revenue.

Multidisciplinary Approach

Traditionally, RCM used a silo approach where each clinical department was responsible for its own functions and contributions to the **revenue cycle.** However, this linear approach was often reactive in nature, and rather than promoting communication between departments, it tended to foster hostility and division. The twenty-first century approach is for healthcare facilities to take a new multidisciplinary approach to RCM. This recent, dynamic approach promotes teamwork among various clinical departments by creating an RCM team composed of representatives from all revenue cycle areas. An emphasis on education encourages all team members to be updated on changing market forces such as payer trends, government and regulatory modifications, and organization strategy. As result of higher understanding of all members' contributions and importance to the revenue cycle, this modern management style has influenced the team to take a proactive approach to reimbursement issues.

Components of the Revenue Cycle

Each section of the revenue cycle is vital to creating efficient and compliant reimbursement processes. Although each area is responsible for its own functions and tasks, cooperation from outside departments and clinical areas is often critical for timely and accurate completion and submission of healthcare claims. The major components of the revenue cycle are:

- Preclaims submission activities
- Claim processing activities
- **Accounts receivable**
- Claims reconciliation and collections

Preclaims Submission Activities

Preclaims submission activities comprise tasks and functions from the admitting and case management areas. Specifically, this portion of the revenue cycle is responsible for collecting the patient's and responsible parties' information completely and accurately for determining the appropriate financial class, educating the patient as to his or her ultimate financial responsibility for services rendered, collecting waivers when appropriate, and verifying data prior to procedures/services being performed and submitted for payment. For example, when a Medicare patient arrives for admission into the cardiology unit for a coronary artery stent placement, the admitting representative is responsible for collecting the patient demographic data including the individual's Medicare healthcare identification claim number (HICN). Additionally, the Medicare patient may need to be educated about any annual **deductible** amount or **copayment** responsibilities if the inpatient stay were to last longer than 60 days.

Claims Processing Activities

Claims processing activities include the capture of all billable services, claim generation, and claim corrections. **Charge capture** is a vital component of the revenue cycle. All clinical areas that provide services to a patient must report charges for the services that they have performed. Failure to report charges for these services will result in lost reimbursement for the healthcare facility. Charge capture can be accomplished in a variety of ways depending on the technological capabilities of the healthcare facility.

Order Entry

Electronic order entry systems have been implemented at hospitals to help capture the charge at the point of service delivery. With an electronic order entry system, the charge for the service or supply is automatically transferred to the patient accounting system and posted to the patient's claim. Facilities without electronic systems use paper-based processes such as charge tickets, superbills, or encounter forms to assist in charge collection. With a paper-based process, the paper forms are collected and then entered into the patient accounting system, where the charge is then transferred to the claim. The paper system leaves more room for error as charges can be posted to the wrong patient's account, digits can be transposed during data entry, and backlogs can occur when data entry clerks are absent or pulled off task.

Charge Description Master

Coding is a major portion of charge capture. Claims submission regulations require ICD-9-CM and/or HCPCS codes to be reported on a patient's claim. Several types of visits, such as clinic visits, or services, such as laboratory or radiology, are designed to have procedure codes posted to the claim via the **charge description master (CDM).** During order entry, electronic or paper-based, a unique identifier for each service is entered. This unique identifier triggers a charge from the CDM to be posted to the patient's account. This process is known as **hard coding.**

Different facilities use different terminology for the CDM. Some more common synonyms include chargemaster, charge compendium, service master, price list, service item master, and charge list (Schraffenberger 2005, 117). The CDM is a large database maintained by the facility, which houses the price list for all services provided to patients.

The basic CDM model contains the revenue code, HCPCS code, service description, and price/charge for services and procedures. However, facilities do house other pieces of charge information in the CDM based on their individual needs, such as general ledger key, activity status, and department number. Table 8.1 provides a sample CDM. The CDM is typically under the responsibility of the finance department.

With the growing complexity of coding and billing regulations, many facilities have created a CDM coordinator position. A CDM coordinator should have coding and claims processing knowledge. Many HIM professionals that are interested in revenue cycle management are entering this arena via the CDM coordinator position.

CDM Maintenance

Although the CDM may be managed by one individual or a small unit, CDM maintenance is a joint effort. Influenced by the multidisciplinary approach taken by many RCM teams, each ancillary area and revenue cycle area participates in the maintenance process. Because code sets are modified each year, basic yearly maintenance of the CDM is critical. All code changes must be incorporated into the CDM to ensure proper reimbursement will be obtained. Inclusion of new codes must be coordinated with the ancillary department to ensure that services are properly reported. Further, code changes should be communicated to the ancillary areas so that proper education can be provided to order/charge entry staff.

In addition to yearly maintenance, several other updates may be necessary throughout the year. The Centers for Medicare and Medicaid Services (CMS) releases coding and billing guidance at various times during the fiscal year that may include information that warrants CDM updates. As new services are introduced at a facility, line items will need to be added to the CDM so that services and procedures may be billed for payment. And when claims processing improvements are made, the CDM should

Table 8.1.   Sample charge description master

Department Number	Item Number*	Item Description	Revenue Code	HCPCS Code**	Price***	Active/Inactive Status
700	7008989	Dermagraft (Synth skin graft)	252	C9201	$1,525.00	Active
700	7005202	Minor surgery – $^1/_2$ hour	360		$1,203.00	Active
700	7005203	Regular OR – 1st hour	360		$4,687.00	Active
700	7005205	Regular OR – $^1/_2$ hour	360		$1,682.00	Active
715	7157059	Open heart – 1st hour	360		$5,589.00	Active
715	7157060	Open heart – $^1/_2$ hour	360		$2,782.00	Active
760	7605161	OB/GYN surgery	360		$1,975.00	Active
800	8004557	Rabies Vaccine-IM use	450	90675	$632.00	Active
822	8224210	Albumin 5% saline	250	P9045	$265.00	Active
367	3675839	Speech screening	440	V5362	$298.00	Active
367	3675840	Language screening	440	V5363	$298.00	Active
367	3675841	Dysphagia screening	440	V5364	$298.00	Active
200	2578961	Venipuncture	300	G0001	$18.00	Inactive
200	2578989	Venipuncture	300	36415	$18.00	Active
110	1478951	MRI upper extremity w/o dye	610	73218	$817.00	Active
110	1478952	MRI upper extremity with dye	610	73219	$857.00	Active
110	1478953	MRI upper extremity w/o & with dye	610	73220	$897.00	Active

*Also called charge code, charge number, item code, service code and service number.

**When blank, HCPCS code is determined via coding in HIM department.

***Price is fictitious and should not be used for rate setting.

always be reviewed and modified to ensure that the components are up-to-date and will efficiently facilitate the claims processing changes.

Many healthcare facilities have contracted with maintenance companies to help keep the CDM up-to-date. Many consulting companies provide Web-based or software-based updating systems that allow the facility to easily make changes to the CDM. In addition to providing up-to-date code sets and regulations, many of these companies provide consultation services that assist facilities in the charge capture process.

Failure to effectively maintain the CDM puts a facility at risk for compliance violations and lost reimbursement as outlined in table 8.2. With the implementation of PPS in various healthcare settings, it is vital that the correct information be reported to third party payers. Because key information used to determine payment is transmitted to the claim via the CDM, it is critical that the CDM always be precise. Whereas the focus of the CDM may have been simply the charge value in the past, it is clearly now the accuracy of the entire line item.

Coding by HIM

Other types of visits, such as inpatient or complex ambulatory surgery, require the diagnoses and operating room procedures to be coded by health information management (HIM) professionals. During the coding process, medical records are viewed and read by the coding staff. All diagnoses and procedures are identified, coded, and then abstracted into the HIM coding system. This system then transfers the diagnoses and procedure codes to the patient accounting system where they are posted to the patient's claim prior to submission for payment.

Auditing and Review

Once all data have been posted to a patient's account, the claim can be reviewed for accuracy and completeness. Many facilities have internal auditing systems known as scrubbers. The auditing system runs each claim through a set of edits specifically designed for that third party payer. The auditing system identifies data that has failed edits and flags the claim for correction. Examples of errors that cause claim rejections or denials if not caught by the scrubber are:

- Incompatible dates of service

- Nonspecific or inaccurate diagnosis and procedure codes

- Lack of medical necessity

- Inaccurate revenue code assignment

The auditing process prevents facilities from sending incomplete or inaccurate claims to the payer. Facilities that do not have an editing system may perform a hand audit of a sample of claims. HIM and reimbursement specialists review claims with the medical record to determine if all services, diagnoses, and procedures were accurately reported. If errors are found, they can be corrected before claim submission.

Submission of Claims

Once reviewed and corrected, the claim can be submitted to the third party payer for payment. The Health Insurance Portability and Accountability Act of 1996 (HIPAA) added a new part to the Social Security Act titled Administrative Simplification.

Table 8.2.   Charge description master maintenance issues

Issue	Possible Result	Risk Area
Undercharging for services	Under payment	Lost revenue
Overcharging for services	Over payment	Compliance
Incorrect HCPCS or diagnosis code	Claims rejection/denial	Lost revenue
Incorrect revenue code	Claims rejection/denial	Lost revenue

The purpose of this section is to improve the efficiency and effectiveness of the healthcare delivery system. Through this section, Medicare has established standards and requirements for the electronic exchange of certain health information (DHHS 2003a, 8381). The Final Rule on Standards for Electronic Transactions and Code Sets, also known as the Transactions Rule, identified eight electronic transactions and six code sets (see tables 8.3 and 8.4). This Rule ensures that all providers, third party payers, claims clearinghouses, and so forth, use the same sets of codes to communicate coded health information, therefore ensuring standardization for systems and applications across the healthcare continuum. Not only does this support standardization, but it also supports administrative simplification.

Table 8.3. HIPAA electronic transactions

Healthcare claims or equivalent encounter information
Eligibility for a health plan
Referral certification and authorization
Healthcare claim status
Enrollment and disenrollment in a health plan
Healthcare payment and remittance advice
Health plan premium payments
Coordination of benefits

Source: Department of Health and Human Services. 2003a (February 20). *Federal Register.* 68 (34): 8382.

Table 8.4. HIPAA code sets

International Classification of Diseases, 9th Edition, Clinical Modification, Volumes 1 and 2
International Classification of Diseases, 9th Edition, Clinical Modification, Volume 3
National Drug Codes
Code on Dental Procedures and Nomenclature
Health Care Financing Administration Common Procedure Coding System
Current Procedural Terminology, 4th Edition

Source: Department of Health and Human Services. 2003a (February 20). *Federal Register.* 68 (34): 8382.

Providers can now maintain a select number of code sets at their current version, rather than maintaining different versions (current and old) of many code sets based on payer specification as required in the past.

Healthcare claims, healthcare payment and **remittance advice**, and coordination of benefits are included in the electronic transactions. As of October 16, 2003, all healthcare facilities were required to electronically submit and receive healthcare claims, remittance advices, and coordination of benefits. Thus, today facilities submit claims via the 837I electronic format, which replaces the UB-04 or CMS-1450 billing form. Physicians submit claims via the 837P electronic format, which takes the place of the CMS-1500 billing form.

Accounts Receivable

The accounts receivable department manages the amounts owed to a facility by customers who received services but whose payment will be made at a later date by the patient or his or her third party payer. Once the claim is submitted to the third party payer for reimbursement, the accounts receivable clock begins to tick. Typical performance statistics maintained by the accounts receivable department include days in accounts receivable and aging of accounts. Days in accounts receivable is calculated by dividing the ending accounts receivable balance for a given period by the average revenue per day. Facilities typically set performance goals for this standard. Aging of accounts is maintained in 30-day increments (0–30 days, 31–60 days, and so forth). Facilities monitor the number of accounts and the total dollar value in each increment. The older the account or the longer the account remains unpaid, the less of a chance that the facility will receive reimbursement for the encounter.

Insurance Processing

Once a claim is received by the third party payer (TPP), the insurance processing of the claim begins. Medicare claims for Part A services and hospital-based Medicare Part B services are submitted to a designated **fiscal intermediary.** Fiscal intermediaries (FIs) contract with Medicare to process claims for a specific area or region. The FI determines costs and reimbursement amounts, conducts reviews and audits, and makes payments to providers for covered services on behalf of Medicare. Part B claims for services rendered by physicians and for medical supplies are submitted to a designated **Medicare carrier.** Like the FI, the carrier determines charges allowed by Medicare and makes payment to physicians and suppliers on behalf of Medicare.

Benefits Statements

In addition to processing the claim for payment, TPPs prepare an **explanation of benefits (EOB)** that is delivered to the patient. The EOB is a statement that describes services rendered, payment covered, and benefits limits and denials. Specifically for Medicare patients, FIs and carriers prepare **Medicare Summary Notices (MSNs).** The MSN details amounts billed by the provider, amounts approved by Medicare, how much Medicare reimbursed the provider, and what the patient must pay the provider by way of deductible and copayments. EOBs and MSNs are part of the Transactions Rule and are provided to the facility via electronic data interchange (EDI) and are sent to the patient via postal mail.

Remittance Advice

Once the claim is processed by the TPP, a remittance advice (RA) is electronically returned to the provider via the 835A or 835B electronic format. Payments are typically made in batches with the RA sent to the facility and payments electronically transferred to the provider's bank. The RA reports claim rejections, denials, and payments to the facility via EDI.

Claims Reconciliation and Collection

The last component of the revenue cycle is reconciliation and collections. The healthcare facility uses the EOB, MSN, and RA to reconcile accounts. EOBs and MSNs identify the amount owed by the patient to the facility. Collections can contact the patient to collect outstanding deductibles and copayments. RAs indicate rejected or denied line items or claims. Facilities can review the RAs and determine whether the claim error can be corrected and resubmitted for additional payment. If a correction is not warranted, reconciliation can be made via a write-off or adjustment to the patient's account. Once the account has been settled, the revenue cycle is completed. Figure 8.1 provides a flow chart of the revenue cycle.

Check Your Understanding 8.1

1. The first step in the revenue cycle is _____.

2. How are charges for healthcare at all of the points of services collected and reported to the appropriate patient account for entry onto the provider's claim?

3. What do scrubbers do?

Revenue Cycle Management Team

The purpose of a revenue cycle management (RCM) team is to improve the efficiency and effectiveness of the revenue cycle process. Each team will develop different goals and objectives to guide their focus and discussions. Some sample objectives are:

*   To identify issues to improve accounts receivable

*   To communicate issues with appropriate areas

*   To develop educational materials such as a revenue cycle manual

*   To create a map or blueprint on how to bring up new services

*   To review denials and actively discuss the appeal process and successes

*   To discuss **key performance indicators** and measures

Figure 8.1.   Flow chart of the revenue cycle

Once an RCM team establishes goals and objectives, team members must define optimal performance for their facility. Many teams define optimal performance by establishing key performance indicators and by setting a standard for each indicator. Key performance indicators should represent areas that need improvement. The facility should design indicators so that they can be measured to gauge performance improvement. Some sample key performance indicators are:

- Dollar value of discharged not final billed encounters

- Days from discharge to coded

- Number of accounts receivable days

- Percentage and amount of write-offs

- Percentage of nonerror claims (clean claims)

- Percentage of claims returned to provider for correction by third party payers

- Percentage of denials by third party payers

- Percentage of late charges

- Percentage of accurate registrations

Current levels for each key indicator should be determined and compared to the standard. For example, if the standard for key performance indicator "Dollar value of discharged not final billed encounters" is $2 million and the current value is

$10 million, the facility is exceeding the standard by $8 million. Therefore, significant focus should be placed on reducing that total. Perhaps the facility is experiencing a coder shortage or there is a backlog in the prepping and scanning area so the coders are unable to review the records online. The HIM management team must investigate the issues and practice performance improvement techniques to improve the coding and/or record processing procedures so that the standard can be met. Key indicators should be continuously monitored until their related standard is consistently met. Once met, facilities typically review the indicator quarterly or semiannually to ensure continued optimal performance.

RCM Case Study

Facility A submitted one month of Medicare outpatient claims for auditing by the Medicare Outpatient Code Editor (OCE). The data set contained 2,530 claims, 17,710 line items, and $5,457,513 in charges. The results of an OCE audit are displayed in table 8.5.

Several edits were evoked during the audit. In order to improve the revenue cycle process, the RCM team investigates each edit to uncover its root problems.

OCE Edit 41

OCE edit 41 (Invalid revenue code) has been evoked, which usually arises when the revenue code reported on the claim is not in the list of valid revenue codes for HOPPS. When this edit is activated, the claim is returned to the provider for correction. Therefore, this error is delaying payment of several claims and is also costing the facility staff time in rework. Each claim must be corrected and resubmitted to the fiscal intermediary for payment.

Table 8.5.   Hospital A OCE Audit Results

OCE Edit	Edit Description	Violations	Claims Processing Area
01	Invalid diagnosis code	23	Coding
06	Invalid procedure code	21	Coding/CDM
15	Service unit out of range for procedure	46	Order entry
27	Only incidental services reported	16	Order entry/coding/CDM
28	Code not recognized by Medicare; alternate code for same service may be available	54	Coding/CDM
38	Inconsistency between implanted device and implantation procedure	47	Order entry/CDM
41	Invalid revenue code	65	CDM
43	Transfusion or blood product exchange without specification of blood product	15	Order entry/CDM
44	Invalid use of observation revenue code	49	Order entry/CDM
48	Revenue center requires HCPCS code	29	CDM
61	Service can only be billed to the DMERC	14	Order entry/CDM
68	Service provided prior to date of National Coverage Determination (NCD) approval	32	Coding/CDM
71	Claim lacks required device code	28	Order entry/CDM

Clearly, this situation raises revenue code issues. Revenue codes are stored in the charge description master (CDM) and are placed on the claim via charge/order entry. Therefore, a CDM review is warranted because several line items obviously are stored with incorrect revenue codes. Perhaps a program transmittal was incorrectly interpreted or a typing mistake was made during data entry in the CDM.

A review of the sixty-five error claims shows that two line items in the ancillary section of physical therapy have incorrect information. The two line items represent physical therapy evaluation services, which should be reported with revenue code 0424. However, these line items had been assigned revenue code 0425—not a valid revenue code. This was a simple data entry mistake, but it resulted in delayed payment for several claims. This error is easy to correct, but it reveals the need for the CDM update process to be reviewed to identify risk areas for typing errors. Facility A subsequently implements a review component as part of its CDM update process.

OCE Edit 48

OCE edit 48 (Revenue center requires HCPCS code) is triggered when an HCPCS code is not reported with a revenue code on the claim and the revenue center status indicator is not bundled. This edit is not applicable for revenue codes 100x, 210x, 310x, or 905–907. Because this edit is activated, claims are being returned to the facility for correction. Like OCE edit 41, this error is also delaying the payment of several claims and is costing facility A staff time for rework.

Review of these twenty-nine claims reveals they all included the line item number 3268916, which is used to report lithotripsy. Facility A had recently hard coded the lithotripsy services in the CDM, so the RCM team could not understand why the HCPCS code was not appearing on the claim. Further, the lithotripsy unit was contacted and its staff confirmed that they performed thirty-five

procedures last month, so why did only twenty-nine claims evoke this edit? What happened to the other six claims? The RCM team asked the CDM coordinator to review all line items for lithotripsy services.

The CDM review revealed that there were duplicate line items for this service. Apparently the old line item for this service was not marked as inactive when the hard-coding update occurred. Therefore, the CDM contained two active line items for the same service. However, the RCM team was still puzzled because they thought that they had thoroughly educated the charge entry staff about the line item changes. After further investigation the RCM team discovered that one charge entry staff member was on vacation during the training, and upon return to work she was not informed about the line item changes. She had continued to use the old line item number.

Two fixes were implemented. First, line item number 3268916 was marked inactive. Second, the charge entry staff member was scheduled for training immediately. Additionally, the RCM team and coding manager learned two lessons. An additional component was needed to the hard-coding conversion plan to review all old line items for inactive status, and a sign-in sheet was needed to be used for training sessions and followed up for missing attendees to ensure that all staff members would be educated in the future.

OCE Edit 38

OCE edit 38 (Inconsistency between implanted device and implantation procedure) is triggered when an HCPCS code with APC payment status indicator H (pass-through device) is present on the claim, but no APC with a payment status indicator of S (significant), T (surgical), X (ancillary—non-implant) is reported. This edit causes the claim to be returned to the provider for correction.

To determine whether this situation resulted from a CDM error or a flaw in the order entry process, facility A required a claim analysis. Claim review showed that the forty-seven cases evoking OCE edit 38 were all cardiac pacemaker claims. Further investigation of the cardiac encounters revealed that the order entry process included reporting the device code via the CDM, but the facility's chart flow process was bypassing the HIM department. Therefore, the code for the pacemaker insertion procedure was not being coded or reported on the claim.

Not only did facility A require rework and resubmission for these forty-seven claims, but the HIM and cardiac departments had to learn through the RCM team to work together to change claims processing flow.

This case study shows that each claim that evokes an edit from an internal or external auditing system or process should be investigated and corrected if warranted. Facilities should resubmit all possible claims in order to achieve optimal reimbursement. Failure to review and rework error claims will result in significant lost payment. A facility's RCM team should facilitate this process so that efforts can be coordinated and streamlined.

Check Your Understanding 8.2

1. Healthcare facilities should design key performance indicators so they _____.

2. What system is typically used to audit Medicare claims?

3. Describe at least two problems uncovered during the claims audit at facility A.

Summary

The revenue cycle and the management of the processes contained within are vital to obtaining accurate reimbursement. Every piece of healthcare information collected during the cycle contributes to the production of an error-free claim. Effective management of the revenue cycle results in efficient processes that meet key performance indicator standards defining optimal performance. Achieving and maintaining optimal performance levels not only improves revenue but allows the healthcare facility to focus on other areas for improved profitability.

Review Quiz

1. Which provider order entry system is usually more reliable, paper-based or electronic? Why?

2. What are two sources of new charge description master codes?

3. What risk areas are concerns when the charge description master is not properly maintained and revised?

4. How has HIPAA changed claims processing?

5. What are two roles of EDI in claims processing?

6. List the ways discrepancies between submitted charges and paid charges are reconciled by the provider.

7. How do providers decide what optimal performance is for units of their facility?

8. Facility B just completed an analysis of its alarmingly high balance of unpaid claim amounts. What are some key performance indicators a provider's RCM team could use to learn the reason(s) for the surge in unpaid balances?

9. Describe at least three sources of errors that cause claim denials.

10. Use of the charge description master has made manual coding by HIM coders obsolete. True or false?

References and Bibliography

3M Health Information Systems. 2005. *Outpatient Code Editor with Ambulatory Payment Classification Software: Installation and User's Manual.* Software version 6.2.

AHIMA. 1999. Practice Brief: The Care and Maintenance of Charge Masters. *Journal of American Health Information Management Association* 70 (7) 80A–B.

Berkey, Tim. 1998. Reducing accounts receivable through benchmarking and best practices identification. *Journal of American Health Information Management Association* 69:10, 30–34.

Department of Health and Human Services. 2003a (February 20). Health Insurance Reform: Security Standards; Final Rule. *Federal Register* 68 (34): 8333–8381.

Department of Health and Human Services. 2003b (February 20). Health Insurance Reform: Modifications to Electronic Data Transaction Standards and Code Sets. *Federal Register* 68 (34): 8381–8399.

Schraffenberger, Lou Ann. 2005. *Effective Management of Coding Services.* Chicago: American Health Information Management Association.

VHA: 2002. Revenue Cycle Management: The Paradigm Shift to Success. VHA, Inc. Available online from www.vha.com.

Work, M. 2005. Best practices in revenue cycle management. *Journal of American Health Information Management Association* 76:7, 31.

Youmans, Karen. 2004. An HIM spin on the revenue cycle. *Journal of American Health Information Management Association* 75:3, 32–36.

Chapter 9
Quality Issues

Objectives

- To describe origins and evolution of pay for performance
- To describe models of pay for performance
- To explain models of Centers for Medicare and Medicaid Services

Pay-for-Performance Systems

Pay-for-performance systems are a recent trend that link reimbursement, performance, and quality. Driven by rising healthcare costs and studies reporting poor quality, pay-for-performance systems have emerged as a recent trend. Experts predict that these systems will become more and more prevalent.

History and Background

In the landmark report, *Crossing the Quality Chasm,* the Committee on Quality of Health Care in America of the Institute of Medicine stated that the U.S. health-care delivery system needed fundamental change as "quality problems are everywhere, affecting many patients" (Committee on Quality 2001, 1). Thus, as one stratagem in the redesign and restructuring of the healthcare delivery system, the report's authors called for an alignment of payment incentives and quality (Committee on Quality 2001, 5). This alignment is the basis of pay-for-performance systems.

In a guide for the federal Agency for Healthcare Research and Quality (AHRQ), Dudley and Rosenthal define pay for performance (P4P or PFP) as any type of providers' payment system that is based on performance and incentives, including systems that target performance on cost measures (Dudley and Rosenthal 2006, 1). These AHRQ researchers

acknowledge that this definition is broad (Dudley and Rosenthal 2006, 1).

Pay-for-performance systems link rewards and the provision of quality healthcare (Bell and Levinson 2007, 1717). Financial rewards can be bonuses or other incentives, such as higher fee structure. Non-financial rewards include public recognition and reputation (Dudley et al. 2004, n.p.). Quality is often assessed by evidence-based process measures, such as the number of eligible women who receive Papanicolaou tests (Bell and Levinson 2007, 1717). Theoretically, rewards are being used to motivate providers to provide quality healthcare. While, overall research on P4P systems is limited and shows mixed results, recent research shows modest, positive results (See Table 9.1). Despite these modest returns-on-investment, intense interest in and growth of pay-for-performance system continues.

The number of pay-for-performance systems has quickly grown over the past few years. However, prior to the current trend, health plans and employer-payer coalitions sponsored pay-for-performance systems in other guises (Anonymous 2005, 2). For example, in the early 1970s, Dr. Walter McClure advocated the "Buy Right" program (Millenson 2004, 324). This program aimed at corporate purchasers of healthcare combined quality improvement, incentives, and efficiency measures (Millenson 2004, 324). The current

Table 9.1.   Pay for performance: Modest results

Study	Process Measures	Outcomes
Glickman et al. 2007	6 CMS indicators for acute myocardial infarction • Aspirin at arrival • Aspirin at discharge • β-blocker at arrival • β-blocker at discharge • Angiotensin-converting enzyme inhibitor or angiotensin receptor blocker for left ventricular systolic dysfunction • Smoking cessation counseling for recent or active smokers 8 nonCMS indicators for acute myocardial infarction • Glycoproteen llb/llla inhibitor use • Clopidogrel at discharge • Any heparin use • Lipid-lowering medication • Dietary modification counseling • Referral for cardiac rehabilitation • Electrocardiogram within 10 minutes • Cardiac catheterization within 48 hours	For both the CMS indicators and the nonCMS indicators, there were no significant differences in the overall rates of improvements between the 54 pay-for-performance hospitals and the 446 non pay-for-performance hospitals Two individual CMS indicators (aspirin at discharge and smoking cessation counseling) and one nonCMS indicator (lipid-lowering medication at discharge) showed slightly higher rates of improvements at the 54 pay-for-performance hospitals than at the 446 non pay-for-performance hospitals General improvements in quality at pay for performance was 1.6 percent over 3 years
Lindenauer et al. 2007	5 indicators for acute myocardial infarction • Aspirin at arrival • Aspirin at discharge • β-blocker at arrival • β-blocker at discharge • Angiotensin-converting enzyme inhibitor or angiotensin receptor blocker for left ventricular systolic dysfunction 2 indicators for heart failure • Assessment for left ventricular function • Angiotensin-converting enzyme inhibitor or angiotensin receptor blocker for left ventricular systolic dysfunction 3 indicators for pneumonia • Assessment for oxygenation • Initial antibiotics within 4 hours after arrival • Assessment and given pneumococcal vaccination	For 7 of 10 indicators, the 207 pay-for-performance hospitals showed significantly better performance than the 406 non pay-for-performance hospitals. After adjusting for baseline performance and other hospital characteristics, pay for performance was associated with improvements ranging from 2.6 percent to 4.1 percent over 2 years
Rosenthal et al. 2005	3 indicators of clinical quality • Cervical cancer screening • Mammography • Hemoglobin A_{1c}	For 1 indicator (cervical cancer screening), 134 pay-for-performance physician groups showed significantly better performance (3.6 percent) than the 33 non pay-for-performance physicians groups over 31 months of patient treatment Overall, $3.4 million in bonuses were awarded mostly to the already high performers

Sources:

Glickman et al. 2007, June 6. Pay for performance, quality of care, and outcomes in acute myocardial infarction. *Journal of the American Medical Association* 297(21):2373–2380.

Lindenauer, P.K., D. Remus, S. Roman, M.B. Rothberg, E.M. Benjamin, A. Ma, and D.W. Bratzler. 2007, February 1. Public reporting and pay for performance in hospital quality improvement. *New England Journal of Medicine* 356(5):486–496.

Rosenthal, M.B., R. G. Frank, Z. Li, and A.M. Epstein. 2005, October 12. Early experience with pay-for-performance: From concept to practice. *Journal of the American Medical Association* 294(14):1788–1793.

upswing in P4P systems began in 2004 when the number of systems doubled to seventy-eight from the thirty-nine P4P systems in 2003. In 2004, these seventy-eight sponsoring entities were:

- Health plans (54)
- State Medicaid programs (9)
- Employers (6)
- Centers for Medicare and Medicaid Services demonstration projects (5)
- Other plans (4) (Anonymous 2005, 3)

In 2005, over 100 sponsoring entities including health plans, employer-payer coalitions, and Medicare and Medicaid programs had initiated P4P payment systems (Baker and Carter 2005, 3).

Pay-for-performance systems are still evolving. In 2004, they targeted primary care physicians and HMOs (Baker and Carter 2005, 3). At that time, the incentives were annual bonuses based on the measures in the Healthcare Effectiveness Data and Information Set (HEDIS) of the National Committee for Quality Assurance (NCQA) (Baker and Carter 2005, 3). Since 2004, P4P systems have evolved in several ways:

- Expanded to more types of providers, such as preferred provider organizations, medical specialists, and hospitals
- Extended beyond payers and providers to consumers, such as dissemination of performance results in public reports and involvement in consumer-directed care (See chapter 3.)
- Developed more performance measures, such as adoption of health information technologies, specific population measures, clinical practice guidelines (evidence-based, process measures), cost savings, and return on investment
- Advanced incentives to tiered fee schedules (Baker and Carter 2005, 3).

The interest of the Centers for Medicare and Medicaid Services in P4P is a major driver of the spread of the P4P systems in the U.S. Pay-for-performance systems are also a global phenomenon as reflected by discussion in Canada, interest in Australia, and an existing system in Great Britain (See figure 9.1.) (Bell and Levinson 2007, 1717).

An important player in the development of P4P systems is the Leapfrog Group. The Leapfrog Group was initiated in November, 2000, and is supported by the Business Roundtable, the Robert Wood Johnson Foundation, and other contributors (Leapfrog Group and Thomson Medstat 2007, n.p.). By 2005, over 170 Fortune 500 companies and other large public and private purchasers of health benefits representing 36 million enrollees had joined the Leapfrog Group (Robert Wood Johnson Foundation 2005, n.p.). The goal of the Leapfrog Group is to positively affect the quality and affordability of healthcare by "leaping" forward improvements in hospitals' quality and safety through rewards.

Purpose

The rising costs of healthcare have motivated payers to investigate and seek pay-for-performance systems.

Figure 9.1.   Global perspective: Pay-for-performance system in the United Kingdom

The United Kingdom has a comprehensive quality-improvement strategy. For many years, national standards of care have existed for the treatment of major chronic diseases. In 2004, pay for performance was introduced for family physicians at a cost of $3.2 billion (1.8 billion pounds sterling). During the first year, levels of achievement in quality exceeded the government's expectations. Analysts compared quality trends between clinical indicators for which financial incentives were provided and clinical indicators for which financial incentives were not provided. Analysis revealed that the improvement in quality reflected a continuing trend that had begun before the introduction of pay for performance. However, the introduction of pay for performance did modestly accelerate the improvement in some diseases. Finally, the analysts noted that government experts acknowledge that the improvements in performance could have been obtained at a lower cost.

Source of content: Campbell, S., D. Reeves, E. Kontopantelis, E. Middleton, B. Sibbald, and M. Roland. 2007, July 12. Quality of care in England with the introduction of pay for performance. *New England Journal of Medicine* 357(2):181–190.

Underpinning this decision is the payers' perception that quality has not concomitantly improved with the increasing costs. Thus, sponsors of P4P systems typically list the following goals:

- Reward the provision of quality care
- Improve the quality of care
- Control costs directly
- Control costs indirectly by reducing errors and inappropriate utilization (Dudley and Rosenthal 2006, 1).

These goals are broad and all-inclusive. Some healthcare organizations may have additional sub-goals, such as achieving a competitive edge through a focus on cost-effective quality or a market advantage. Finally, though, as the variation in goals demonstrates, pay-for-performance systems cannot be "one-size-fits-all"; instead, these systems must be tailored to the health plan, governmental purchaser, or employer-payer coalition.

Advantages and Disadvantages

Both advantages and disadvantages can accrue to healthcare organizations that implement P4P systems.

The advantages include:

- Demonstrated commitment to providing quality care
- Establishment of infrastructure for reporting on quality
- Rewards for providing quality healthcare
- Transparent process of rewards
- Ability to focus on underserved or high-risk groups (Bell and Levinson 2007, 1718)

Similarly, the disadvantages include:

- Implementation of intervention that is not evidence-based (paucity of literature on P4P)

- Potential for unintended consequences, such as poor quality in unmeasured processes or inappropriate reduction of needed services
- Lack of accepted model with each system uniquely tailored for healthcare organization
- Difficult to measure processes and outcomes in populations of patients or clients with complex diseases and conditions
- Difficult to assess measures involving patients' or clients' compliance, such as smoking cessation
- Potential that costs of implementation could be better spent on other efforts
- Better documentation of care rather than actual better quality of care (Bell and Levinson 2007, 1718)

Thus, despite having significant disadvantages, P4P systems are firmly entrenched in public and private healthcare payment systems. With physicians and payers believing that the current system needs reform, P4P systems seem to be an opportunity for all parties to collaborate to improve healthcare.

Models

As P4P is an emerging payment system, effective models based on practice are few. Moreover, there is a paucity of research that takes a comprehensive approach, focusing instead on one or two factors (Damberg et al. 2005, 67; Dudley 2005, 1821). Thus, many models exist for P4P.

Two key considerations in the design of existing models of P4P systems are:

- Recipient of reward or penalty (individual or group)
- Mechanism of payment

Based on these two key considerations, the current models fit two major categories:

- Reward-based

  —Individual, group, hospital, or region

  —Rewards (compensation) when targets met or exceeded

  —Higher fee schedule for superior performance

  —Increased payment rates for superior providers

- Penalty-based

  —Individual, group, hospital, or region

  —Compensation withheld when targets not met or performance not improved

  —Lower fee schedule for inferior performance (Bell and Levinson 2007, 1717)

Given that pay-for-performance systems are incentive-based, determination of rewards must be fair and transparent. Moreover, the amount of rewards must be sufficient to induce change in behavior.

Unfortunately, fairness and transparency are difficult when determination of whom to reward is problematic. When multiple providers are involved, as is the case with many patients, the provider of the care, be it an individual or a group is difficult to determine. For example, one research study of Medicare claims found that Medicare beneficiaries saw a median of two primary care physicians and five specialists working in four different physician groups (Pham et al. 2007, 1132–1133). Moreover, for one-third of Medicare beneficiaries, their assigned physicians were changed from one year to the next with 97 percent being changed to different physician groups (Pham et al. 2007, 1134). Overall, no more than half of their visits could be assigned under current pay-for-performance models (Pham et al. 2007, 1136). Thus, implementing pay-for-performance for providers treating a majority of Medicare patients would be difficult. However, a study of HMOs revealed data that are relevant and useful. HMOs that did not require enrollees to designate a gatekeeper (primary care provider), a characteristic of Medicare, were less likely to implement pay for performance (Rosenthal et al. 2006, 1901). Thus, Rosenthal and colleagues recommend that, in the design Medicare's pay-for-performance program, this experience from HMOs be utilized (Rosenthal et al. 2006, 1901). Finally, in terms of fairness, experts recommend that multiple levels of incentives exist with lowered payments associated with partial achievement of targets and that incentives be tied to improvements, not just baselines (Rosenthal and Dudley 2007, 741).

The sufficient amount of the incentive varies by the setting and situation. In one study, albeit set in 1984, $2.00 was sufficient to make an impact (Hickson et al. 1987, 346-347). Yet, in another study $10,000 was insufficient to make an impact (Joachim et al. 2003, 294, 297). Based on the experience of HMOs, Rosenthal and colleagues observe that bonuses should be 5 percent or more of payments because this rate is prevalent among private payers (Rosenthal et al. 2006, 1902). Finally, Goldfield and colleagues suggest that, to be effective, the incentives must be large enough to make providers take notice (Goldfield et al. 2005, 32–33). They recommend that 20 percent is an amount substantial enough to make providers "relentlessly" pursue quality (Goldfield et al. 2005, 33). Moreover, they recommend that this 20 percent be carved out of current payments rather than bonuses on top of current payments (Goldfield et al. 2005, 33). They take this controversial stance because they believe that dramatic changes need to be made to the current healthcare delivery system—and that pay-for-performance systems that put providers at significant financial risk are the means to achieve these changes and quality improvement (Goldfield et al. 2005, 32–33).

One reward-based model is the Leapfrog Hospital Rewards Program, a standardized hospital incentive program (Leapfrog Group 2006, 1). Any of the following five clinical areas is measured for improvement:

- Coronary artery bypass graft

- Percutaneous coronary intervention

- Acute myocardial infarction

- Community acquired pneumonia

- Deliveries and newborn care (Leapfrog Group 2006, 1)

This model attempts to motivate improvements in effectiveness, efficiency, and quality through rewards and public reporting.

Another model is the statewide project in California (Damberg et al. 2005, 68). While some pay-for-performance systems involve one healthcare insurance plan or one hospital, this project involved 7 health plans, 215 physician organizations (45,000 physicians), purchasers, consumer-advocate groups, and 6.5 million enrollees. The goal of this collaborative effort was to have a substantial impact by implementing financial and nonfinancial incentives to improve quality of healthcare (Damberg et al. 2005, 67). The project's core objectives were:

- Collaboration (combined effort of stake-holders—health plans, physician organization, purchasers, and consumers)

- Measurement (clinical quality, patient experience, and infrastructure)

- Reward (financial—risk-adjusted bonus payments and nonfinancial—report cards providing public recognition)

- Accountability (all stakeholders have role, including a public scorecard)

This project sought to reform the healthcare delivery system through re-engineering rather than incremental improvements.

Operations

Most healthcare organizations that implement P4P systems begin small and expand operations over time. Key advantages to incremental implementation are:

- Measures are tested before full-scale use

- Providers have time to prepare

- Sponsors can evaluate policies, procedures, and results before full-scale use (Dudley and Rosenthal 2006, 12).

Incremental implementations can be pilot projects that focus on:

- Specific providers, patient populations, or geographic areas

- National measures

- Existing administrative or billing data

- Volunteers

- Specific processes, such as data collection, reporting, or benchmarking (Dudley and Rosenthal 2006, 12).

The Centers for Medicare and Medicaid Services (CMS) used an incremental implementation. The CMS withheld 0.4 percent of the payment update from hospitals that did not participate in the publicly report a set of quality measures (Dudley and Rosenthal 2006, 12).

Researchers at the Agency for Healthcare Research and Quality recommend that P4P systems should focus on the following targets:

- Most significant problems in terms of quality or cost

- Proportion of population covered by the service or provider

- Availability of valid and reliable performance measures (Dudley and Rosenthal 2006, 6).

Success of operations also depends on other factors such as the characteristics of the incentives, the organizational infrastructure, the culture of quality, and effective leadership (See table 9.2.).

Analysis of organizational data may reveal problems in delivery of services in terms of quality and cost. Sources of these data include quality and utilization reports, claims data, lawsuits, and patients' or clients' complaints. The literature may also suggest problems prevalent in many healthcare organizations that could become the basis of the P4P.

Pay-for-performance systems should focus on services or providers that affect many patients or enrollees. While services or providers that affect only a few enrollees are important to those few patients or enrollees, the overall impact of changing behaviors will be small. Moreover, there may be little, if any, return on investment. Thus, experts recommend focusing on services or providers that affect a large proportion of the healthcare organizations' populations (Dudley and Rosenthal 2006, 6). In addition to these considerations, other experts recommended that the problems be important to patients or clients (Damberg et al. 2005, 68).

Using reliable and valid performance measures is critical. Reliable measures are consistent over time, site, and data collectors. Valid measures are clinically relevant and scientifically sound Sources of these performance measures are:

- Joint Commission (Core Measures and ORYX Noncore Measures)

- National Quality Measures Clearinghouse

- National Quality Forum (endorsed consensus standards)

- National Committee for Quality Assurance [Healthcare Effectiveness Data and Information Set (HEDIS)]

- Hospital Quality Alliance (Hospital CAHPS)

Table 9.2. Additional factors in success of pay-for-performance systems

Factors	Features
Characteristics of the Incentive	• Magnitude that is affected by overarching payment system, such as fee-for-service or capitation, or other requirements, such as accreditation • Provision of additional directly revenue or indirectly through reduced costs • Ability to determine using organizational health information technology the proportion of providers' patients to which the incentive applies • Return on investment as affected by risk, complexity, and socioeconomic factors • Individual, group, hospital, or region (incentives beyond individual involve sophisticated data collection and algorithms)
Infrastructure of Health Information Technologies	• Ability to collect data for measures • Ability to manipulate data for reporting • Capability to provide timely and reliable feedback • Capability to calculate incentives, especially for group recipients of incentives
Shared Culture of Quality	• Obtain buy-in of all stakeholders • Collaborative focus among healthcare personnel, including physicians, nurses, allied health providers, administrators, and technical and clerical staff on quality and quality improvement • Collective actions among all healthcare personnel • Shared accountability
Effective Leadership	• Communication • Clear goals • Effectual teams • Efficient management

Content synthesized from multiple sources, including Campbell et al. 2005, 38; Damberg et al. 2005, 76; Dudley 2005, 1822.

- AQA alliance (formerly Ambulatory Care Quality Alliance)

- Agency for Healthcare Research and Quality [Consumer Assessment of Healthcare Providers and Systems (CAHPS®)]

- Leapfrog measures (Dudley and Rosenthal 2006, 6–17).

In addition, specialty medical organizations, such as the American College of Rheumatology; American Diabetes Association; National Heart, Lung, and Blood Institute; and National Osteoporosis Foundation provide disease-specific guidelines that some organizations adopt as measures.

Types of performance measures are structure, process, and outcome. Many pay-for-performance measures are focused on evidence-based processes, such as prescribing appropriate medications for patients. However, some measures are structure, such as the existence of health information technology and its degree of implementation. The classic outcome measure is mortality rates

Some experts recommend that the measures be within the control of providers, such as ordering appropriate laboratory tests or prescribing correct medications, rather than measures dependent upon patients' or clients' compliance (Damberg et al. 2005, 68). Experts also recommended that both administrative data and clinical data be used, as administrative data cannot represent all processes of care (Damberg et al. 2005, 77). Other experts noted that measures should be adjusted for risk and socioeconomic status (Casalino et al. 2007, 495; Tabak et al. 2007, 790). Adoption of unreliable or invalid performance measures may have unintended and undesirable consequences and contrary results (Casalino et al. 2007, 495).

Analysts explored the functioning of P4P systems for physicians who cared for patients with multiple chronic diseases (Boyd et al. 2005, 717). Many medical specialty groups have disseminated

clinical practice guidelines for each of these chronic diseases. The P4P systems have adopted many of the clinical practice guidelines or standards derived from them, as evidence of the provision of quality of care (superior performance). Thus, these systems reward physicians for providing the elements of the guidelines. Unfortunately, the guidelines are single-disease guidelines; they were developed for each single disease in isolation, not for complex combinations of these chronic diseases. The analysts targeted guidelines for combinations of the following fifteen common diseases: hypertension, chronic heart failure, stable angina, atrial fibrillation, hypercholesterolemia, diabetes mellitus, osteoarthritis, chronic obstructive pulmonary disease, and osteoporosis (Boyd et al. 2005, 717). The analysts found that single-disease clinical practice guidelines "do not provide an appropriate, evidence-based foundation for assessing quality of care in older adults with several chronic diseases" (Boyd et al. 2005, 720). Moreover, utilizing these clinical practice guidelines to assess the care of these complex cases could lead to inaccurate judgments regarding the quality of care provided, erroneous calculations of rewards, and, potentially, creation of disincentives to treating these patients (Boyd et al. 2005, 722).

Operations of pay-for-performance systems depend upon the reliable and timely measurement of the quality of care (Bell and Levinson 2007, 1718). Internal organizational systems of data collection need to be in place, such as clinical data capture, administrative databases, provider surveys, patient surveys, and longitudinal claims data. This measurement would be greatly enhanced by an infrastructure of health information technology, such as electronic health records and data warehouses. However, electronic health records and other health information technologies are not widely utilized in the U.S. healthcare system. This impediment to measurement presents a challenge to successful implementation of P4P.

Centers for Medicare and Medicaid Services—Linking Quality to Reimbursement

The Centers for Medicare and Medicaid Services has articulated their vision for healthcare quality—the right care for every person every time (CMS 2007b, 3). From this vision and with the support of various laws, CMS has made significant strides to link quality to reimbursement. The Medicare Modernization Act of 2003 established the framework for CMS to meld together quality and reimbursement. The MMA established the Reporting of Hospital Quality Data for Annual Payment Update (RHQDAPU) program. The move to a pay for performance (P4P) component within IPPS, and other medical settings, was further strengthened by the Deficit Reduction Act of 2005 when a call for a Value Based Purchasing (VBP) program was signed into law. It appears that P4P within CMS PPS is inevitable as positive results from various demonstration projects have been recorded.

Although quality may have improved, at what cost must surely be addressed. Discussed in this section are the most recent CMS P4P initiatives and the acute care P4P demonstration project.

Reporting of Hospital Quality Data for Annual Payment Update (RHQDAPU)

Formerly named the National Hospital Reporting Initiative (NVHRI), the RHQDAPU is a quality-based pay-for-performance program of CMS. Introduced in section 501(b) of the MMA, this program requires that hospitals report quality information for established quality measures. When implemented, failure to submit quality data results in that facility's standardized amount to be reduced by .4 percent. Therefore, if a facility did not report quality data in FY 2006 (2005 hospital data) the market basket adjustment would decrease from 3.7% to 3.3%. When implemented in FY 2006, hospitals were instructed to report on ten quality measures:

Heart Attack (5)

- Was aspirin given to the patient upon arrival to the hospital?

- Was aspirin prescribed when the patient was discharged?

- Was a beta-blocker given to the patient upon arrival to the hospital?

- Was a beta-blocker prescribed when the patient was discharged?

- Was an ACE inhibitor given for the patient with heart failure?

Heart Failure (2)

- Did the patient get an assessment of his or her heart function?

- Was an Ace inhibitor given to the patient?

Pneumonia (3)

- Was an antibiotic given to the patient in a timely way?

- Had a patient received a pneumococcal vaccination?

- Was the patient's oxygen level assessed?

While the MMA created the requirement for hospitals to report quality information, the Deficit Reduction Act (DRA) expanded it. DRA changed the penalty for noncompliance from .4 percent reduction to the payment update to 2 percent for FY 2007 and years thereafter. The standardized amount reduction applies only with respect to the fiscal year involved, and will not be taken into account for computing the applicable percentage increase for a subsequent fiscal year. Additionally, the DRA requires that the quality reporting measures be expanded beginning in 2007.

The DRA provides the Secretary of Health and Human Services with the discretion to replace any quality measures, requires that CMS establish procedures for making quality data available to the public after ensuring that a hospital has the opportunity to review, in advance, its data, and requires that quality measures of process, structure, outcome, patients' perspective on care, efficiency and costs of care are reported on the CMS Web site.

For FY 2007, facilities continued to report the original ten quality measures for remainder of 2005 data. Starting with CY 2006 **third quarter** data, the reporting requirements expanded to include twenty-one measures.

Expanded Measures

Heart Attack (Acute Myocardial Infarction)

- Aspirin at arrival

- Aspirin prescribed at discharge

- ACE inhibitor (ACE-I) or Angiotensin Receptor Blocker (ARBs) for left ventricular systolic dysfunction

- Beta blocker at arrival

- Beta blocker prescribed at discharge

- Thrombolytic agent received within 30 minutes of hospital arrival

- Percutaneous coronary intervention (PCI) received within 120 minutes of hospital arrival

- Adult smoking cessation advice/counseling

Heart Failure (HF)

- Left ventricular function assessment

- ACE inhibitor (ACE-I) or Angiotensin Receptor Blocker (ARBs) for left ventricular systolic dysfunction

- Discharge instructions

- Adult smoking cessation advice/counseling

Pneumonia (PNE)

- Initial antibiotic received within 4 hours of hospital arrival

- Oxygenation assessment

- Pneumococcal vaccination status

- Blood culture performed before first antibiotic received in hospital

- Adult smoking cessation advice/counseling

- Appropriate initial antibiotic selection

- Influenza vaccination status

Surgical Care Infection Prevention (SCIP)

- Prophylactic antibiotic received within 1 hour prior to surgical incision

- Prophylactic antibiotics discontinued within 24 hours after surgery end time

Once again in FY 2008, CMS expanded the quality measures and included a 30-day mortality rate for pneumonia in Medicare patients. Other measures were proposed but had not yet been adopted by the National Quality Forum (NQF) and therefore, were not adopted by CMS. Measurement specifications for each of the measures and the supporting evidence basis for each measure can be found in the *Specifications Manual for National Hospital Quality Measures* at www.qualitynet.org. This is a joint manual maintained by CMS and the Joint Commision. Under this program, quality data is reported for both Medicare and nonMedicare patients. Submitted data must pass the validation requirement of a minimum of 80 percent reliability. CMS uses a two-step process, which includes a chart review. Facilities have been instructed to submit data through the QualityNet Exchange secure website at www.qnetexchange.org. Data populates the Hospital Compare Web site, www.hospitalcompare.hhs.gov.

In addition to expanding the quality measures, CMS implemented the HCAHPS® (Hospital Consumer Assessment of Healthcare Providers and Systems) patient survey for FY 2007 (Oct. 1, 2006). HCAHPS® is designed to make apples-to-apples comparisons of patients' perspectives on hospital care including communications with doctors, communications with nurses, responsiveness of hospital staff, cleanliness and quietness of the hospital, pain control, communication about medicines, and discharge information. CMS expects to report the first three quarters of survey data in late 2007.

Expansion to Outpatient Areas

Section 109(a) and (b) of the Tax Relief and Health Care Act of 2006 (MIEA-TRHCA) extended the financial ramification and requirement of reporting quality results to the hospital outpatient and ambulatory surgical centers areas. This law established the Hospital Outpatient Quality Data Reporting Program (HOP QDRP) for hospital outpatient departments.

CMS had originally proposed that the outpatient measures mirror the inpatient measures for this new provision of HOP QDRP. However, this was met with great opposition from the healthcare community. Therefore, CMS stated that outpatient-specific measures would be created and implemented for the outpatient area. In the 2008 final rule for OPPS/ASCs, the following seven quality measures were finalized:

- ED-AMI-1-Aspirin at arrival
- ED-AMI-2-Median time to fibrinolysis
- ED-AMI-3-Fibrinolytic therapy received within 30 minutes of arrival
- ED-AMI-4-Median time to electro-cardiogram (ECG)
- ED-AMI-5-Median time to transfer for Primary PCI
- PQRI #20—Perioperative care: timing of antibiotic prophylaxis
- PQRI #21—Perioperative care: selection of prophylactic antibiotic

Therefore, outpatient facilities will be required to report quality data on outpatient-specific measures beginning with services provided in April, 2008. Hospitals must meet administrative requirements and data collection and submission requirements under the HOP QDRP. Facilities that do not meet these requirements or those that choose not to participate in the quality program will receive a 2 percent reduction in their HOPPS rate for CY 2009. Validation requirements will effect 2 percent reduction starting in CY 2010.

Although section 109(b) of MIEA-TRHCA established the requirement of reporting quality data for the ambulatory surgical center setting, rulemaking for this has been delayed. In CY 2008, ASCs are moving to an APC-based reimbursement system. Therefore, CMS is delaying the implementation of the quality reporting requirement so that ASCs can become familiar with a new payment system during CY 2008.

Hospital-Acquired Conditions

Section 5001(c) of Pub.L. 109-171 of the Deficit Reduction Act (DRA) requires the Secretary to implement the Hospital-Acquired Conditions provision to IPPS. This additional component of pay for performance utilizes reported ICD-9-CM diagnosis codes and the present-on-admission (POA) indicator to identify quality issues. The Secretary must identify, by October 1, 2007 (FY 2008) at least two conditions that are:

- High cost or high volume or both
- Result in the assignment of a case to a DRG that has a higher payment when present as a secondary diagnosis
- Could reasonably have been prevented through the application of evidence-based guidelines

For discharges occurring on or after October 1, 2008 (FY 2009), the DRA mandates that CMS perform a quality adjustment to the MS-DRG payment for certain conditions that were not present on hospital admission, but were acquired during the hospital stay. Hospitals will not receive the higher weighted MS-DRG payment for cases in which one of the selected conditions was not present on admission, but was acquired after admission and during the hospital encounter. That is, the case would be paid as though that secondary diagnosis was not present. CMS may revise the list, but two conditions must be present on the list at all times. Section 5001(c) also requires hospitals to submit a POA indicator for reportable diagnoses on the UB-04 (there is a list of excluded ICD-9-CM codes) when reporting payment information for discharges on or after October 1,

2007 (FY 2008). Therefore, hospitals have one year to implement and tighten their POA procedures prior to reimbursement impact taking place.

In the FY 2008 IPPS final rule, CMS finalized the conditions that will be included in the hospital-acquired conditions provision that is set for implementation in FY 2009 (discharges occurring on or after October 1, 2008). CMS has selected eight conditions/categories for implementation.

The eight conditions/categories are:

1. Catheter-associated urinary tract infections
2. Pressure ulcers
3. Serious preventable event—Object left in surgery
4. Serious preventable event—Air embolism
5. Serious preventable event—Blood incompatibility
6. Vascular catheter-associated infections
7. Mediastinitis after coronary artery bypass graft (CABG)
8. Falls and fractures, dislocations, intracranial injury, crushing injury and burns

Several other conditions under consideration for inclusion into the hospital-acquired conditions provision for FY 2009. The conditions are:

1. Staphylococcus aureus septicemia
2. Deep vein thrombosis (DVT)/pulmonary embolism (PE)
3. Ventilator associated pneumonia (VAP) and other types of pneumonia

Conditions under further consideration for future years are:

1. Clostridium difficile-associated disease (CDAD)

2. Methicillin-resistant Staphylococcus aureus (MRSA)

3. Wrong surgery performed on wrong body part, wrong patient, or the wrong surgery

The Hospital-Acquired Conditions provision will only apply when the selected conditions are the only MCC or CC present on the claim. Therefore, if a nonselected MCC or CC is not the claim, the case will continue to be assigned to the higher paying MCC or CC DRG, and there will be no saving to Medicare from the case. This provision will apply in a small minority of cases because it is rare that one of the selected conditions would be the only MCC or CC present on the claim.

Value-Based Purchasing

The DRA requires the implementation of a value-based purchasing (VBP) plan for IPPS beginning with FY 2009 (October 1, 2008–September 30, 2009). CMS has established value-based purchasing demonstration projects for the acute care setting, physician services, nursing homes, home health arena, and dialysis centers. (See www.cms.hhs.gov/ DemoProjectsEvalRpts/MD/list.asp#TopOfPage for information on the active CMS demonstration projects). The DRA also requires CMS to develop a plan for implementation. As established by Congress, the plan must consider the following issues:

- The ongoing development, selection, and modification process for measures of quality and efficiency in hospital inpatient settings

- The reporting, collection, and validation of quality data

- The structure of payment adjustments, including the determination of thresholds of improvements in quality that would substantiate a payment adjustment, the size of such payments, and the sources of funding for the payments

- The disclosure of information on hospital performance (CMS 2007b, 2).

CMS created the Hospital Pay for Performance Workgroup to prepare plan options, create a draft plan, and finalize the CMS VBP plan. As stated in the *Medicare Hospital Value-Based Purchasing Plan Issues Paper,* it expected that CMS will adhere to the following guiding principles in establishing the Medicare Hospital VBP program:

- The VBP program will be budget neutral

- The VBP program will build on the existing Medicare performance measurement and reporting infrastructure, specifically the components for the RHQDAPU

- The VBP performance measures will apply to a broad range of care delivered in the acute care setting and will address clinical quality, patient-centered care, and efficiency

- CMS will continue to work collaboratively with the Hospital Quality Alliance (HQA), National Quality Forum (NQF), and the Joint Commission

- The design of the VBP program will avoid creating additional disparities in healthcare and to reduce existing disparities.

- CMS will develop and implement ongoing evaluation process to assess impact, examine the utility of the measures and monitor unintended consequences of the program (CMS 2007b, 4–6).

While the CMS workgroup frames and builds the VBP program, several demonstration projects are in progress. Discussed in the next section is the VBP demonstration project for IPPS services.

Premier Hospital Quality Incentive Demonstration (HQID)

The Premier Hospital Quality Incentive Demonstration provides financial rewards to those facilities which demonstrate high quality of care in established clinical areas (CMS 2007a, 1). The goal of the demonstration is to identify if providing financial incentives for quality improvements does in fact result in significant advancement in the quality of inpatient care. Starting on October 1, 2003, over 260 Premier hospitals are participating in this demonstration project. Recently, the demonstration project was extended, and will continue on through fiscal year 2009 (six year demonstration project (FYs 2004–2009).

The participating facilities provide data on thirty quality measures related to five clinical conditions. The clinical conditions are:

- Heart attack

- Heart failure

- Pneumonia

- Coronary artery bypass graft

- Hip and knee replacements

As part of this demonstration project, CMS identifies hospitals with the highest quality performance in each of the five clinical areas. Hospitals scoring in the top 10 percent in each clinical area receive a 2 percent bonus payment in addition to the regular Medicare DRG (as of FY 2008 MS-DRG) payment for the measured condition. Hospitals in the second highest 10 percent receive a 1 percent bonus payment. In the third year of the demonstration, hospitals that do not achieve absolute improvements above the demonstration's first year composite score baseline (the lowest 20 percent) for that condition will have their DRG payments reduced by 1 or 2 percent, depending on how far their performance is below the baseline.

The results of years one and two have been published by Premier via white papers which are available at www.premierinc.com/qualitydemo. During the first year of the demonstration project, CMS awarded 8.85 million in bonus payments. In aggregate, quality of care improved in all five clinical areas. This preliminary data suggested that P4P programs do have the ability to influence increased efforts in quality of care areas. During the second year, CMS provided $8,690,477 in incentive payments to 115 top-performing hospitals (CMS 2007a, 5). Table 9.3 provides quality improvement figures from year two of the demonstration project. Clearly, the participating hospitals are providing a higher level of quality care. As results are provided for years 3–6, CMS will continue to utilize this valuable data to establish and enhance their VBP program.

Summary

Pay-for-performance (P4P) systems link financial rewards and the provision of healthcare. The landmark report, *Crossing the Quality Chasm* (CQHA 2001), is a key reason for the realignment of payment incentives and quality in the healthcare deliv-

Table 9.3.   Composite quality scores for Premier HQID years one and two

Clinical Area	Year One	Year Two
Acute myocardial infarction	87.5%	94.4%
Heart failure	64.5%	82.4%
Community-acquired pneumonia	69.3%	85.8%
Coronary artery bypass graft	84.8%	93.8%
Hip and knee replacement	84.6%	93.4%

CMS/Premier Hospital. 2007a. *Quality Incentive Demonstration Project White Paper.* Second year. 5.

ery system. The Centers for Medicare and Medicaid Services and other large purchasers of healthcare are driving the change. Key considerations in the design of models of P4P systems are recipient of the incentive and mechanism of payment. Operational considerations include a focus on significant problems and on issues affecting many enrollees or providers, the use of valid and reliable performance measures, the characteristics of the incentives, the organizational infrastructure, the culture of quality, and effective leadership.

Check Your Understanding 9.2

1. What is the ramification for hospitals that do not participate or do not submit sufficient data under the Reporting of Hospital Quality Data for Annual Payment Update (RHQDAPU) program?

2. The same quality indicators are utilized under RHQDAPU and HOP QDRP. True or False?

3. What criteria must be met for the Secretary of Health and Human Services to include a condition on the Hospital-Acquired Conditions provision list?

4. What are four of the eight categories initially monitored for the Hospital-Acquired Condition provision of IPPS?

5. What piece of legislation mandated CMS to develop a value-based purchasing program?

6. What hospital alliance is participating in the CMS VBP demonstration project for inpatient hospital services? How many hospitals are participating in the demonstration project?

Review Quiz

1. What three components do pay-for-performance systems typically link?

2. Why did pay-for-performance systems emerge?

3. What incentives are typically aligned in pay-for-performance systems?

4. The very first pay-for-performance systems emerged in the early 1990s. True or False?

5. The Centers for Medicare and Medicaid Services has attempted to "brake" the trend of pay-for-performance systems because experts believe the linkage of quality with reward will jeopardize the care of patients. True or False?

6. List three other countries investigating pay-for-performance systems for their healthcare delivery systems.

7. Withholding compensation would be considered a penalty-based model of pay-for-performance. True or False?

References

Anonymous. 2005, April. Changing the dial on quality: What will pay-for-performance reimbursement strategies mean for providing better care? *Quality Letter for Healthcare Leaders* 17(4):2–8.

Baker, C., and B. Carter. 2005, First Quarter. *Provider Pay-for-Performance Incentive Programs: 2004 National Study Results.* San Francisco, CA: Med-Vantage. Available online from http://www.medvantageinc.com/Pdf/mv_2004_P4P_National_Study_Results-Exec_Summary.pdf. Accessed on 17 October 2007.

Bell, C.M., and W. Levinson. 2007, June 5. Pay for performance: Learning about quality. *Canadian Medical Association Journal* 176(12):1717–1719.

Boyd, C.M., J. Darer, C. Boult, L.P. Fried, L. Boult, and A.W. Wu. 2005, August 10. Clinical practice guidelines and quality of care for older patients with multiple comorbid diseases. *Journal of the American Medical Association* 294(6):716–724.

Campbell, S., D. Reeves, E. Kontopantelis, E. Middleton, B. Sibbald, and M. Roland. 2007, July 12. Quality of care in England with the introduction of pay for performance. *New England Journal of Medicine* 357(2):181–190.

Campbell, S., A. Steiner, J. Robison, D. Webb, A. Raven, S. Richards, and M. Roland. 2005, January. Do personal medical services contracts improve quality of care? A multi-method evaluation. *Journal of Health Services Research and Policy* 10(1):31–39.

Casalino, L.P., G.C. Alexander, L. Jin, and R.T. Konetzka. 2007, March-April. General internists' views on pay-for-performance and public reporting of quality scores: A national survey. *Health Affairs* 26(2):492–499.

Centers for Medicare & Medicaid Services. 2007a. *Fact Sheet: Premier Hospital Quality Incentive Demonstration (HQID) Extension.* Available online from www.cms.hhs.gov.

Center for Medicare & Medicaid Services (CMS). 2007b. *Medicare Hospital Value-Based Purchasing Plan Issues Paper.* Available online from www.cms.hhs.gov.

Centers for Medicare & Medicaid Services. 2007. *Premier Hospital Quality Incentive Demonstration Fact Sheet.* Available online from www.cms.hhs.gov.

Centers for Medicare & Medicaid Services (CMS) / Premier Hospital. 2007a. *Quality Incentive Demonstration Project White Paper, Second Year.* Available online from www.premierinc.com/quality-safety.

Committee on Quality of Health Care in America of the Institute of Medicine. 2001. *Crossing the Quality Chasm: A New Health System for the 21st Century.* Washington, DC: National Academy Press.

Damberg C.L., K. Raube, T. Williams, and S.M. Shortell. 2005, April–June. Paying for performance: Implementing a statewide project in California. *Quality Management in Health Care* 14(2):66–79.

Department of Health and Human Services. 2006 (November 24) Medicare Program; Revisions to Hospital Outpatient Prospective Payment System and Calendar Year 2007 Payment Rates; Final Rule. *Federal Register* Vol. 71 No. 226 pages 67960–68401

Department of Health and Human Services. 2007 (August 2) Medicare Program; Proposed Changes to Hospital Outpatient Prospective Payment System and Calendar Year 2008 Payment Rates; Proposed Rule. *Federal Register* Vol. 72 No. 448 page 42801

Department of Health and Human Services. 2007 (August 22) Medicare Program; Revisions to Inpatient Prospective Payment System and Fiscal Year 2008 Payment Rates; Final Rule. *Federal Register* Vol. 72 No. 162 pages 47130–48175

Department of Health and Human Services. 2007 (November 27) Medicare Program; Medicare and Medicaid Programs; Interim and Final Rule. *Federal Register* Vol. 72 No. 227 pages 66860–66876.

Dudley, R.A. 2005, October 12. Pay-for-performance research: How to learn what clinicians and policy makers need to know. *Journal of the American Medical Association* 294(14):1821–1823.

Dudley, R.A., A. Frolich, D.L. Robinowitz, J.A. Talavera, P. Broadhead, and H.S. Luft. 2004, July. *Strategies To Support Quality-based Purchasing: A Review of the Evidence.* Technical Review 10. (Prepared by the Stanford-University of California San Francisco Evidence-based Practice Center under Contract No. 290-02-0017). AHRQ Publication No. 04-0057. Rockville, MD: Agency for Healthcare Research and Quality. Available online from http://www.ncbi.nlm.nih.gov/books/bv.fcgi?rid=hstat2.chapter.11920 Accessed on 17 October 2007.

Dudley, R.A., and M.B. Rosenthal. 2006, April. *Pay for Performance: A Decision Guide for Purchasers.* AHRQ Publication No. 06-0047. Rockville, MD: Agency for Healthcare Research and Quality. Available online from http://www.ahrq.gov/qual/p4pguide.pdf. Accessed on 16 October 2007.

Glickman, S.W, Fang-Shu, O., DeLong, E.R, et al. 2007, June 6. Pay for performance, quality of care, and outcomes in acute myocardial infarction. *Journal of the American Medical Association* 297(21):2373–2380.

Goldfield, N., R. Burford, R. Averill, B. Boissonnault, W. Kelly, T. Kravis, and N. Smithline. 2005, January–March. Pay for performance: An excellent idea that simply needs implementation. *Quality Management in Health Care* 14(1):42–44.

Hickson, G.B., W.A. Altemeier, and J.M. Perrin. 1987, September. Physician reimbursement by salary or fee-for-service: Effect on physician practice behavior in a randomized prospective study. *Pediatrics* 80(3):344–350.

Leapfrog Group. 2006, December 13. *Factsheet: The Leapfrog Hospital Rewards Program.* Available online from https://leapfrog.medstat.com/rewards/tools/FactSheet.pdf. Accessed on 17 October 2007.

Leapfrog Group and Thomson Medstat. 2007, January 13. *Welcome.* Available online from https://leapfrog.medstat.com/rewards/. Accessed on 17 October 2007.

Lindenauer, P.K., D. Remus, S. Roman, M.B. Rothberg, E.M. Benjamin, A. Ma, and D.W. Bratzler. 2007, February 1. Public reporting and pay for performance in hospital quality improvement. *New England Journal of Medicine* 356(5):486–496.

Millenson, M.L. 2004, October. Pay for performance: The best worst choice. *Quality and Safety in Health Care* 13(5):323–324.

Pham, H.H., D. Schrage, A.S. O'Malley, B. Wu, and P.B. Bach. 2007, March 15. Care patterns in Medicare and their implications for pay for performance. *New England Journal of Medicine* 356(11):1130–1139.

Premier Inc. 2007. Overview of CMS Hospital Quality Incentive Demonstration Project, Available online from http://www.premierinc.com/quality-safety/tools-services/p4p/hqi.

Robert Wood Johnson Foundation. 2005, November 15. *Pay for Performance Improving Health Care Quality and Changing Provider Behavior; but Challenges Persist.* Available online from http://www.rwjf.org/newsroom/newsreleasesdetail.jsp?productid=21847. Accessed on 17 October 2007.

Rosenthal, M.B., and R.A. Dudley. 2007, February 21. Pay-for-performance: Will the latest payment trend improve care? *Journal of the American Medical Association* 297(7): 740–744.

Rosenthal, M.B., R. G. Frank, Z. Li, and A.M. Epstein. 2005, October 12. Early experience with pay-for-performance: From concept to practice. *Journal of the American Medical Association* 294(14):1788–1793.

Rosenthal, M.B., B.E. Landon, S-L.T. Normand, R.G. Frank, A.M. Epstein. 2006, November 2. Pay for performance in commercial HMOs. *New England Journal of Medicine* 355(18):1895–1902.

Roski, J., R. Jeddeloh, L. An, H. Lando, P. Hannan, C. Hall, and S-H. Zhu. 2003, March. The impact of financial incentives and a patient registry on preventive care quality: Increasing provider adherence to evidence-based smoking cessation guidelines. *Preventive Medicine* 36(3):291–299.

Tabak, Y.P., R.S. Johannes, and J.H. Silber. 2007, August. Using automated clinical data for risk adjustment: Development and validation of six disease-specific mortality predictive models for pay-for-performance. *Medical Care* 45(8):789–805.

Williams, J. 2006. Making the Grade with Pay for Performance; Lessons from Best-Performing Hospitals, *Healthcare Financial Management*, December 2006, p 78–85.

Appendix A
Glossary

Abuse: Unknowing or unintentional submission of an inaccurate claim for payment.

Accounts receivable: Department in a healthcare facility that manages the amounts owed to the facility by customers who have received services but whose payment is made at a later date.

Actual charge: Amount provider actually bills a patient, which may differ from the allowable charge.

Adjacent episodes of care: Episodes of home health that are contiguous and separated by no more than 60 days.

Adverse selection: Enrollment of excessive proportion of persons with poor health status in a healthcare plan or healthcare organization

AHA *Coding Clinic for HCPCS*:   Official coding guidance for HCPCS Level II procedure, service, and supply codes.

AHIMA Standards of Ethical Coding: Standards developed by the Council on Coding and Classification of the American Health Information Management Association to give health information coding professionals ethical guidelines for performing their coding and grouping tasks.

Allowable charge: Average or maximum amount the third party payer will reimburse providers for the service.

Allowable fee: *See* Allowable charge.

Ambulatory payment classification (APC):   Hospital outpatient prospective payment system (HOPPS). The classification is a resource-based reimbursement system. The payment unit is the ambulatory payment classification group (APC group).

Ambulatory payment classification group (APC group):   Basic unit of the ambulatory payment classification (APC) system. Within a group, the diagnoses and procedures are similar in terms of resources used, complexity of illness, and conditions represented. A single payment is made for the outpatient services provided. APC groups are based on HCPCS/CPT codes. A single visit can result in multiple APC groups. APC groups consist of five types of service: significant procedures, surgical services, medical visits, ancillary services, and partial hospitalization. The APC group was formerly known as ambulatory visit group (AVG) and ambulatory patient group (APG).

Ambulatory surgery center (ASC):   Free-standing, outpatient facility in which outpatient surgeries are performed.

Ambulatory surgery center (ASC) payment group: Payment made to an ambulatory surgery center (ASC) for facility-related costs. A fixed payment rate for procedures designated to be ASC procedures. ASC procedures are classified into nine payment groups. A fixed payment rate is designated for each group. The ASC facility payment in each group is a single rate adjusted for geographic variation. This prospectively determined rate covers the cost of standard overhead items (nursing care, supplies, equipment, and use of facility). It does not include physicians' fees and some other medical items and services (such as prostheses).

Ambulatory surgery center list (ASC list): Procedures that Medicare will cover when they are performed in the ambulatory setting.

Ancillary services: Professional healthcare services such as radiology, laboratory, or physical therapy.

Appeal: Request for reconsideration of denial of coverage or rejection of claim.

Arithmetic mean length of stay (AMLOS): Sum of all lengths of stay in a set of cases divided by the number of cases. The national average number of days patients within a given diagnosis related group (DRG) are hospitalized.

Average length of stay (ALOS): Average number of days patients are hospitalized. Statistic is calculated by dividing the total number of hospital bed days in a certain period by the admissions or discharges during the same period.

Bad debt: Services for which healthcare organizations expected, but did not receive, payment.

Balanced Budget Act of 1997 (BBA): Legislation that effected several aspects of the healthcare industry including the hospital outpatient prospective payment system (HOPPS), fraud and abuse, and programs of all-inclusive care for elderly (PACE).

Base (payment) rate: Rate per discharge for operating and capital-related components for an acute care hospital.

Base year: Cost reporting period upon which a rate is based.

Benchmarking: The process of comparing performance to a preestablished standard or performance of another facility or group.

Beneficiary: An individual who is eligible for benefits from a health plan.

Benefit: Healthcare service for which the healthcare insurance company will pay. *See also* Covered service.

Benefit cap: Total dollar amount that a healthcare insurance company will pay for covered healthcare services during a specified period, such as a year or lifetime.

Block grant: Fixed amount of money given or allocated for a specific purpose, such as a transfer of governmental funds to cover health services.

Budget neutrality: Adjusting payment rates so total expenditures are equal to specified past periods, often mandated under federal acts and regulations.

Budget neutrality adjustor (BN adjustor): Percentage, weight, proportion, or other mechanism that alters payment in order to maintain budget neutrality.

Bundling: Combination of supply and pharmaceutical costs or medical visits with associated procedures or services for one lump sum payment.

Calendar year (CY): Twelve-month period (year) that begins January 1 and ends December 31.

Capitation: Method of payment for health services in which an individual or institutional provider is paid a fixed, per capita amount for each person enrolled without regard to the actual number or nature of services provided or number of persons served.

Carrier: Entity that has a contract with the Centers for Medicare and Medicaid Services (CMS) to determine and make Medicare payments for Part B benefits.

Carve out: Contracts that separate out services or populations of patients or clients to decrease risk and costs

Case: Patient, resident, or client with a given condition or disease.

Case management: Coordination of individuals' care over time and across multiple sites and providers, especially in complex and high-cost cases. Goals include continuity of care, cost-effectiveness, quality, and appropriate utilization.

Case mix: Set of categories of patients (type and volume) treated by a healthcare organization and representing the complexity of the organization's case load.

Case-mix diagnoses: Diagnoses in the home health prospective payment system that feed into the home health case-mix grouper.

Case-mix group (CMG):   Class of functionally similar discharges in the inpatient rehabilitation facility prospective payment system (IRF PPS). Basis of similarity is impairment, functional capability, age, and comorbidities.

Case-mix index (CMI):   Single number that compares the overall complexity of the healthcare organization's patients to the complexity of the average of all hospitals. Typically, the CMI is for a specific period and is derived from the sum of all diagnosis related group (DRG) weights, divided by the number of Medicare cases.

Case-based payment: Type of prospective payment method in which the third party payer reimburses the provider a fixed, preestablished payment for each case.

Catastrophic expense limit: Specific amount, in a certain time frame such as one year, beyond which all covered healthcare services for that policyholder or dependent are paid at 100 percent by the healthcare insurance plan. (*See also* Maximum out-of-pocket cost and Stop-loss benefit.)

Centers for Medicare and Medicaid Services (CMS):   A division of the Department of Health and Human Services (DHHS) that is responsible for administering the Medicare program and the federal portion of the Medicaid program; responsible for maintaining the procedure portion of the International Classification of Diseases, 9th revision, Clinical Modification (ICD-9-CM). Prior to 2001 was named the Health Care Financing Administration (HCFA).

Certificate holder: Member of a group for which the employer or association has purchased group healthcare insurance. *See also* Insured, Member, Policyholder, *and* Subscriber.

Charge: Price assigned to a unit of medical or health service, such as a visit to a physician or a day in a hospital. The charge for a service may be unrelated to the actual cost of providing the service. *See also* Fee.

Charge capture: The process of collecting all services, procedures, and supplies provided during patient care.

Charge description master: Database used by healthcare facilities to house the price list for all services provided to patients.

Charity care: Services for which healthcare organizations did not expect payment because they had previously determined the patients' or clients' inability to pay.

Cherry picking: Targeting the enrollment of healthy patients to minimize healthcare costs.

Civilian Health and Medical Program: Veterans Administration (CHAMPVA):   A benefits program administered by the Department of Veterans Affairs for the spouse or widow(er) and for the children of a veteran who meets specified criteria.

Claim: Request for payment, or itemized statement of healthcare services and their costs provided by a hospital, physician's office, or other healthcare provider. Claims are submitted for reimbursement to the healthcare insurance plan by either the policy or certificate holder or the provider. Also called bills for Medicare Part A and Part B services billed through fiscal intermediaries and for Part B physician or supplier services billed through carriers.

Clean claim: Request for payment that contains only accurate information (no errors in data).

Clinical risk group (CRG): Capitated, prospective payment system that predicts future healthcare expenditures for populations.

Closed panel: Type of health maintenance organization that provides hospitalization and physicians' services through its own staff and facilities (also known as staff model or group model).

Code range: Applicable set of diagnosis or procedure codes.

Coding Clinic for ICD-9-CM: Official coding guidance for the International Classification of Diseases, 9th revision, Clinical Modification (ICD-9-CM) diagnosis and procedure codes.

Coding compliance plan: A component of an HIM compliance plan or a corporate compliance plan that focuses on the unique regulations and guidelines with which coding professionals must comply.

Cognitive: Related to mental abilities, such as talking, memory, and problem solving.

Coinsurance: Cost-sharing in which the policy or certificate holder pays a preestablished percentage of eligible expenses after the deductible has been met. The percentage may vary by type or site of service.

Community (-based premium) rating: Method of determining healthcare premium rates by geographic area (community) rather than by age, health status, or company size. This method increases the size of the risk pool. Costs are increased to younger, healthier individuals who are, in effect, subsidizing older or less healthy individuals.

Comorbidity: Preexisting condition that, because of its presence with a specific diagnosis, causes an increase in length of stay by at least one day in approximately 75 percent of the cases (as in complication and comorbidity [CC]).

Compliance: Managing a coding or billing department according to the laws, regulations, and guidelines that govern it.

Compliance officer: Designated individual who monitors the compliance process at a healthcare facility.

Compliance program guidance: Information provided by the Office of Inspector General (OIG) of the Department of Health and Human Services (DHHS) to assist healthcare organizations with the development of compliance plans and programs.

Complication: Condition that arises during the hospital stay that prolongs the length of stay at least one day in approximately 75 percent of the cases (as in complication and comorbidity [CC)]).

Consumer-directed (driven) healthcare plan (CDHP): Managed care organization characterized by influencing patients and clients to select cost-efficient healthcare through the provision of information about health benefit packages and through financial incentives.

Contracted discount rate: Type of fee-for-service reimbursement in which the third party payer has negotiated a reduced (discounted) fee for its covered insureds. *See also* Discounted fee-for-service.

Conversion factor (CF): National dollar multiplier which sets the allowance for the relative values; a constant.

Coordination of benefits (COB): Method of integrating benefits payments from all health insurance sources to ensure that payments do not exceed 100 percent of the covered healthcare expenses.

Copayment: Cost-sharing measure in which the policy or certificate holder pays a fixed dollar amount (flat fee) per service, supply, or procedure that is owed to the healthcare facility by the patient. The fixed amount that the policyholder pays may vary by type of service, such as $20.00 per prescription or $15.00 per physician office visit.

Core-based statistical area (CSBA): Statistical geographic entity consisting of the county or counties associated with at least one core (urbanized area or urban cluster) of at least 10,000 population, plus adjacent counties having a high degree of social and economic integration with the core as measured through commuting ties with the counties containing the core. Metropolitan and micropolitan statistical areas are two components of CBSAs.

Cost-of-living adjustment (COLA): Alteration that reflects a change in the consumer price index (CPI), which measures purchasing power between time periods. The CPI is based on a market basket of goods and services that a typical consumer buys.

Cost report: Report required from providers on an annual basis in order for the Medicare program to make a proper determination of amounts payable to providers under its provisions.

Cost-sharing: Provision of a healthcare insurance policy that requires policyholders to pay for a portion of their healthcare services; a cost-control mechanism.

Covered condition: Health condition, illness, injury, disease, or symptom for which the healthcare insurance company will pay.

Covered service (expense): Specific service for which a healthcare insurance company will pay. *See also* Benefit.

Customary, prevailing, and reasonable (CPR): Type of retrospective fee-for-service payment method in which the third party payer pays for fees that are customary, prevailing, and reasonable.

CPT Assistant: Official coding guidance for CPT codes.

Creditable coverage: Prior health care coverage that is taken into account to determine the allowable length of preexisting condition exclusion periods (for individuals entering group health plan coverage). Includes healthcare insurance through a group health plan or health maintenance organization (HMO), federal employees health benefits program, military healthcare plan (TRICARE), Indian Health Service (IHS), state high risk pools, Medicare, Medicaid, coverage under the Consolidated Omnibus Budget Reconciliation Act (COBRA), or other public health plan. Excluded from creditable coverage are accidental death and dismemberment plan, automobile medical payment insurance, disability insurance, and workers' compensation.

Credited coverage: Reduction of waiting period for preexisting condition based on previous creditable coverage. Credited coverage may be calculated on a day-by-day basis or other method that is at least as favorable to the individual. To receive credit for previous creditable coverage, the lapse (break) in coverage cannot exceed 63 days.

Critical access hospital (CAH): Small facility that gives limited outpatient and inpatient hospital services to people in rural areas.

Critical care services: Evaluation and management of critically ill or critically injured patients.

Current Procedural Terminology (CPT): Coding system created and maintained by the American Medical Association that is used to report diagnostic and surgical services and procedures.

Current Procedural Terminology (CPT) Category I Code: A CPT code that represents a procedure or service that is consistent with contemporary medical practice and is performed by many physicians in clinical practice in multiple locations.

Current Procedural Terminology (CPT) Category II Code: A CPT code that represents services and/or test results that contribute to positive health outcomes and quality patient care.

Current Procedural Terminology (CPT) Category III Code: A CPT code that represents emerging technologies for which a Category I Code has yet to be established.

Deductible: Annual amount of money that the policyholder must incur (and pay) before the health insurance will assume liability for the remaining charges or covered expenses.

Defensive medicine: Medical tests, visits, and procedures to avert or prevent medical litigation, to reduce medical liability, and to avoid claims of malpractice. Defensive medicine is associated with increased costs of healthcare that do not benefit patients or clients.

Dependent: An insured's spouse and unmarried children, claimed on income tax. The maximum age of dependent children varies by policy. A common ceiling is 19 years of age, with continuation to age 23 provided the child is a full-time student at an accredited school, primarily dependent upon the covered employee for support and maintenance, and is unmarried. Some healthcare insurance polices also allow same sex domestic partners to be listed as dependents.

Diagnosis related group (DRG): Inpatient classification that categorizes patients who are similar in terms of diagnoses and treatments, age, resources used, and lengths of stay. Under the prospective payment system (PPS), hospitals are paid a set fee for treating patients in a single DRG category, regardless of the actual cost of care for the individual.

Discounted fee-for-service: Type of fee-for-service reimbursement in which the third party payer has negotiated a reduced ("discounted") fee for its covered insureds. *See also* Contracted discount rate.

Discounting: Reducing the payment in the hospital outpatient prospective payment system (HOPPS) (payment status indicator = T). In the CMS's discounting schedule, Medicare will pay 100 percent of the Medicare allowance for the principle procedure (exclusive of deductible and copayment) and 50 percent (50 percent discount) of the Medicare allowance for each additional procedure. For example, if two CT scans (APC group 0349) are performed in the same visit, the first is reimbursed at the full APC group rate, the second at 50 percent of the APC group rate.

Disease management: Program focused on preventing exacerbations of chronic diseases and on promoting healthier life styles for patients and clients with chronic diseases.

Disproportionate share hospital (DSH): Healthcare organizations that meet governmental criteria for percentages of indigent patients.

Editor: Logic (algorithms) within computer software that evaluates data.

Encounter: Professional, direct personal contact between a patient and a provider who delivers services or is professionally responsible for services delivered to a patient. Face-to-face contact between a patient and a provider who has primary responsibility for assessing and treating the condition of the patient at a given contact and exercises independent judgment in the care of the patient.

Endorsement: Language or statements within a healthcare insurance policy providing additional details about coverage or lack of coverage for special situations that are not usually included in standard policies. May function as a limitation or exclusion.

Episode of care: One or more healthcare services given by a provider during a specific period of relatively continuous care in relation to a particular health or medical problem or situation. In home health, the episode of care is all home care services and nonroutine medical supplies delivered to a patient during a 60-day period. In the home health prospective payment system (HHPPS), the episode of care is the unit of payment.

Episode-of-care reimbursement: Healthcare payment method in which providers receive one lump sum for all the care they provide related to a condition or disease. *See also* Episode of care.

Etiologic diagnosis: Underlying cause of the problem that led to the condition requiring admission to an inpatient rehabilitation facility.

Evidence of insurability: Statement or proof of a health status necessary to obtain healthcare insurance, especially private healthcare insurance.

Evidence-based clinical practice guideline: Explicit statement that guides clinical decision making and has been systematically developed from scientific evidence and clinical expertise to answer clinical questions. Systematic use of guidelines is termed evidence-based medicine.

Exclusion: Situation, instance, condition, injury, or treatment that the healthcare plan states will not be covered and for which the healthcare plan will pay no benefits (synonym is impairment rider).

Exclusive provider organization (EPO): Hybrid managed care organization that is sponsored by self-insured (self-funded) employers or associations and exhibits characteristics of both health maintenance organizations and preferred provider organizations.

Explanation of benefits (EOB): Report sent from a healthcare insurer to the policyholder and to the provider that describes the healthcare service, its cost, applicable cost-sharing, and the amount the healthcare insurer will cover. The remainder is the policyholder's responsibility.

False Claims Act: Legislation passed during the Civil War that prohibits contractors from making a false claim to a governmental program; used to reinforce healthcare fraud and abuse.

Federal Employees' Compensation Act of 1916 (FECA): A benefit program that ensures that civilian employees of the federal government are provided medical, death, and income benefits for work-related injuries and illnesses.

Fee: Price assigned to a unit of medical or health service, such as a visit to a physician or a day in a hospital. A fee for a service may be unrelated to the actual cost of providing the service. *See also* Charge.

Fee schedule: Third party payer's predetermined list of maximum allowable fees for each healthcare service.

Fee-for-service (FFS) reimbursement: Healthcare payment method in which providers retrospectively receive payment for each service rendered.

Fiscal intermediary (FI): Local payment branch of the Medicare program. Intermediaries are public or private insurance companies that contract with the Centers for Medicare and Medicaid Services (CMS) to act as agents of the federal government in dealing directly with participating providers of Medicare services. An intermediary is usually, but not necessarily, an insurance company, such as Blue Cross. FIs reimburse for inpatient or hospital services (Part A Medicare) and some Part B services.

Fiscal year: Yearly accounting period; the twelve month period on which a budget is planned. The federal fiscal year is October 1st through September 30th of the next year. Some state fiscal years are July 1st through June 30th of the next year. Often, agencies and companies match their fiscal years to the state and federal governments with which they contract.

Formulary: List of preferred drugs including brand-name and generic.

Fraud: Intentionally making a claim for payment that one knows to be false.

Functional independent assessment tool: Standardized tool to measure the severity of patients' impairments in rehabilitation settings. The tool captures characteristics that reflect the functional status of patients. Patients with lower scores on the tool have less independence and need more assistance than patients with higher scores.

Functional status: Patient's ability to perform the activities of daily living.

Gatekeeper: Health care provider or entity responsible for determining the healthcare services a patient or client may access. May be a primary care provider, a utilization review or case management agency, or a managed care organization.

Geographic practice cost index (GPCI): Index based on relative difference in the cost of a market basket of goods across geographical areas. A separate GPCI exists for each element of the relative value unit (RVU), which includes physician work, practice expenses, and malpractice. GPCIs are a means to adjust the RVUs, which are national averages, to reflect local costs of service.

Geometric mean length of stay (GMLOS): Statistically adjusted value of all cases of a given diagnosis related group (DRG), allowing for the outliers, transfer cases, and negative outlier cases that would normally skew the data. The GMLOS is used to compute hospital reimbursement for transfer cases.

Global payment method: Method of payment in which the third party payer makes one consolidated payment to cover the services of multiple providers who are treating a single episode of care.

Group practice model: Type of health maintenance organization (HMO) in which the HMO contracts with a medical group and reimburses the group on a fee-for-service or capitation basis. *See also* Closed panel.

Group practice without walls (PWW): Type of integrated delivery system in which the individual physicians share administrative systems but maintain their separate practices and offices distributed over a geographic area. (Also known as clinic without walls [CWW]).

Grouper: Computer program that uses specific data elements to assign patients, clients, or residents to groups, categories, or classes.

Guarantor: Person who is responsible for paying the bill or guarantees payment for healthcare services. Patients who are adults are often their own guarantor. Parents guarantee payments for the healthcare costs of their children.

Hard coding: Use of the charge description master to code repetitive services.

Health Care Procedure Coding System (HCPCS): Coding system created and maintained by the Centers for Medicare and Medicaid Services (CMS) that provides codes for procedures, services, and supplies not represented by a Current Procedural Terminology (CPT) code.

Health Information Technology (HIT): The use of electronic devices and media to collect, store, and retrieve healthcare information.

Health Insurance Portability and Accountability Act of 1996 (HIPAA): Significant piece of legislation aimed at improving healthcare data transmission among providers and insurers; designated code sets to be used for electronic transmission of claims.

Health insurance prospective payment system (HIPPS) code: Five-character alphanumeric code used in the home health prospective payment system (HHPPS) and in the inpatient rehabilitation facility prospective payment system (IRF PPS). In the HHPPS, the HIPPS code is derived or computed from the home health resource group (HHRG). In the IRF PPS, the HIPPS code is derived from the case-mix group and comorbidity. Reimbursement weights for each HIPSS code correspond to the levels of care provided.

Health maintenance organization (HMO): Entity that combines the provision of healthcare insurance and the delivery of healthcare services. Characterized by: (1) organized healthcare delivery system to a geographic area, (2) set of basic and supplemental health maintenance and treatment services, (3) voluntarily enrolled members, and (4) predetermined fixed, periodic prepayments for members' coverage. Prepayments are fixed without regard to actual costs of healthcare services provided to members.

High-cost outlier. *See* Outlier.

High-cost threshold: Criterion to assess whether technologies would be inadequately paid under the inpatient prospective payment system (IPPS). The sum of the geometric mean and the lesser of .75 of the national adjusted operating standardized payment amount (increased to reflect the difference between costs and charges) or .75 of one standard deviation of mean charges by diagnosis related group (DRG).

Hold harmless: Status in which one party does not hold the other party responsible.

Home Assistance Validation and Entry (HAVEN) System: Computer software for the collection and submission of the data elements in the Outcome Assessment Information Set (OASIS). HAVEN is used in the home health prospective payment system (HHPPS).

Home health agency (HHA): Organization that provides services in the home. These services include skilled nursing care, physical therapy, occupational therapy, speech therapy, and personal care by home health aides.

Home health resource group (HHRG): Classifications (groups) for the home health prospective payment system (HHPPS) derived from the data elements in the Outcome Assessment Information Set (OASIS). The HHRG is a six-character alphanumeric code that represents a severity level in three domains.

Hospital Outpatient Prospective Payment System (HOPPS): The reimbursement system created by the Balanced Budget Act of 1997 for hospital outpatient services rendered to Medicare beneficiaries; maintained by the Centers for Medicare and Medicaid Services (CMS).

Hospital Outpatient Quality Data Reporting Program (HOP QDRP): Quality-based pay-for-performance program implemented for HOPPS facilities in CY 2009. Hospitals must report data for measures established by CMS in order to receive a full HOPPS rate update.

Hospital Payment Monitoring Program (HPMP): Coding compliance monitoring program created by the 7th Scope of Work which ensures that proper payment is made for Medicare beneficiary admissions; administered by regional Quality Improvement Organizations (QIOs).

Hospital within hospital (HwH): Long-term care hospital physically located within another hospital

ICD-9-CM Coordination and Maintenance Committee: Committee composed of representatives from the National Center for Health Statistics (NCHS) and the Centers for Medicare and Medicaid Services (CMS) that is responsible for maintaining the United States' clinical modification version of the International Classification of Diseases, 9th revision (ICD-9-CM) code sets.

Impairment group code (IGC): Multidigit code that represents the primary reason for a patient's admission to an inpatient rehabilitation facility.

Indemnity health insurance: Traditional, fee-for-service healthcare plan in which the policyholder pays a monthly premium and a percentage of the usual, customary, and reasonable healthcare costs, and the patient can select the provider.

Independent practice association (IPA) or organization (IPO): Type of health maintenance organization (HMO) in which participating physicians maintain their private practices, and the HMO contracts with the independent practice association. The HMO reimburses the IPA on a capitated basis; the IPA may reimburse the physicians on a fee-for-service or a capitated basis.

Indian Health Service (IHS):   An agency within the Department of Health and Human Services (DHHS) responsible for upholding the federal government's obligation to promote healthy American Indian and Alaskan native people, communities, and cultures.

Indirect medical education (IME) adjustment: Percentage increase in Medicare reimbursement to offset the costs of medical education that a teaching hospital incurs.

Inpatient rehabilitation facility patient assessment instrument (IRF PAI): Data collection tool specific to rehabilitation facilities.

Inpatient Rehabilitation Validation and Entry (IRVEN): Computer software for data entry in inpatient rehabilitation facilities (IRFs). Captures data for the IRF Patient Assessment Instrument (IRF PAI) and supports electronic submission of the IRF PAI. Also allows data import and export in the standard record format of the Centers for Medicare and Medicaid Services (CMS).

Insurance: Reduction of a person's (insured's) exposure to risk of loss by having another party (insurer) assume the risk.

Insured: Individual or entity that purchases healthcare insurance coverage. *See also* Certificate holder, Member, Policyholder, *and* Subscriber.

Integrated delivery system (IDS): Generic term for the separate legal entity that healthcare providers form to offer a comprehensive set of healthcare services to a population. Other terms are health delivery network, horizontally integrated system, integrated services network (ISN), and vertically integrated system.

Integrated provider organization (IPO): Corporate, managerial entity that includes one or more hospitals, a large physician group practice, other healthcare organizations, or various configurations of these businesses.

International Classification of Diseases, 9th Revision, Clinical Modification (ICD-9-CM): Coding and classification system used to report diagnoses in all healthcare settings and inpatient procedures and services.

Interrupted stay: Discharge in which the patient was discharged from the inpatient rehabilitation facility and returned within three calendar days.

Key performance indicator: Area identified for needed improvement through benchmarking and continuous quality improvement.

Labor-related share (portion, ratio): Sum of facilities' relative proportion of wages and salaries, employee benefits, professional fees, postal services, other labor-intensive services, and the labor-related share of capital costs from the appropriate market basket. Labor-related share is typically 70 to 75 percent of healthcare facilities' costs. Adjusted annually and published in the *Federal Register*.

Late enrollee: Individual who does not enroll in a group healthcare plan at the first opportunity, but enrolls later if the plan has a general open enrollment period.

Length of stay (LOS): Number of days a patient remains in a healthcare organization. The statistic is the number of calendar days from admission to discharge including the day of admission, but not the day of discharge. This statistic may have an impact on prospective reimbursement.

Limitation: Qualification or other specification that reduces or restricts the extent of the healthcare benefit.

Local Coverage Determination (LCD): Reimbursement and medical necessity policies established by regional fiscal intermediaries. New format for Local Medical Review Policies (LMRPs). LCDs and LMRPs vary from state to state.

Local Medical Review Policy (LMRP): *See* Local Coverage Determination (LCD).

Long-term care diagnosis related group (LTC-DRG): Inpatient classification that categorizes patients who are similar in terms of diagnoses and treatments, age, resources used, and lengths of stay. Under the prospective payment system (PPS), hospitals are paid a set fee for treating patients in a single DRG category, regardless of the actual cost of care for the individual. LTC-DRGs are exactly the same as the DRGs for the inpatient prospective payment system (IPPS). *See also* Diagnosis related group (DRG).

Long-term care hospital (LTCH): Hospitals that provide general acute care and specialized services to patients who have longer than average lengths of stay. These patients may have chronic diseases or acute diseases that require long-term therapies. The Centers for Medicare and Medicaid Services (CMS) has two ways to categorize hospitals as LTCHs. First, an LTCH has an average length of stay for Medicare patients that is twenty-five days or longer. Second, an LTCH can be a hospital excluded from the inpatient prospective payment system and that has an average length of stay for all patients that is twenty days or longer.

Low-utilization payment adjustment (LUPA): Payment adjustment applied when a home health agency provides four or fewer visits in an episode of care.

Major diagnostic category (MDC): Highest level in hierarchical structure of the federal inpatient prospective payment system (IPPS). The twenty-five MDCs are primarily based on body system involvement, such as MDC No. 06, Diseases and Disorders of the Digestive System. However, a few categories are based on disease etiology, for example, Human Immunodeficiency Virus Infections.

Malpractice (MP): Element of the relative value unit (RVU); costs of the premiums for professional liability insurance.

Managed care: Payment method in which the third party payer has implemented some provisions to control the costs of healthcare while maintaining quality care. Systematic merger of clinical, financial, and administrative processes to manage access, cost, and quality of healthcare.

Managed care organization (MCO): Entity that integrates the financing and delivery of specified healthcare services. Characterized by (1) arrangements with specific providers to deliver a comprehensive set of healthcare services, (2) criteria for selecting providers, (3) quality assessment and utilization review, and (4) incentives for members to use plan providers. Also known as coordinated care organization.

Management (medical) service organization (MSO): Specialized entity that provides management services and administrative and information systems to one or more physician group practices or small hospitals. An MSO may be owned by a hospital, physician group, physician-hospital organization, integrated delivery system, or investors.

Market basket: Mix of goods and services appropriate to the setting, such as home health services or skilled nursing facilities.

Market basket index: Relative measure that averages the costs of a mix of goods and services.

Maximum out-of-pocket cost: Specific amount, in a certain timeframe such as one year, beyond which all covered healthcare services for that policyholder or dependent are paid at 100 percent by the healthcare insurance plan. *See also* Catastrophic expense limit *and* Stop-loss benefit.

Medicaid: Part of the Social Security Act, a joint program between state and federal governments to provide healthcare benefits to low-income persons and families.

Medical emergency: Severe injury or illness (including pain); definition depends upon the healthcare insurer.

Medical foundation: Multipurpose, nonprofit service organization for physicians and other healthcare providers at the local and county levels. As managed care organizations, medical foundations have established preferred provider organizations, exclusive provider organizations, and management service organizations. Emphases are freedom of choice and preservation of the physician–patient relationship.

Medical necessity: Healthcare services and supplies that are proven or acknowledged to be effective in the diagnosis, treatment, cure, or relief of a health condition, illness, injury, disease, or its symptoms and to be consistent with the community's accepted standard of care. Under medical necessity, only those services, procedures, and patient care are provided that are warranted by the patient's condition.

Medicare: Federally funded healthcare benefits program for those persons sixty-five years of age and older, as well as for those entitled to Social Security benefits.

Medicare Administrative Contractor (MAC): Newly established contracting authority to administer Medicare Part A and Part B as required by section 911 of the MMA of 2003. Fifteen Medicare Administrative Contractors will replace Medicare Carriers and Fiscal Intermediaries by 2011. Each MAC will process and manage both Part A and Part B claims.

Medicare Advantage (Part C): Optional managed care plan for Medicare beneficiaries who are entitled to Part A, are enrolled in Part B, and live in an area with a plan. Types of plans available include health maintenance organization, point-of-service plan, preferred provider organization, and provider-sponsored organization (formerly Medicare+Choice).

Medicare carrier: Contractor with Medicare to process Medicare Part B claims; determines charges allowed by Medicare and makes payment to physicians and suppliers on behalf of Medicare.

Medicare Modernization Act of 2003 (MMA): Most significant legislative change to the Medicare Program since its creation; the law created the outpatient prescription drug benefit and provided expanded coverage choices and improved benefits.

Medicare Part A: The portion of Medicare that provides benefits for inpatient hospital services.

Medicare Part B: An optional and supplemental portion of Medicare that provides benefits for physician services, medical services, and medical supplies not covered by Medicare Part A.

Medicare Part C: Also known as Medicare Advantage, this is a managed care option that includes services under Parts A, B and D and additional services that are not typically covered by Medicare; Medicare Part C requires an additional premium; plan known formerly as Medicare+Choice.

Medicare Part D: Medicare drug benefit created by the Medicare Modernization Act of 2003 (MMA) that offers outpatient drug coverage to beneficiaries for an additional premium.

Medicare severity diagnosis related group (MS-DRG): Medicare refinement to the diagnosis related group (DRG) classification system which allows for payment to be more closely aligned with resource intensity.

Medicare Summary Notice: Statement that describes services rendered, payment covered, and benefits limits and denials for Medicare beneficiaries.

Medigap: Type of private insurance policy available for Medicare beneficiaries to supplement Medicare Part A and or Part B coverage.

Member: Individual or entity that purchases healthcare insurance coverage. *See also* Certificate holder, Insured, Policyholder, *and* Subscriber.

Metropolitan division: County or group of counties within a core-based statistical area (CBSA) that contains a core with a population of at least 2.5 million. A metropolitan division consists of one or more main/secondary counties that represent an employment center or centers, plus adjacent counties associated with the main county or counties through commuting ties. *See also* Core-based statistical area.

Metropolitan statistical area (MSA): Core-based statistical area associated with at least one urbanized area that has a population of at least 50,000. The MSA comprises the central county or counties containing the core, plus adjacent outlying counties. *See also* Core-based statistical area (CBSA).

Minimum data set (MDS): Standardized, comprehensive assessment instrument that the Centers for Medicare and Medicaid Services (CMS) requires be completed for residents of skilled nursing facilities. The MDS collects administrative and clinical information. States have the option of having supplemental data collected with the approval of CMS.

Modifier: Two-digit alpha/alphanumeric/numeric code that provides the means by which a physician or facility can indicate that a service provided to the patient has been altered by some special circumstance(s), but for which the basic code description itself has not changed.

Moral hazard: Any change in behavior that occurs as a result of becoming insured.

Mortality: The incidence of death.

Motor: Related to movement of muscles and coordination and includes both large motor skills, such as walking, and fine motor skills, such as buttoning and zipping clothing.

National Center for Health Statistics (NCHS): Organization that developed the clinical modification to the International Classification of Diseases, Ninth Revision (ICD-9); responsible for maintaining and updating the diagnosis portion of the International Classification of Diseases, 9th revision, Clinical Modification (ICD-9-CM).

National Correct Coding Initiative (NCCI): A set of coding regulations to prevent fraud and abuse in physician and hospital outpatient coding; specifically addresses unbundling and mutually exclusive procedures.

National Coverage Determination (NCD): National medical necessity and reimbursement regulations.

National standard episode amount: Set dollar amount (conversion factor, constant, across-the-board multiplier), unadjusted for geographic differences, that is multiplied with the weights of the health insurance prospective payment system (HIPPS) codes in the home health prospective payment system (HHPPS). The amount for each year is published in the *Federal Register*.

National unadjusted copayment: Set dollar amount, unadjusted for geographic differences, that beneficiaries pay under the hospital outpatient prospective payment system (HOPPS).

National unadjusted payment: Product of the conversion factor multiplied by the relative weight, unadjusted for geographic differences.

Network: Physicians, hospitals, and other providers who provide healthcare services to members of a managed care organization. Providers may be associated through formal or informal contracts and agreements.

Network model: Type of health maintenance organization (HMO) in which the HMO contracts with two or more medical groups and reimburses the groups on a fee-for-service or capitation basis. (*See also* Group practice model.)

New technology: Advance in medical technology that substantially improves, relative to technologies previously available, the diagnosis or treatment of Medicare beneficiaries. Applicants for the status in new technology must submit a formal request, including a full description of the clinical applications of the technology and the results of any clinical evaluations demonstrating that the new technology represents a substantial clinical improvement, along with data to demonstrate the technology meets the high cost threshold.

Noncase-mix adjusted component: Amount comprising the noncase-mix component and the noncase mix therapy component.

Noncase-mix component: Standard amount added to the rate for each refined RUG-III group to cover administrative and capital-related costs; this standard amount is added to all groups

Non-case mix therapy component: Standard amount to cover the costs of assessing the residents' needs for therapy and who, subsequently, were determined not to need continued services of therapy.

Nonlabor share (portion, ratio): Facilities' operating costs not related to labor (typically 25 to 30 percent). *See also* Labor-related share.

Nonroutine medical supplies (NRS): Supplies that are not bundled into typical (routine) medical care for home health, such as catheter bags, urinary and stool collection pouches, irrigation trays, and appliance cleaners.

Nursing component: Amount comprising nursing per diem amount and nursing index.

Nursing per diem amount: Standard amount which includes direct nursing care and the cost of nontherapy ancillary services.

Nursing index: Ratio based on the amount of staff time, weighted by salary levels, associated with each refined RUG-III group; applying this ratio to the nursing per diem is the case-mix adjustment.

Observation: Service in which providers observe and monitor a patient to decide whether the patient needs to be admitted to inpatient care or can be discharged to home or an outpatient area, usually charged by the hour.

Office of Inspector General (OIG): A division of the Department of Health and Human Services (DHHS) that investigates issues of noncompliance in the Medicare and Medicaid programs such as fraud and abuse.

Office of Inspector General (OIG) Workplan: Yearly plan released by the OIG that outlines the focus for reviews and investigates in various healthcare settings.

Operating room (OR) procedure: Procedure that physician panel classified as occurring in the operating room in most hospitals. Presence of an OR procedure groups a case to a surgical diagnosis related group (DRG).

Operation Restore Trust: A 1995 joint effort of the Department of Health and Human Services (DHHS), Office of Inspector General (OIG), the Centers for Medicare and Medicaid Services (CMS), and the Administration of Aging (AOA) to target fraud and abuse among healthcare providers.

Out-of-pocket: Payment made by the policyholder or member.

Outcome Assessment Information Set (OASIS): Set of data elements that represent core items of a comprehensive assessment for an adult home care patient. OASIS is used to measure patient outcomes in outcome-based quality improvement (OBQI). This assessment is performed on every patient who receives services from home health agencies that participate in the Medicare or Medicaid programs. The OASIS is the basis of the home health prospective payment system (HHPPS).

Outlier: Cases in prospective payment systems with unusually long lengths of stay or exceptionally high costs; day outlier or cost outlier, respectively.

Outpatient code editor (OCE): *See* Editor.

Outpatient Service Mix Index (SMI): The sum of the weights of ambulatory payment classification groups for patients treated during a given period divided by the total volume of patients treated.

Packaging: Combination of an ancillary service with its related procedure or service for one lump-sum payment in the hospital outpatient prospective payment system.

Partial hospitalization: Program of intensive psychotherapy that is provided in a day outpatient setting and is designed to keep patients with severe mental conditions from being hospitalized in an inpatient unit.

Pass-through: Exception to the Medicare prospective payment systems (PPSs) for a high-cost service. The exception minimizes the negative financial impact of the lump-sum payments of the PPSs. Pass-throughs are not included in the PPSs and are passed through to cost-based (retrospective) payment mechanisms. In the hospital outpatient prospective payment system (HOPPS), the Centers for Medicare and Medicaid Services (CMS) created exceptions for some expensive drugs, pharmaceuticals, biologicals, and devices. Rather than being bundled or packaged, these exceptions to the CMS's HOPPS are "passed-through" the HOPPS to other payment mechanisms (payment status indicators F, G, H, and J). The inpatient prospective payment system (IPPS) passes through the costs of medical education and organ acquisition and some capital costs.

Payment Error Prevention Program (PEPP): Payment compliance program established under the 6th Scope of Work to help healthcare facilities identify simple mistakes that are causing payment errors; monitored by Quality Improvement Organizations (QIOs).

Payment status indictor (PSI). Alphabetic code that provides payment information in the hospital outpatient prospective payment system (HOPPS). There are two types of indicators. The first type designates one of three major categories of reimbursement *outside* the ambulatory patient classification (APC) system (A, C, and E). The second type gives directions related to payment rules for APC payments (D, F, G, H, K, L, N, P, S, T, V, and X).

Per diem (per day): Type of prospective payment method in which the third party payer reimburses the provider a fixed rate for each day a covered member is hospitalized.

Per member per month (PMPM): Amount of money paid monthly for each individual enrolled in a capitation-based health insurance plan.

Physician care group (PCG): Type of outpatient prospective payment method for physician services in which patients are classified into similar, homogenous categories.

Physician work (WORK): Component or element of the relative value unit (RVU) that should cover the physician's salary. This work is the time the physician spends providing a service and the intensity with which that time is spent. The four elements of intensity are: (a) mental effort and judgment, (b) technical skill, (c) physical effort, and (d) psychological stress.

Physician-hospital organization (PHO): Hybrid type of integrated delivery system that is a legal entity formed by a hospital and a group of physicians.

Point-of-service (POS) healthcare insurance plan: Plan in which members choose how to receive services at the time they need the services, also known as open-ended HMOs.

Policy: Binding contract issued by a healthcare insurance company to an individual or group in which the company promises to pay for healthcare to treat illness or injury (also known as health plan agreement and evidence of coverage).

Policyholder: Individual or entity that purchases healthcare insurance coverage. *See also* Insured, Certificate holder, Member, *and* Subscriber.

Practice expenses (PE):   Element of the relative value unit (RVU) that covers the physician's overhead costs, such as employee wages, office rent, supplies, and equipment. There are two types, facility and nonfacility.

Practice without walls (PWW):   *See* Group practice without walls (PWW).

Preadmission certification: *See* Prior approval (authorization).

Preadmission review: *See* Prior approval (authorization).

Preauthorization: *See* Prior approval (authorization).

Preauthorization(precertification)number: Control number issued when a healthcare service is approved.

Precertification: *See* Prior approval (authorization).

Pre-existing condition: Disease, illness, ailment, or other condition (whether physical or mental) for which, within six months before the insured's enrollment date of coverage, medical advice, diagnosis, care, or treatment was recommended or received. Healthcare coverage may be denied for a period of time for a preexisting condition. The Health Insurance Portability and Accountability Act (HIPAA) constrains the use of exclusions for preexisting conditions and establishes requirements exclusions for preexisting conditions must satisfy.

Preferred provider organization (PPO):   Entity that contracts with employers and insurers to render, through a network of providers, healthcare services to a group of members. Members can choose to use the healthcare services of any physician, hospital, or other healthcare provider. Members who choose to use the services of in-network (in-plan) providers have lower out-of-pocket expenses than members who choose to use the services of out-of-network (out-of-plan) providers.

Premium: Amount of money that policyholder or certificate holder must periodically pay a healthcare insurance plan in return for healthcare coverage.

Prescription management: Cost control measure that expands the use of a formulary to include patient education; electronic screening, alert, and decision-support tools; expert and referent systems; criteria for drug utilization; point-of-service order entry; electronic prescription transmission; and patient-specific medication profiles.

Pricer: Software module in Medicare claims processing systems, specific to certain benefits, used in pricing claims and calculating payment rates and payments, most often under prospective payment systems.

Primary care physician (PCP):   Physician who provides, supervises, and coordinates the healthcare of a member. Family and general practitioners, internists, pediatricians, and obstetricians/gynecologists are primary care physicians. *See also* Primary care provider.

Primary care provider (PCP):   Healthcare provider who provides, supervises, and coordinates the healthcare of a member. The PCP makes referrals to specialists and for advanced diagnostic testing. Family and general practitioners, internists, pediatricians, and obstetricians/gynecologists are primary care physicians. Other PCPs include nurse practitioners and physician assistants. *See also* Primary care physician.

Primary insurer (payer):   Entity responsible for the greatest proportion or majority of the healthcare expenses. *See* Secondary insurer.

Principal diagnosis: Reason established after study to be chiefly responsible for occasioning the admission of the patient to the hospital for care.

Prior approval (authorization):   Process of obtaining approval from a healthcare insurance company before receiving healthcare services (also known as precertification).

Program for Evaluation Payment Patterns Electronic Report (PEPPER): A benchmarking database maintained by the Texas Medical Foundation that supplies individual QIOs with hospital data to determine state benchmarks and monitor hospital compliance.

Programs of All-Inclusive Care for Elderly (PACE): A joint Medicare–Medicaid venture that allows states to choose a managed care option for providing benefits to the frail elderly population.

Prospective payment method: Type of episode-of-care reimbursement in which the third party payer establishes the payment rates for healthcare services in advance for a specific time period.

Prospective payment system (PPS): Method of reimbursement in which payment rates for healthcare services are established in advance for a specific time period. The predetermined rates are based on average levels of resource use for certain types of healthcare.

Provider: Physician, clinic, hospital, nursing home, or other healthcare entity (second party) rendering the care.

Provider-sponsored organization (PSO): Type of point-of-service plan in which the physicians that practice in a regional or community hospital organize the plan.

Quality Improvement Organization (QIO): Medicare contractor that is responsible for carrying a specified scope of work during a three-year period; monitors and assists healthcare facilities with quality, payment, treatment denial, and health information technology issues.

Quintile: Portion of a frequency distribution containing one-fifth of the total cases.

Recovery Audit Contractor (RAC): The result of successful demonstration project required by the MMA 0f 2003. RACs ensure correct payments are made by Medicare for Part A and Part B claims.

Refined case-based payment method: Case-based payment method enhanced to include patients from all age groups or from regions of the world with varying mixes of diseases and differing patterns of healthcare delivery.

Regression analysis: Statistical technique that uses an independent variable to predict the value of a dependent value. In the inpatient psychiatric facility prospective payment system (IPF PPS), patient demographics and length of stay (independent variables) were used to predict cost of care (dependent variable).

Rehabilitation facility: Facility specializing in the restorative processes and therapies that develop and maintain self-sufficient functioning consistent with individuals' capabilities. Rehabilitative services restore function after an illness or injury. Services are provided by physiatrists, nurses, and physical, occupational, and speech therapists.

Rehabilitation impairment category (RIC): Clusters of impairment group codes (IGCs) that represent similar impairments and diagnoses. RICs are the larger umbrella division within the inpatient rehabilitation facility prospective payment system (IRF PPS). From the RICs, the case-mix groups (CMGs) are determined.

Reimbursement: Compensation or repayment for healthcare services already rendered.

Relative value scale (RVS): System designed to permit comparisons of the resources needed or appropriate prices for various units of service. It takes into account labor, skill, supplies, equipment, space, and other costs for each procedure or service.

Relative value unit (RVU): Unit of measure designed to permit comparison of the amount of resources required to perform various provider services by assigning weights to such factors as personnel time, level of skill, and sophistication of equipment required to render service. In the resource-based relative value scale (RBRVS), the RVU reflects national averages and is the sum of the physician work, practice expenses, and malpractice. RVUs are adjusted to local costs through the geographic practice cost indexes (GPCIs). *See also* Physician work, Practice expenses, Malpractice, *and* Geographic practice cost index.

Relative weight (RW): Assigned weight that reflects the relative resource consumption associating with a payment classification or group. Higher payments are associated with higher relative weights.

Remittance advice: Report sent by third party payer that outlines claim rejections, denials, and payments to the facility; sent via electronic data interchange.

Reporting of Hospital Quality Data for Annual Payment Update Program (RHQDAPU): Created by the MMA of 2003, is a quality-based pay-for-performance initiative under IPPS. Annual update to the IPPS rate is reduced if program requirements are not met.

Resource utilization group (RUG): Classification for resources used in nursing homes. Patients are classified into one of forty-four possible RUGs based on resident information collected in the minimum data set (MDS). The RUG subsequently classifies residents into seven payment categories.

Resource-based relative value scale (RBRVS): Type of retrospective fee-for-service payment method that classifies health services based on the cost of providing physician services in terms of effort, practice expense (overhead), and malpractice insurance.

Retrospective payment method: Type of fee-for-service reimbursement in which providers receive recompense after health services have been rendered.

Revenue cycle: The regularly repeating set of events that produces revenue.

Revenue cycle management: The supervision of all administrative and clinical functions that contribute to the capture, management, and collection of patient service revenue.

Rider: Document added to a healthcare insurance policy that provides details about coverage or lack of coverage for special situations that are not usually included in standard policies. May function as an exclusion or limitation.

Risk: Probability of incurring loss.

Risk pool: Group of people who will be covered by the healthcare insurance plan.

Rural area: Geographic area outside an urban area and its constituent counties or county equivalents. *See also* Core-based statistical area (CBSA) *and* Metropolitan statistical area (MSA).

Scope of Work: The contract specifications for quality improvement organizations (QIOs) to complete during their three-year contract period.

Second opinion: Cost containment measure to prevent unnecessary tests, treatments, medical devices, or surgical procedures.

Secondary insurer (payer): Entity responsible for the remainder of the healthcare expenses after the primary insurer pays. *See* Primary insurer.

Self-insured plan: Method of insurance in which the employer or other association itself administers the health insurance benefits for its employees or their dependents, thereby assuming the risks for the costs of healthcare for the group.

Self-pay: Type of fee-for-service reimbursement in which the patients or their guarantors pay a specific amount for each service received.

Short-stay outlier: Hospitalization that is five-sixths of the geometric length of stay for the long-term care diagnosis related group (LTC-DRG).

Social Security Act: Federal legislation providing support for state public health activities and healthcare services for mothers and children; amended in 1965 to establish the Medicare and Medicaid programs.

Sole community hospital: Hospital that, by reason of factors such as isolated location, weather conditions, travel conditions, or absence of other hospitals (as determined by the Secretary of the Department of Health and Human Services [DHHS]), is the sole source of patient hospital services reasonably available to individuals in a geographical area who are entitled to benefits.

Staff model: Type of health maintenance organization (HMO) that provides hospitalization and physicians' services through its own staff and facilities (also known as closed panel).

Standard federal rate: National base payment amount in the prospective payment system for long-term care hospitals (PPS for LTC). This amount is multiplied with the relative weight of the long-term care diagnosis related group (LTC-DRG) to calculate the unadjusted payment. Published annually in the *Federal Register*.

Standardized payment: National base amount in the inpatient rehabilitation facility prospective payment system (IRF PPS). This amount is multiplied with the relative weight of the case mix group to calculate the unadjusted payment. Published annually in the *Federal Register*.

State Children's Health Insurance Program (SCHIP): A state–federal partnership created by the Balanced Budget Act of 1997 that provides health insurance to children of families whose income level is too high to qualify for Medicaid but too low to purchase healthcare insurance.

Stop-loss benefit: Specific amount, in a certain timeframe such as one year, beyond which all covered healthcare services for that policyholder or dependent are paid at 100 percent by the healthcare insurance plan. *See also* Maximum out-of-pocket cost *and* Catastrophic expense limit.

Subcapitation: Portion of capitated rate that is based to specialists for carved-out services

Subscriber: Individual or entity that purchases healthcare insurance coverage. *See also* Certificate holder, Insured, Member, *and* Policyholder.

Supplemental insurance: Additional healthcare insurance that fills in gaps (supplements) in comprehensive insurance or Medicare benefits; may be a cash benefit, per diem, or other form.

Teaching hospital: Hospital engaged in an approved graduate medical education residency program in medicine, osteopathy, dentistry, or podiatry.

Temporary Assistance for Needy Families Program (TANF): Replaced the Aid to Families with Dependent Children program; this program provides states with grant money designated to provide low-income families with assistance.

Therapy component: Amount comprising the therapy per diem amount and therapy index.

Therapy index: Ratio based on the amount of staff time, weighted by salary levels, associated with each refined RUG-III group; applying this ratio to the therapy per diem is the case-mix adjustment

Therapy per diem amount: Standard amount which includes physical, occupational, and speech-language therapy services provided to beneficiaries in a Part A stay

Third opinion: Cost containment measure to prevent unnecessary tests, treatments, medical devices, or surgical procedures.

Third party payer: Insurance company or health agency that pays the physician, clinic, or other healthcare provider (second party) for the care or services to the patient (first party). An insurance company or healthcare benefits program that reimburses healthcare providers and/or patient for covered medical services.

Third party payment: Payments for healthcare services made by an insurance company or health agency on behalf of the insured.

Title: Short name of a diagnosis related group (DRG), such as DRG 1, Craniotomy Age > 17 Except for Trauma.

Transfer: Discharge of a patient from a hospital and readmission to postacute care or another acute care hospital on the same day.

TRICARE: The healthcare program for active duty and retired members of one of the seven uniformed services administered by the Department of Defense; formerly known as Civilian Health and Medical Program of the Uniformed Services (CHAMPUS).

TRICARE Extra: A healthcare program available for active duty family members (ADFM) that requires an annual deductible and a 20 percent copayment for services rendered by a TRICARE network provider.

TRICARE for Life (TFL): Secondary coverage for TRICARE beneficiaries who become entitled to Medicare Part A.

TRICARE Prime: The managed care option for the TRICARE program available for active duty family members (ADFM) who live or work within fifty miles or an hours drive of a military treatment facility.

TRICARE Prime Remote: The managed care option for the TRICARE program available for active duty family members (ADFM) who live or work in remote areas.

TRICARE Standard: A healthcare program available for active duty family members (ADFM) that requires an annual deductible plus 25 percent cost sharing of charges for services rendered by a TRICARE authorized provider.

Trim point: Numeric value that identifies atypically long lengths of stay (LOS) or high costs (long stay outliers and cost outliers, respectively). Commonly trim points are plus or minus three standard deviations from the mean. *See also* Outlier.

Unbundling: The fraudulent process in which individual component codes are submitted for reimbursement rather than one comprehensive code.

Uncompensated care: Overall measure of services provided for which no payments were received from the patient, client, or third party payer

Underwriting: Process of identifying and classifying individuals' or groups' risk.

Upcoding: The fraudulent process of submitting codes for reimbursement that indicates a more complex or higher paying services than that which the patient actually received.

Urban area: Core-based statistical area (CBSA).

Usual, customary, and reasonable (UCR): Type of retrospective fee-for-service payment method in which the third party payer pays for fees that are usual, customary, and reasonable, wherein "usual" is for usual for the individual provider's practice; "customary" means customary for the community; and "reasonable" is reasonable for the situation.

Utilization review: The process of determining whether a patient's medical care is necessary according to established guidelines and regulations. Cost containment measure that assesses the appropriateness of the setting for the healthcare service in the continuum of care and the level of service.

Value based purchasing (VBP): CMS plan which provides incentives hospitals to improve quality. Financial rewards are given to those facilities that perform at the highest level.

Wage index: Ratio that represents the relationship between the average wages in a healthcare setting's geographic area and the national average for that healthcare setting. Wage indexes are adjusted annually and published in the *Federal Register*.

Waiting period: Time between the effective date of a healthcare insurance policy and the date the healthcare insurance plan will assume liability for expenses related to certain health services, such as those related to preexisting conditions.

Withhold: Portion of providers' capitated payments that managed care organizations deduct and hold in order to create an incentive for efficient or reduced use of healthcare services (also known as physician contingency reserve [PCR]).

Withhold pool: Aggregate amount withheld from all providers' capitation payments as an amount to cover expenditures in excess of targets.

Workers' Compensation: Medical and income insurance coverage for employees who suffer from a work-related injury or illness.

World Health Organization (WHO): Organization that created and maintains the International Classification of Diseases (ICD) used throughout the world to collect morbidity and mortality information.

Appendix B
Additional Readings
and Resources

Coding and Compliance

Coding Ethically

Developing a Coding Compliance Policy Document, AHIMA Practice Brief

The Codes to Watch: Identifying the DRGs Most Prone to Payment Error

Diagnosis Coding and Medical Necessity: Rules and Reimbursement

Sample Advance Beneficiary Notice (ABN)

Internet Resources for Accurate Coding and Reimbursement Practices

Managed Care

Can You Manage Managed Care?

Revenue Cycle

The Care and Maintenance of Charge Masters, AHIMA Practice Brief

Coding Connections in Revenue Cycle Management

Key Points of the UB-04

Charge Capture and the Physician Revenue Cycle

Coding Ethically

June Bronnert, RHIA, CCS

With the many reimbursement issues and regulatory requirements surrounding coding, it is sometimes necessary for coders to refamiliarize themselves with what it means to code ethically. AHIMA's Coding Policy and Strategy Committee developed the Standards of Ethical Coding, which were approved by AHIMA's Board of Directors in 2000.[1] The standards were developed to help coders address these issues.

While it is recommended that all those performing coding functions follow the standards, credentialed coders are required to follow this code in order to maintain their credentials. Coders sometimes take for granted the ethical decisions they face on a daily basis. What are the standards and how should coders follow them? This article will present various situations and potential action items coders may engage in to abide by the Standards of Ethical Coding.

The Standards

1. Coding professionals are expected to support the importance of accurate, complete, and consistent coding practices for the production of quality healthcare data.

2. Coding professionals in all healthcare settings should adhere to the ICD-9-CM (International Classification of Diseases, 9th revision, Clinical Modification) coding conventions, official coding guidelines approved by the Cooperating Parties, the CPT (Current Procedural Terminology) rules established by the American Medical Association, and any other official coding rules and guidelines established for use with mandated standard code sets. Selection and sequencing of diagnoses and procedures must meet the definitions of required data sets for applicable healthcare settings.

3. Coding professionals should use their skills, their knowledge of currently mandated coding and classification systems, and official resources to select the appropriate diagnostic and procedural codes.

4. Coding professionals should only assign and report codes that are clearly and consistently supported by physician documentation in the health record.

5. Coding professionals should consult physicians for clarification and additional documentation prior to code assignment when there is conflicting or ambiguous data in the health record.

6. Coding professionals should not change codes or the narratives of codes on the billing abstract so that meanings are misrepresented. Diagnoses or procedures should not be inappropriately included or excluded because payment or insurance policy coverage requirements will be affected. When individual payer policies conflict with official coding rules and guidelines, these policies should be obtained in writing whenever possible. Reasonable efforts should be made to educate the payer on proper coding practices in order to influence a change in the payer's policy.

7. Coding professionals, as members of the healthcare team, should assist and educate physicians and other clinicians by advocating proper documentation practices, further specificity, and resequencing or inclusion of diagnoses or procedures when needed to more accurately reflect the acuity, severity, and the occurrence of events.

8. Coding professionals should participate in the development of institutional coding policies and should ensure that coding policies complement, not conflict with, official coding rules and guidelines.

9. Coding professionals should maintain and continually enhance their coding skills, as they have a professional responsibility to stay abreast of changes in codes, coding guidelines, and regulations.

10. Coding professionals should strive for optimal payment to which the facility is legally entitled, remembering that it is unethical and illegal to maximize payment by means that contradict regulatory guidelines.[2]

Coding compliance plans usually include AHIMA's standards, and coders agree that coding behaviors should follow accordingly. However, what does this mean when performing the day-to-day coding tasks, when records are on your desk waiting to be coded? You know that a coding backlog is building due to various open positions, and your supervisor informs you that the current productivity standards are being reviewed for a potential increase. You have just received the latest edition of *CPT Assistant,* but it, along with the previous issue, remains unopened and unread on your desk.

The ethical standards are a part of these everyday situations and should provide a guide when making decisions on how to handle these events. Assessment of coder performance should take into account adherence to each of these standards.

Case Study

A Medicare patient presents to the laboratory for a complete blood count but forgets to bring the physician's order. Registration calls the physician's office, and they fax over the physician's order. However a diagnosis is not present on the order. When the encounter is ready for coding, the coder must query the physician for more documentation. The coder also knows that the test is covered by a local coverage determination, so the coder asks the physician to provide a medically necessary diagnosis. What standards does this violate?

The coder in this situation violates multiple standards:

Standard 4. Coding professionals should only assign and report codes that are clearly and consistently supported by physician documentation. It is not appropriate to refer to coverage determinations to pinpoint diagnoses that support medical necessity, nor is it acceptable to pick up diagnoses from prior records if they are not documented in the current visit record. This would be an example of a leading query. All HIM departments should carefully review their physician query forms to ensure that they comply with AHIMA's practice brief "Developing a Physician Query Process," which can be found online in the FORE Library: HIM Body of Knowledge at www.ahima.org.

Standard 5. Coding professionals should consult physicians for clarification of conflicting or ambiguous data.

Standard 6. Diagnoses or procedures should not be inappropriately included or excluded because payment or insurance policy coverage requirements will be affected.

Out of Compliance?

The second standard states that coding professionals in all settings should adhere to the ICD-9-CM and CPT coding conventions as published by the cooperating parties for ICD-9-CM and American Medical Association, respectively. While this appears to be basic, coders may often be out of compliance with this standard, which occurs in the following situations:

- Misidentification of the principal diagnosis that results in an inaccurate Diagnosis Related Group (DRG) assignment

- Misassignment of a CPT code that reports a procedure more complex than actually performed, resulting in a higher-weighted Ambulatory Payment Classification (APC)

- Assignment of multiple CPT codes when only one is necessary to obtain higher APC reimbursement

Coding professionals are also responsible for maintaining continuing education through a variety of methods, the most common being seminars, audio seminars, or quizzes. However, coding professionals need to be responsible for reviewing the official sources of coding advice, *Coding Clinic for ICD-9-CM* and *CPT Assistant*. The department management is responsible for making these resources available to all coders, but coders are responsible for reading them. The "Minutes of the Coordination and Maintenance Committee for ICD-9-CM" and the book *CPT Update: An Insider's View* are excellent resources to understand the rationales behind the coding changes. If a coder does not comply with the above, he or she would be violating both standards 3 and 9.

The final standard of ethical coding states that coding professionals should strive for optimal payment to which the facility is legally entitled. This means the appropriate reimbursement for the services rendered, paid as expeditiously as feasible. Acute care inpatient facilities failing to validate DRG assignments are not only demonstrating poor revenue cycle management but also violating this standard by not verifying proper reimbursement.

Potential Violations

Pamela R. Yokubaitis's article "Are Ethics Guiding Your Workplace?" quotes Michael Daigneault's eight "reasons" that people give for ethical lapses:

- I have to cut corners to meet my goals.

- I lack the time or resources to do what is right.

- My peers expect me to act this way.

- My superiors want results, not excuses.

- I don't think it is really wrong or illegal.

- Others would think it is a good choice.

- No one will ever know the difference.

- I am afraid to do what I know is right.[3]

Do not let yourself fall into one of these categories. Be knowledgeable of the standards and how they influence your professional career. If a violation of these standards occurs, AHIMA has a process for reporting the allegations. A completed and signed form is submitted to AHIMA by either another AHIMA member, HIM professional, employer, or regulatory agency representative within one year of the alleged violation. A professional conduct committee has a complaint review subcommittee review the allegation. This subcommittee may either dismiss the case, proceed with an additional investigation, or proceed with a formal hearing. Various disciplinary actions could occur ranging from a letter of complaint dismissal to revocation of certification.

Coders will be faced with ethical challenges most days, and it is important to know the standards and how they apply in order to make the best decisions possible when solving your ethical dilemmas.

Notes

1. AHIMA. "Standards of Ethical Coding." *Journal of AHIMA* 71, no. 3 (2000): insert.

2. Ibid.

3. Yokubaitis, Pamela R. "Are Ethics Guiding Your Workplace?" *Journal of AHIMA* 74, no. 8 (2003): 66–68.

Developing a Coding Compliance Policy Document

Organizations using diagnosis and procedure codes for reporting healthcare services must have formal policies and corresponding procedures in place that provide instruction on the entire process—from the point of service to the billing statement or claim form. Coding compliance policies serve as a guide to performing coding and billing functions and provide documentation of the organization's intent to correctly report services. The policies should include facility-specific documentation requirements, payer regulations and policies, and contractual arrangements for coding consultants and outsourcing services. This information may be covered in payer/provider contracts or found in Medicare and Medicaid manuals and bulletins.

Following are selected tenets that address the process of code selection and reporting. These tenets may be referred to as coding protocols, a coding compliance program, organizational coding guidelines, or a similar name. These tenets are an important part of any organization's compliance plan and the key to preventing coding errors and resulting reimbursement problems. Examples are taken from both outpatient and inpatient coding processes for illustration purposes only. This document cannot serve as a complete coding compliance plan, but will be useful as a guide for creating a more comprehensive resource to meet individual organizational needs.

A coding compliance plan should include the following components:

- A general policy statement about the commitment of the organization to correctly assign and report codes

Example: Memorial Medical Center is committed to establishing and maintaining clinical coding and insurance claims processing procedures to ensure that reported codes reflect actual services provided, through accurate information system entries.

- The source of the official coding guidelines used to direct code selection

Example: ICD-9-CM code selection follows the Official Guidelines for Coding and Reporting, developed by the cooperating parties and documented in *Coding Clinic for ICD-9-CM*, published by the American Hospital Association.

Example: CPT code selection follows the guidelines set forth in the CPT manual and in *CPT Assistant,* published by the American Medical Association.

- The parties responsible for code assignment. The ultimate responsibility for code assignment lies with the physician (provider). However, policies and procedures may document instances where codes may be selected or modified by authorized individuals

Example: For inpatient records, medical record analyst I staff are responsible for analysis of records and assignment of the correct ICD-9-CM codes based on documentation by the attending physician.

Example: Emergency department evaluation and management levels for physician services will be selected by the physician and validated by outpatient record analysts using the HCFA/AMA documentation guidelines. When a variance occurs, the following steps are taken for resolution (The actual document should follow with procedure details).

- The procedure to follow when the clinical information is not clear enough to assign the correct code

Example: When the documentation used to assign codes is ambiguous or incomplete, the physician must be contacted to clarify the information and complete/amend the record, if necessary. (The actual document should follow with details of how the medical staff would like this to occur, e.g., by phone call, by note on the record, etc.). Standard protocols for adding documentation to a record must be followed, in accordance with the applicable laws and regulations.

- Specify the policies and procedures that apply to specific locations and care settings. Official coding guidelines for inpatient reporting and outpatient/physician reporting are different. This means that if you are developing a facility-specific coding guideline for emergency department services, designate that the coding rules or guidelines only apply in this setting

Example: When reporting an injection of a drug provided in the emergency department to a Medicare beneficiary, the appropriate CPT code for the administration of the injection is reported in addition to the evaluation and management service code and drug code. CPT codes are reported whether a physician provides the injection personally or a nurse is carrying out a physician's order. This instruction does not always apply for reporting of professional services in the clinics, because administration of medication is considered bundled with the corresponding evaluation and management service for Medicare patients.

Example: Diagnoses that are documented as "probable," "suspected," "questionable," "rule-out," or "working diagnosis" are not to have a code assigned as a confirmed diagnosis. Instead, the code for the condition established at the close of the encounter should be assigned, such as a symptom, sign, abnormal test result, or clinical finding. This guideline applies only to outpatient services.

- Applicable reporting requirements required by specific agencies. The document should include where instructions on payer-specific requirements may be accessed

Example: For patients with XYZ care plan, report code S0800 for patients having a LASIK procedure rather than an unlisted CPT code.

Example: For Medicare patients receiving a wound closure by tissue adhesive only, report HCPCS Level II code G0168 rather than a CPT code.

Many of these procedures will be put into software databases and would not be written as a specific policy. This is true with most billing software, whether for physician services or through the charge description master used by many hospitals.

- Procedures for correction of inaccurate code assignments in the clinical database and to the agencies where the codes have been reported

Example: When an error in code assignment is discovered after bill release and the claim has already been submitted, this is the process required to update and correct the information system and facilitate claim amendment or correction (The actual document should follow with appropriate details).

- Areas of risk that have been identified through audits or monitoring. Each organization should have a defined audit plan for code accuracy and consistency review and corrective actions should be outlined for problems that are identified

Example: A hospital might identify that acute respiratory failure is being assigned as the principal diagnosis with congestive heart failure as a secondary diagnosis. The specific reference to *Coding Clinic* could be listed with instructions about correct coding of these conditions and the process to be used to correct the deficiency.

- Identification of essential coding resources available to and used by the coding professionals

Example: Updated ICD-9-CM, CPT, and HCPCS Level II code books are used by all coding professionals. Even if the hospital uses automated encoding software, at least one printed copy of the coding manuals should be available for reference.

Example: Updated encoder software, including the appropriate version of the NCCI edits and DRG and APC grouper software, is available to the appropriate personnel.

Example: *Coding Clinic* and *CPT Assistant* are available to all coding professionals.

- A process for coding new procedures or unusual diagnoses

Example: When the coding professional encounters an unusual diagnosis, the coding supervisor or the attending physician is consulted. If, after research, a code cannot be identified, the documentation is submitted to the AHA for clarification.

- A procedure to identify any optional codes gathered for statistical purposes by the facility and clarification of the appropriate use of E codes

Example: All ICD-9-CM procedure codes in the surgical range (ICD-9-CM Volume III codes 01.01–86.99) shall be reported for inpatients. In addition, codes reported from the nonsurgical section include the following (Completed document should list the actual codes to be reported).

Example: All appropriate E codes for adverse effects of drugs must be reported. In addition, this facility reports all E codes, including the place of injury for poisonings, all cases of abuse, and all accidents on the initial visit for both inpatient and outpatient services.

- Appropriate methods for resolving coding or documentation disputes with physicians

Example: When the physician disagrees with official coding guidelines, the case is referred to the medical records committee following review by the designated physician liaison from that group.

- A procedure for processing claim rejections

Example: All rejected claims pertaining to diagnosis and procedure codes should be returned to coding staff for review or correction. Any chargemaster issues should be forwarded to appropriate departmental staff for corrections. All clinical codes, including modifiers, must never be changed or added without review by coding staff with access to the appropriate documentation.

Example: If a claim is rejected due to the codes provided in the medical record abstract, the billing department notifies the supervisor of coding for a review rather than changing the code to a payable code and resubmitting the claim.

- A statement clarifying that codes will not be assigned, modified, or excluded solely for the purpose of maximizing reimbursement. Clinical codes will not be changed or amended merely due to either physicians' or patients' request to have the service in question covered by insurance. If the initial code assignment did not reflect the actual services, codes may be revised based on supporting documentation. Disputes with either physicians or patients are handled only by the coding supervisor and are appropriately logged for review

Example: A patient calls the business office saying that her insurance carrier did not pay for her mammogram. After investigating, the HIM coding staff discover that the coding was appropriate for a screening mammogram and that this is a noncovered service with the insurance provider. The code is not changed and the matter is referred back to the business office for explanation to the patient that she should contact her insurance provider with any dispute over coverage of service.

Example: Part of a payment is denied and after review, the supervisor discovers that a modifier should have been appended to the CPT code to denote a separately identifiable service. Modifier –25 is added to the code set and the corrected claim is resubmitted.

Example: A physician approaches the coding supervisor with a request to change the diagnosis codes for his patient because what she currently has is a pre-existing condition that is not covered by her current health plan. The coding supervisor must explain to the physician that falsification of insurance claims is illegal. If the physician insists, the physician liaison for the medical record committee is contacted and the matter is turned over to that committee for resolution if necessary.

- The use of and reliance on encoders within the organization. Coding staff cannot rely solely on computerized encoders. Current coding manuals must be readily accessible and the staff must be educated appropriately to detect inappropriate logic or errors in encoding software. When errors in logic or code crosswalks are discovered, they are reported to the vendor immediately by the coding supervisor

Example: During the coding process, an error is identified in the crosswalk between the ICD-9-CM Volume III code and the CPT code. This error is reported to the software vendor, with proper documentation and notification of all staff using the encoder to not rely on the encoder for code selection.

- Medical records are analyzed and codes selected only with complete and appropriate documentation by the physician available. According to coding guidelines, codes are not assigned without physician documentation. If records are coded without the discharge summary or final diagnostic statements available, processes are in place for review after the summary is added to the record

Example: When records are coded without a discharge summary, they are flagged in the computer system. When the summaries are added to the record, the record is returned to the coding professional for review of codes. If there are any inconsistencies, appropriate steps are taken for review of the changes.

Additional Elements

A coding compliance document should include a reference to the AHIMA Standards of Ethical Coding, which can be downloaded from AHIMA's Web site at www.ahima.org. Reference to the data quality assessment procedures must be included in a coding compliance plan to establish the mechanism for determining areas of risk. Reviews will identify the need for further education and increased monitoring for those areas where either coding variances or documentation deficiencies are identified.

Specific and detailed coding guidelines that cover the reporting of typical services provided by a facility or organization create tools for data consistency and reliability by ensuring that all coders interpret clinical documentation and apply coding principles in the same manner. The appropriate medical staff committee should give final approval of any coding guidelines that involve clinical criteria to assure appropriateness and physician consensus on the process.

The format is most useful when organized by patient or service type and easily referenced by using a table of contents. If the facility-specific guidelines are maintained electronically, they should be searchable by key terms. Placing the coding guidelines on a facility Intranet or internal computer network is a very efficient way to ensure their use and it also enables timely and efficient updating and distribution. Inclusion of references to or live links should be provided to supporting documents such as Uniform Hospital Discharge Data Sets or other regulatory requirements outlining reporting procedures or code assignments.

Prepared by

AHIMA's Coding Practice Team and reviewed by the Coding Policy and Strategy Committee and the Society for Clinical Coding Data Quality Committee

The Codes to Watch: Identifying the DRGs Most Prone to Payment Error

Kimberly Hrehor, MHA, RHIA, CHE

Monitoring codes prone to payment error is an important part of an organization's ongoing efforts to verify coding accuracy. Data from the Hospital Payment Monitoring Program (HPMP) helps identify codes most prone to errors such as over- and undercoding. Organizations can use these data to strengthen their compliance programs.

Collecting Random Samples from the States

The Centers for Medicare and Medicaid Services (CMS) has monitored Medicare inpatient payment error rates for inpatient prospective payment system (PPS) services since the Payment Error Prevention Program (PEPP) was initiated in the fall of 1999. In fall 2001 PEPP was renamed the Hospital Payment Monitoring Program. The purpose of the program remained the same: to measure, monitor, and reduce the incidence of improper payments for Medicare inpatient PPS-reimbursed services. Under this contract activity, quality improvement organizations (QIOs, formerly known as peer review organizations, or PROs) work with hospitals to identify and prevent payment errors. As a payment efficiency program, HPMP serves to protect the Medicare Trust Fund. The calculated payment error rates are also a crucial contributor to the annual fiscal statements for the agency.

To measure and monitor inpatient payment error rates, in 2001 CMS began randomly sampling final action reimbursed claims from each state, Puerto Rico, and the District of Columbia. The corresponding medical records are screened for medical necessity and validated for Diagnosis Related Group (DRG) coding errors by the clinical data abstraction centers. All records failing the screening are referred to the QIOs for full case review. An internal quality-control sample of 10 percent of records that did not fail screening is also sent for review, but error rates determined from the sample are not included in the calculated payment error rates.

In fiscal years 2000 and 2001 the sample included approximately 58,000 cases; in fiscal year 2002 the sample contained approximately 53,000 cases. Currently CMS is sampling 62 cases per state per month (except for Alaska, where 48 records are sampled monthly), an annual total of approximately 38,500 cases. At the time of this article, the latest data analyzed was from fiscal year 2002. Data for 2003 is now available for analysis, and data for 2004 is expected next year.

How Payment Errors Are Calculated

Payment errors identified in the reviews are categorized into six types:

- DRG coding errors

- Admission denials (medical necessity and appropriateness of setting)

- Billing errors

- Technical denials (recoupment of hospital reimbursement for failure to submit a medical record or for submitting a medical record that lacks necessary documentation)

- Combined DRG coding errors and admission denials

- Maryland length-of-stay errors (Maryland is a non-PPS state, and providers in the state are not reimbursed by Medicare under a DRG system.)

Payment errors are measured by dollars in error, which are calculated by determining the difference between what the hospital was paid on the originally sampled claim and what the correct payment should have been. Thus, for unnecessary admissions the dollars in error are equal to the entire reimbursement for the claim and represent an overpayment. For DRG changes, the dollars in error are equal to the difference between what the hospital was paid and the correct DRG payment. This could result in an overpayment to the hospital (in cases of overcoding) or in an underpayment to the hospital (in cases of undercoding).

The absolute value of dollars in error represents the total dollars in error, regardless of whether the hospital was overpaid or underpaid. The net dollars in error represent the net amount of dollars in error, taking into account overpayments and underpayments.

Of the six error types, DRG coding errors have not comprised a large proportion of overall dollars in error. In fiscal year 2002 DRG errors comprised 2.9 percent of the net dollars in error and 30.1 percent of the absolute value of dollars in error nationwide (see "Payment Error Snapshot," below). However, the trend over fiscal years 2000, 2001, and 2002 indicates an increase in net dollars in error for DRG changes, while the absolute value of dollars in error decreased from fiscal years 2000 to 2001 and increased from 2001 to 2002. What does this mean? In essence, the net dollars in error for the nation reflected more undercoding than overcoding in 2000, which remained true, though to a lesser extent, in 2001. However, in 2002 the statistics paint a different picture: hospitals were, overall, overcoding.

Payment Error Snapshot

A national sample of DRG codes in fiscal year 2002 shows $4.8 million in overall error (absolute value of error). The positive net error amount of $330,110 indicates that more errors among the sample resulted from overpayments than underpayments.

Error Type	Description	Claims	Net Error Amount	% of Total Payment*	% of Total Net Error Amount	Absolute Value of Error Amount†	% of Total Payment*	% of Total Absolute Value of Error Amount
1	DRG Change	2,090	$330,110	0.1%	2.9%	$4,805,624	1.3%	30.1%
2, 5	Admission Denials‡	2,293	$8,806,431	2.3%	76.7%	$8,806,431	2.3%	55.2%
3	Billing Errors	293	$1,126,099	0.3%	9.8%	$1,126,099	0.3%	7.1%
4	Technical Denials	132	$1,057,941	0.3%	9.2%	$1,057,941	0.3%	6.6%
6	Maryland LOS Error	136	$166,134	0%	1.4%	$166,134	0%	1.0%
	Total	4,944	$11,486,715	3.1%		$15,962,229	4.2%	

* Total sample was 52,728 claims and total payment was $376,322,491.

† The absolute value of the error amount is the positive value of the error amount and is calculated claim by claim.

‡ Error type 2 = admission/prohibited action denial and error type 5 = admission denial and DRG change.

Overcoding: Top DRGs for Net Dollars in Error

The top 10 DRGs for net dollars in error due to overcoding in fiscal year 2002 are shown in the table below. Note that in some cases the net amount is equal to the absolute value amount. This occurs when all cases for that particular DRG were overcoded. Where these values differ, it indicates that one or more claims for that DRG were undercoded.

Many of the DRGs in this figure are familiar in terms of payment errors. Several have been studied by the Office of the Inspector General.[2-5] Many QIOs also have conducted PEPP or HPMP projects related to these DRGs. For the most part, these are high-paying DRGs.

Original DRG	Claims	Net Error Amount	Absolute Value of Error Amount
468 Extensive OR procedure unrelated to principal diagnosis	31	$233,946	$234,953
475 Respiratory system diagnosis with ventilator support	10	$127,912	$127,912
415 OR procedure for infectious & parasitic diseases	11	$113,665	$113,665
416 Septicemia age >17	32	$103,342	$107,333
014 Specific cerebrovascular disorders except TIA	44	$76,437	$78,128
483 Tracheostomy except for face, mouth & neck diagnoses	2	$63,876	$63,876
316 Renal failure	34	$62,192	$82,743
514 Cardiac defibrillator implant w/ cardiac cath	3	$49,694	$49,694
403 Lymphoma & non-acute leukemia w/ cc	14	$48,819	$48,819
076 Other resp system OR procedures w/ cc	6	$39,876	$39,876

Undercoding: Top DRGs for Net Dollars in Error

Sorting DRG errors by net dollars in error selects the top DRGs that were undercoded. A few of these DRGs may also be familiar as payment errors, as some QIOs may have conduct-ed PEPP projects related to undercoding. Note that the net error amounts are for the most part lower than the amounts for overcoding shown above.

Original DRG		Claims	Net Error Amount	Absolute Value of Error Amount
109	Coronary bypass w/o PTCA or cardiac cath	7	-$54,404	$54,404
088	Chronic obstructive pulmonary disease	36	-$47,595	$69,467
149	Major small & large bowel procedures w/o cc	4	-$42,666	$42,666
090	Simple pneumonia & pleurisy age >17 w/o cc	25	-$39,515	$40,856
143	Chest pain	35	-$35,119	$35,404
175	GI hemorrhage w/o cc	21	-$32,885	$32,885
320	Kidney & urinary tract infections age >17 w cc	47	-$31,885	$54,660
094	Pneumothorax w/ cc	3	-$31,540	$33,337
479	Other vascular procedures w/o cc	10	-$29,101	$39,648
116	Other permanent cardiac pacemaker implant	7	-$28,337	$66,610

Top DRGs for Absolute Value of Dollars in Error

Ranking the results by absolute value of dollars in error provides another way to identify DRGs prone to payment errors. Seven of these DRGs make the top-10 overcoding or undercoding lists. Some, like DRG 079 (Respiratory infections and inflammations age >17 w/ cc), have a small net error amount but a large absolute value error amount. This indicates that both overcoding and undercoding occur, and hospitals are encouraged to focus on making sure the DRG is correct so that payment is correct.

Original DRG		Claims	Net Error Amount	Absolute Value of Error Amount
468	Extensive OR procedure unrelated to principal diagnosis	31	$233,946	$234,953
475	Respiratory system diagnosis with ventilator support	10	$127,912	$127,912
415	OR procedure for infectious & parasitic diseases	11	$113,665	$113,665
416	Septicemia age >17	32	$103,342	$107,333
079	Respiratory infections & inflammations age >17 w/ cc	23	$1,670	$106,752
089	Simple pneumonia & pleurisy age >17 w/ cc	65	-$5,643	$97,432
144	Other circulatory system diagnoses w/ cc	37	$11,755	$84,907
316	Renal failure	34	$62,192	$82,743
014	Specific cerebrovascular disorders except TIA	44	$76,437	$78,128
088	Chronic obstructive pulmonary disease	36	-$47,595	$69,467

Top DRGs for Frequency

DRGs associated with the highest dollars in error are not necessarily the errors that occur the most frequently. The top DRGs by volume of claims in error are identified below. Al-though the dollars associated with these errors may not be as great, they are worth watching simply due to their volume.

Original DRG	Claims	Net Error Amount	Absolute Value of Error Amount
089 Simple pneumonia & pleurisy age >17 w/ cc	65	-$5,643	$97,432
296 Nutritional & misc. metabolic disorders age >17 w/ cc	65	-$10,396	$61,184
182 Esophagitis, gastroent & misc digest disorders age >17 w/ cc	60	-$900	$57,203
140 Angina pectoris	53	-$27,737	$28,423
127 Heart failure & shock	52	-$5,142	$65,597
320 Kidney & urinary tract infections age >17 w cc	47	-$31,885	$54,660
014 Specific cerebrovascular disorders except TIA	44	$76,437	$78,128
144 Other circulatory system diagnoses w/ cc	37	$11,755	$84,907
088 Chronic obstructive pulmonary disease	36	-$47,595	$69,467
143 Chest pain	35	-$35,119	$35,404

Top Change Pairs by Volume

Lastly, there are some DRGs that have a tendency to be changed to another DRG. These have been identified as "DRG change pairs," and the top 10 by volume of claims are listed here. Of the 10 pairs, only two (DRGs 014-015 and 089-088) are changes to lower-paying DRGs.

Original DRG	Revised DRG	Claims	Net Error Amount	Absolute Value of Error Amount	Change
140 Angina pectoris	132 Atherosclerosis w/ cc	39	-$14,089	$14,089	Higher
090 Simple pneumonia & pleurisy age >17 w/o cc	089 Simple pneumonia & pleurisy age >17 w/ cc	20	-$32,254	$32,254	Higher
175 GI hemorrhage w/o cc	174 GI hemorrhage w/ cc	20	-$32,242	$32,242	Higher
014 Specific cerebrovascular disorders except TIA	015 Transient ischemic attack & precerebral occlusions	16	$30,791	$30,791	Lower
089 Simple pneumonia & pleurisy age >17 w/ cc	079 Respiratory infections & inflammations age >17 w/ cc	13	-$38,862	$38,862	Higher
183 Esophagitis, gastroent. & misc. digest disorders age >17 w/o cc	182 Esophagitis, gastroent & misc. digest disorders age >17 w/ cc	12	-$10,007	$10,007	Higher
125 Circulatory disorders except AMI, w/ card cath. w/o complex diag.	124 Circulatory disorders except AMI, w/ card cath & complex diag	12	-$16,936	$16,936	Higher
089 Simple pneumonia & pleurisy age >17 w/ cc	088 Chronic obstructive pulmonary disease	11	$6,561	$6,561	Lower
143 Chest pain	132 Atherosclerosis w/ cc	11	-$5,818	$5,818	Higher
096 Bronchitis & asthma age >17 w/ cc	088 Chronic obstructive pulmonary disease	11	-$4,989	$4,989	Higher

Monitoring Coding Accuracy

How can HIM coding professionals use this information? First, hospitals should ensure they have a strong coding compliance program.[6,7] HIM coding professionals should ensure that there is a process to randomly verify coding accuracy. They should also be aware of the error-prone DRGs identified in these tables. However, they should not limit their monitoring to these DRGs alone. HIM professionals are encouraged to review DRGs that are high in volume within their facility as well as others that have been associated with a high rate of payment errors or involve high reimbursement, such as DRG 475.

HIM professionals can also contact the HPMP department in their state's QIO. The QIO may be able to share data analysis related to DRG errors within the state and provide tools to assist hospitals with the identification and prevention of DRG errors. To locate state QIOs, visit the American Health Quality Association's Web site at www.ahqa.org and click on the "QIO Locator" link.

Notes

1. Centers for Medicare and Medicaid Services. "Fiscal Year 2002 Payment Error Cause Analysis." 2003. Unpublished data.

2. Office of the Inspector General, Office of Evaluations and Inspections. "DRG 79 Validation Study Update: Respiratory Infections and Inflammations." 1993. Available online at http://oig.hhs.gov/oei/reports/oei-12-89-00193.pdf.

3. Office of the Inspector General, Office of Evaluations and Inspections. "Medicare Payments for DRG 296: Nutritional and Miscellaneous Metabolic Disorders." 1999. Available online at http://oig.hhs.gov/oei/reports/oei-03-98-00490.pdf.

4. Office of the Inspector General, Office of Evaluations and Inspections. "Medicare Payments for Septicemia." 1999. Available online at http://oig.hhs.gov/oei/reports/oei-03-98-00370.pdf.

5. Office of the Inspector General, Office of Evaluations and Inspections. "Medicare Payments for DRG 475: Respiratory System Diagnosis with Ventilator Support." 1999. Available online at http://oig.hhs.gov/oei/reports/oei-03-98-00560.pdf.

6. Hanna, Joette. "Constructing a Coding Compliance Plan." *Journal of AHIMA* 73, no. 7 (2002): 48–56.

7. Office of the Inspector General. "The Office of Inspector General's Compliance Program Guidance for Hospitals." 1998. Available online at http://oig.hhs.gov/authorities/docs/cpghosp.pdf.

The analysis upon which this publication is based was performed under Contract Number 500-02-TX03, funded by the Centers for Medicare and Medicaid Services, an agency of the US Department of Health and Human Services. The content of this publication does not necessarily reflect the views or policies of the Department of Health and Human Services, nor does mention of trade names, commercial products, or organizations imply endorsement by the US government. The author assumes full responsibility for the accuracy and completeness of the ideas presented.

Diagnosis Coding and Medical Necessity: Rules and Reimbursement

Janis Cogley, RN, CPC, CCS-P, CHC

Introduction

The origins of using diagnosis codes in hospitals and other healthcare settings goes back to the early 1950s when the US Public Health Service and the Veterans Administration extended the concept of using the International Classification of Diseases to hospital indexing of medical record storage and retrieval. However, the linkage of diagnosis codes to the concept of medical necessity did not occur until 1965 when Title XVIII and IX were added to the Social Security Act, the Medicare and Medicaid programs. The foundation of the Medicare and Medicaid programs is the concept of medical necessity and thus, the importance of diagnosis coding was elevated beyond a mere indexing of data.

The focus of my presentation is on how the bond between diagnosis coding and medical necessity impacts reimbursement of healthcare services. The presentation will explore the various rules in place for diagnosis coding and its importance in supporting the medical necessity of the services performed. The intent of this paper is to provide background information regarding the International Classification of Diseases and a discussion of the importance of medical necessity to the Medicare and Medicaid programs.

Background Information Regarding ICD-9-CM Coding

In 1968, the US Public Health Service published a product, the *Eighth Revision International Classification of Diseases, Adapted for Use in the United States.* This publication became commonly known as ICDA-8, and, beginning in 1968, it served as the basis for coding diagnostic data for both official morbidity and mortality statistics in the US. The current *International Classification of Diseases, Ninth Revision, Clinical Modification (ICD-9-CM)* is based on the official version of the World Health Organization's Ninth Revision, Internal Classification of Diseases (ICD-9).[1]

The term "clinical" is used to emphasize the modification's intent: to serve as a useful tool to classify morbidity data for indexing medical records, medical care review, and ambulatory and other medical care programs, as well as for basic health statistics. To describe the clinical picture of the patient, the codes must be more precise than those needed only for statistical groups and trend analysis. In January 1979, ICD-9-CM was made the single classification system intended primarily for use in the US.

Physicians have been required by law to submit diagnosis codes for Medicare reimbursement since the passage of the Medicare Catastrophic Coverage Act of 1988. This Act requires physician offices to include the appropriate diagnosis codes when billing for services provided to Medicare or Medicaid beneficiaries on or after April 1, 1989. At that time, the Centers for Medicare and Medicaid Services (CMS, formerly HCFA) designated ICD-9-CM as the coding system that physicians must use.

CMS considers *Coding Clinic,* published quarterly by the American Hospital Association, to be the official source for coding guidelines. Hospitals should follow the Coding Clinic guidelines to assure accuracy in ICD-9-CM coding and DRG assignment. Obviously, the guidelines are far too lengthy to include here, but every hospital, physician practice, and other healthcare organization should maintain current versions of the guidelines applicable to their healthcare system. For example, the *Coding Clinic* defines certain terms as follows:

> **Principal Procedure** is the diagnosis that was performed for definitive treatment rather than one performed for diagnostic or exploratory purposes, or was necessary to take care of a complication. If two procedures appear to meet this definition, then the one most related to the principal diagnosis should be selected as the principal procedure.

> **Significant Procedure** is a significant procedure as defined by the Uniform Hospital Discharge Data Set—one that is surgical in nature, carries a procedural or anesthetic risk or requires specialized training.

> **Documentation** means the documentation that must be present in the medical record to substantiate a procedure was medically necessary and that it was performed. A procedure should not be coded from the title of a procedure; the narrative description of the procedure needs to be read and the correct codes need to be determined based on the narrative description. Procedures that are integral to another procedure are not coded separately, for example, the closure.[2]

General guidelines, coding conventions, and chapter-specific guidelines apply to all healthcare settings. Coding sequencing instructions in Volumes I, II, and III of ICD-9-CM take precedence over any guidelines. Each year, major additions and changes to the coding guidelines are published by the cooperating parties and are effective on October first of that year. The *Coding Clinic* purpose is to assist users in coding and reporting accurately when the ICD-9 manual itself does not provide clear direction.

The official guidelines have four sections. They may be generally described as:

- General coding guidelines
- Guidelines for reporting principal diagnosis for inpatient services
- Guidelines for reporting additional diagnosis codes for inpatient services
- Coding guidelines for outpatient services

The major distinctions between inpatient and outpatient reporting are:

- Definitions for principal versus "first listed" diagnosis codes

- The ability to code or not code "rule out" diagnoses

- More common application of V codes and signs/symptoms coding for outpatient services

The proper ICD-9-CM code is the highest level of detail according to the number of digits available. That is, if a code can be described by a four-digit code rather than a three-digit code, then the four-digit code should be selected; similarly, if a five-digit code is available, that code would represent the highest level of detail and should be selected. Codes that are not specified to the highest order possible are considered truncated and may result in a claim denial.

Several other common coding problem areas that may be confusing for physicians and facility coders are:

- The use of E codes. In the past, coders were advised by various payers not to use E codes. Worker's compensation and auto insurers usually require these codes because they provide more detailed information regarding the cause of an accident resulting in an injury. Coders should report E codes when the circumstances warrant it.

- The assignment of a "first listed" diagnosis in the outpatient setting. Often facility coders who are accustomed to applying inpatient coding guidelines for first listed and additional diagnosis code selections have a difficult time adapting to the diagnosis coding requirements for an outpatient setting. The outpatient coding guidelines state that, "For ambulatory surgery, code the diagnosis for which the surgery was performed. If the post-operative diagnosis is known to be different from the pre-operative diagnosis at the time the diagnosis is confirmed, select the post-operative diagnosis for coding since it is most definitive."[3]

- Coders fail to be as specific in their coding as the documentation supports. They select a generic or unlisted diagnosis when a more specific detailed one is available. This may be the result of relying exclusively on the diagnosis codes that are preprinted on an encounter form or another form. Often the forms are not updated to reflect additions, deletions, and description changes that occur at least once a year. The most applicable and specific diagnostic code must be selected when physicians are ordering diagnostic services (clinical diagnostic labs, radiology, and medicine diagnostic services).

- Diagnostic services are often subject to payment limitations based on medical necessity. The failure to provide the most applicable diagnoses may result in the service being denied. Physician practices as well as facilities should ensure that they have procedures in place to verify questionable and/or vague diagnosis codes. In addition, they need to tie in the diagnosis data to the completion of an

Advance Beneficiary Notice (ABN) when the medical necessity is questionable and the patient is a Medicare beneficiary.

- Preventive services diagnosis coding also may present a unique challenge to coders. Medicare does not typically cover "preventive" services except under specific criteria and frequency limitations. Thus, it is important to report the applicable diagnosis codes to receive payment for medically necessary preventive services.

- When a psychiatric diagnosis is listed as the primary diagnosis for a Medicare patient, the services provided may be reduced as a result of the Outpatient Mental Health Treatment Limitation. Psychiatric diagnoses should be coded when they apply, but, if a medically indicated condition other than a psychiatric diagnosis is more appropriate, it should be coded first.

- Coders should assure that services requiring modifiers are properly supported with applicable diagnosis codes. For example, attaching of a "59" modifier to identify a separately excised lesion may require a separate diagnosis code for each excision and/or specimen obtained since the lesions may vary in tissue type. Providing distinct diagnoses for both services will support the necessity for performing and billing both services.

Selecting the correct diagnosis code based on the documentation requires an excellent understanding of the coding guidelines and good cooperation of the physician to provide a detailed description of why he/she provided certain services.

Background Information Regarding Medical Necessity

"Notwithstanding any other provision of this title, no payment may be made under part A or part B for any expenses incurred for items or services- (1)(A) which, except for items and services described in the succeeding subparagraph, are not reasonable and necessary for the diagnosis and treatment of illness or injury to improve the functioning of a malformed body member."

—Social Security Act Chapter XVIII, Section 1862(a) (1)

Some services that are covered under the Medicare program may be limited in coverage due to certain diagnoses, frequency parameters, etc. For example, the payment for a vitamin B-12 injection is limited to diagnoses such as pernicious anemia, gastrointestinal disorder, neuropathies, etc. Therefore, if the criteria are not met, the service will be denied. A procedure may be denied as not reasonable and necessary if it is considered investigational, experimental, or of questionable usefulness. A service may be denied as not reasonable and necessary if it is done more frequently than CMS' policy guidelines specify. When a facility or physician practice is aware of a situation, which Medicare may deny, and they give the Medicare beneficiary an ABN prior to the service and the service is denied, the full charge may be collected from the patient.

Medical necessity denials occur as a result of a National Coverage Determination (NCD) or a Local Coverage Determination (LCD). Between December 2003 and December 2005, Medicare carriers and fiscal intermediaries (FI) are converting their Local Medicare Review Policies (LMRPs) to LCDs.

NCDs and LCDs specify the clinical circumstances under which a service is covered (including whether the circumstances are considered reasonable and necessary). Local coverage decisions may vary in number and content from carrier to carrier and FI to FI.

For example, HGSA administrators, a Medicare carrier for Pennsylvania, has 18 policies under the category "surgical services." Trailblazer, a carrier covering several different states, has only seven LCDs under the surgical service category. Arkansas Blue Cross and Blue Shield, who also functions as a Medicare carrier for several states, has only eight policies under this category.

LCDs may be general, or more specific, and provide narrative descriptions of diagnoses that support the medical necessity of a specific service. In some cases, they may have a detailed list of ICD-9-CM codes under which the service will be considered as reasonable and necessary. The best reference for both NCDs and LCDs is the CMS Web site at www. cms.hhs.gov.

Another important section of the Social Security Act is 1842 (a) (2) (B), which requires Medicare carriers and FIs to apply "safeguards against unnecessary utilization of services furnished by providers." The safeguards may entitle prepayment screens, prepayment reviews, and postpayment reviews to identify inappropriate, medically unnecessary, or excessive services and to take actions where questionable practice patterns are found.

Both prepayment and postpayment reviews use the same set of medical policies. In general, claims received by carriers and FIs are processed on the assumption that providers have the integrity to submit correct information on claims. The claim information, however, must be supported by the medical documentation in the provider's file and must be made available upon request to a carrier or an FI.

The key elements of the medical review process are:

- Monitoring patterns of Medicare claim submissions to identify statistical deviations

- Identifying physicians and suppliers whose utilization patterns differ from medically recognized standards, criteria, and peer norms

- Recovering any inappropriate program expenditures resulting from abuse or over-utilization of services

- Educating physicians and other healthcare providers to prevent future abuse of program funds

- Recommending administrative sanctions under 1128 (a) and 1826 (d) (2) of the Social Security Act when physicians and other healthcare providers fail to correct their inappropriate practices

CMS requires that before carriers and FIs assign significant resources to examine a provider claim to identify potential problems, that a probe audit be conducted. A probe review will be of a small number of claims and will not exceed 100 claims. Providers will be asked to submit any and all medical documentation applicable to the claims in question.

The probe review results may be classified as minor, moderate, or major. If a minor problem is detected, the carrier or FI will educate the provider on appropriate billing procedures, pursue recoupment of claims paid in error, and may conduct further analysis at a later date to ensure the problem was corrected. If a moderate problem is detected, additional action may be to place the provider under a prepayment review until they have demonstrated correction of the billing procedures. When a major problem is detected, in addition to a prepayment review, further sampling may be conducted, payment may be suspended, and a referral may be placed to the Benefit Integrity unit for investigation of fraud or abuse.

Fraud is the intentional deception or misrepresentation that an individual knows to be false, and knowing that the deception could result in some unauthorized benefit to himself/herself or some other person. Examples of fraud are:

- Billing for services and supplies that were not provided
- Misrepresenting the diagnosis for a patient to justify the services or equipment furnished
- Altering claim forms to obtain a high payment amount
- Unbundling (exploding) charges or upcoding
- Participating in schemes that involve collusion between a provider and a beneficiary, that result in higher costs or charges to the Medicare program (for example, kickbacks)

The term abuse describes incidents or practices of providers that are inconsistent with accepted sound medical practices. Abuse may directly or indirectly result in unnecessary costs to the program, improper reimbursement, or program reimbursement for services that fail to meet professionally recognized standards of care or which are medically unnecessary. CMS identifies the overutilization of medical and healthcare services, which occurs when a patient receives services that are not medically necessary or reasonable, as the leading type of abuse.

References

The Social Security Act
Medicare Program Integrity Manual, Chapter 13, Section 1
CMS Web site for NCDs and LCDs
Medicare Claims Processing Manual
ICD-9-CM Official Guidelines for Coding and Reporting, Effective October 1, 2003.
Coding Clinic, American Hospital Association

Endnotes

1. *2004 ICD-9-CM Expert for Physicians,* Volumes 1 and 2.

2. *Coding Clinic,* fourth quarter 1990, page 5.

3. *2004 ICD-9-CM Expert for Hospitals.*

Sample Advance Beneficiary Notice

Patient's Name: _____ Medicare # (HICN): _____

ADVANCE BENEFICIARY NOTICE (ABN)

NOTE: You need to make a choice about receiving these health care items or services.

We expect that Medicare will not pay for the item(s) or service(s) that are described below. Medicare does not pay for all of your health care costs. Medicare only pays for covered items and services when Medicare rules are met. The fact that Medicare may not pay for a particular item or service does not mean that you should not receive it. There may be a good reason your doctor recommended it. Right now, in your case, **Medicare probably will not pay for –**

Items or Services:

Because:

The purpose of this form is to help you make an informed choice about whether or not you want to receive these items or services, knowing that you might have to pay for them yourself. Before you make a decision about your options, you should **read this entire notice carefully.**
 x Ask us to explain, if you don't understand why Medicare probably won't pay.
 x Ask us how much these items or services will cost you (**Estimated Cost: $**_____),
    in case you have to pay for them yourself or through other insurance.

PLEASE CHOOSE **ONE** OPTION. CHECK **ONE** BOX. **SIGN & DATE** YOUR CHOICE.

Option 1. YES.   I want to receive these items or services.

I understand that Medicare will not decide whether to pay unless I receive these items or services. Please submit my claim to Medicare. I understand that you may bill me for items or services and that I may have to pay the bill while Medicare is making its decision. If Medicare does pay, you will refund to me any payments I made to you that are due to me. If Medicare denies payment, I agree to be personally and fully responsible for payment. That is, I will pay personally, either out of pocket or through any other insurance that I have. I understand I can appeal Medicare's decision.

Option 2. NO.   I have decided not to receive these items or services.
I will not receive these items or services. I understand that you will not be able to submit a claim to Medicare and that I will not be able to appeal your opinion that Medicare won't pay.

_____   _____
      Date   **Signature of patient or person acting on patient's behalf**

NOTE: Your health information will be kept confidential. Any information that we collect about you on this form will be kept confidential in our offices. If a claim is submitted to Medicare, your health information on this form may be shared with Medicare. Your health information which Medicare sees will be kept confidential by Medicare.

OMB Approval No. 0938-0566   Form No. CMS-R-131-G   (June 2002)

Internet Resources for Accurate Coding and Reimbursement Practices

The availability of valuable information on the Internet has a positive impact on how the health information coding profession meets today's coding and reimbursement challenges. Coding professionals have access to Internet resources that assist with legislation, coding questions, coding education, payer policy, and clinical research. The Internet has also made it possible to network with coding professionals on a national level in virtual communities of practice.

This Internet resource guide was developed as a convenient resource for coding professionals in all settings. The list is not exhaustive, nor does inclusion on this list represent AHIMA's endorsement. All URLs were accurate at press time but keep in mind the dynamic nature of Web content.

Recommended Resources	Description	Sponsoring Organization	Web Site
Health Insurance Portability and Accountability Act (HIPAA) Administrative Simplification			
Standards for Code Sets	Under HIPAA, this is any set of codes used to encode data elements, such as tables of terms, medical concepts, medical diagnostic codes, or medical procedure codes.		
Current Dental Terminology (CDT)	The official code set used to report medical services and procedures performed by dental professionals.	American Dental Association	www.ada.org/prof/resources/topics/cdt/index.asp and www.ada.org
Healthcare Common Procedure Coding System (HCPCS) Level I — Current Procedural Terminology (CPT)	The official code set used to report procedures and services provided by healthcare professionals and outpatient institutions.	American Medical Association	www.ama-assn.org/ama/pub/category/3113.html and https://catalog.ama-assn.org/Catalog/home.jsp
Healthcare Common Procedure Coding System (HCPCS) Level II — HCPCS National Codes	The official code set used by healthcare professionals and outpatient institutions to report products, supplies, and services not included in the CPT code set.	Centers for Medicare and Medicaid Services	www.cms.hhs.gov/medicare/hcpcs/default.asp
International Classification of Diseases 9th Revision Clinical Modification (ICD-9-CM Volumes I and II)	The official coding classification system used by healthcare professionals and institutions to report morbidity and mortality information.	National Center for Health Statistics, Centers for Disease Control	www.cdc.gov/nchs/icd9.htm
International Classification of Diseases 9th Revision Clinical Modification (ICD-9-CM Volume III)	The official code set used by inpatient hospital institutions to report procedural information.	Centers for Medicare and Medicaid Services	www.cms.hhs.gov/payment systems/icd9/default.asp
National Drug Code (NDC)	A coding system for pharmacies to report services, supplies, drugs, and biologic information.	US Food and Drug Administration	www.fda.gov/cder/ndc/ preface.htm

Recommended Resources	Description	Sponsoring Organization	Web Site
Standards for Electronic Transactions	Under HIPAA, this is a transaction that complies with the applicable HIPAA standard.		
Designated Standard Maintenance Organization (DSMO)	The DSMO was established in the final HIPAA rule and is charged with maintaining the standards for electronic transactions, developing or modifying an adopted standard.	Secretary of the Department of Health and Human Services	www.hipaa-dsmo.org
Accredited Standards Committee X12 (ASC X12)	ASC X12 is a designated committee under the DSMO that develops uniform standards for cross-industry exchange of business transactions through electronic data interchange standards.	Secretary of the Department of Health and Human Services	www.x12.org
Dental Content Committee (DeCC) of the American Dental Association	DeCC is the designated committee under the DSMO responsible for addressing standard transaction content on behalf of the dental sector of the healthcare community.	Secretary of the Department of Health and Human Services	www.ada.org/prof/resources/ topics/dentalcontent.asp
Health Level Seven (HL7)	HL7 is a designated organization under the DSMO that addresses issues at the seventh, or application, level of healthcare systems interconnections.	Secretary of the Department of Health and Human Services	www.hl7.org
National Council for Prescription Drug Programs (NCDP)	A designated committee under the DSMO that specializes in developing standards for exchanging prescription and payment information.	Secretary of the Department of Health and Human Services	www.ncpdp.org
National Uniform Billing Committee (NUBC)	A designated committee under the DSMO that is responsible for identifying data elements and designing the CMS-1500.	Secretary of the Department of Health and Human Services	www.nubc.org
National Uniform Claim Committee (NUCC)	The national group that replaced the Uniform Claim Form Task Force in 1995 and developed a standard data set to be used in the transmission of noninstitutional provider claims to and from third-party payers.	Secretary of the Department of Health and Human Services	www.nucc.org
Other Electronic Transaction Resources			
Electronic Data Interchange (EDI)	A standard transmission format using strings of data for business information communicated among the computer systems of independent organizations.	Centers for Medicare and Medicaid Services	www.cms.hhs.gov/providers/ edi
National Provider Identifier (NPI)	An alphanumeric identifier used to identify individual healthcare providers for Medicare billing purposes and intended for use with all insurance plans.	Centers for Medicare and Medicaid Services	www.cms.hhs.gov/provider update/regs/cms0045f.pdf
Washington Publishing Company (WPC)	WPC manages and distributes EDI from organizations that develop, maintain, and implement EDI standards. The WPC home page provides implementation guides such as the X12N HIPAA Implementation Guide, educational resources, and additional HIPAA tools.	Washington Publishing Company	www.wpc-edi.com/ Default_ 40.asp
Workgroup for Electronic Data Interchange (WEDI)	A subgroup of Accreditation Standards Committee X12 that has been involved in developing electronic data interchange standards for billing transactions.	Centers for Medicare and Medicaid Services	www.wedi.org

Recommended Resources	Description	Sponsoring Organization	Web Site
Official ICD-9-CM Resources			
Coding Clinic for ICD-9-CM	Official publication for ICD-9-CM coding guidelines and coding advice as approved by the four cooperating parties.	American Hospital Association	www.hospitalconnect.com/ ahacentraloffice/coding/ icd-9-cm_prod.jsp
ICD-9-CM Guidelines for Coding and Reporting	Official coding guidelines developed to assist coding professionals in situations where the ICD-9-CM does not provide instruction.	National Center for Health Statistics, Centers for Disease Control	www.cdc.gov/nchs/datawh/ ftpserv/ftpicd9/ftpicd9. htm#guidelines
ICD-9-CM Volumes I and II Code Updates (Coordination and Maintenance Committee and addenda)	Addendum to the annual (biannual effective April 2005) diagnosis code updates and Coordination and Maintenance Committee reports.	National Center for Health Statistics, Centers for Disease Control	www.cdc.gov/nchs/about/ot heract/icd9/maint/maint.htm
ICD-9-CM Volume III Code Updates	Addendum to the annual (biannual effective April 2005) procedure code updates.	Centers for Medicare and Medicaid Services	www.cms.hhs.gov/payment systems/icd9/default.asp
HCPCS Level I CPT Resources			
Category I, II, III Updates	Category I CPT Codes: Code revisions are published annually and become effective at the beginning of each year. Category II CPT Codes: Code revisions are released electronically each July. The revisions are published in the CPT book and become effective at the beginning of the next year.Category III CPT Codes: New codes are distributed electronically on a semiannual basis and published in the CPT book annually.	American Medical Association	www.ama-assn.org/ama/pub/ category/3884.html
CPT Assistant	A monthly newsletter that provides official CPT coding advice.	American Medical Association	https://catalog.ama-assn.org/ Catalog/home.jsp
CPT Change Requests	CPT code modification process and request for changes.	American Medical Association	www.ama-assn.org/ama/pub/ category/3112.html
CPT Errata	Electronic list that provides corrections to the annual CPT category code changes.	American Medical Association	www.ama-assn.org/ama/pub/ category/3896.html
HCPCS Level II Resources			
Code Updates and Code Modification Process	National codes are published annually and go into effect at the beginning of each year. Temporary codes can be revised quarterly and the changes are made available electronically and published on an annual basis.	Centers for Medicare and Medicaid Services	www.cms.hhs.gov/medicare/ hcpcs
Coding Clinic on HCPCS	Coding resource newsletter that provides accurate coding advice for the users of HCPCS.	American Hospital Association	www.hospitalconnect.com/ ahacentraloffice/coding/ hcpcs_ prod.jsp

Recommended Resources	Description	Sponsoring Organization	Web Site
CDT Resources			
CDT Updates	Code revisions are published and effective biannually at the beginning of odd-numbered years.	American Dental Association	www.ada.org/prof/resources/topics/cdt/index.asp
Additional Coding Classification Systems, Nomenclatures, and Vocabularies			
Diagnostic and Statistical Manual of Mental Disorders, Fourth Edition (DSM-IV)	A nomenclature to standardize the diagnostic process for patients with psychiatric disorders; includes codes that correspond to ICD-9-CM codes.	American Psychiatric Association	www.appi.org/dsm.cfx
Alternative Billing Concepts (ABC) Codes	Contains more than 4,000 codes that describe what is said, done, ordered, prescribed, or distributed by providers of alternative medicine. Disciplines covered by this system include acupuncture, holistic medicine, massage therapy, homeopathy, naturopathy, ayurvedic medicine, chiropractors, and midwifery.	Alternative Link	www.alternativelink.com/ali/home
Home Health Care Classification (HHCC) System	A taxonomy of nursing diagnoses and nursing interventions.	The HHCC System emerged from the federally funded Home Care Project conducted at Georgetown University School of Nursing.	www.sabacare.com
International Statistical Classification of Diseases and Related Health Problems, Tenth Revision (ICD-10)	The ICD-10 version of the disease classification system developed by the World Health Organization is used to report morbidity and mortality information worldwide. Effective with deaths occurring in 1999, the US replaced ICD-9 with ICD-10 for mortality reporting.	World Health Organization	www.cdc.gov/nchs/about/major/dvs/icd10des.htm
International Statistical Classification of Diseases, Tenth Revision, Clinical Modification (ICD-10-CM)	The future US coding classification system for healthcare professionals and institutions to report morbidity and mortality data.	National Center for Health Statistics, Centers for Disease Control	www.cdc.gov/nchs/about/otheract/icd9/abticd10.htm
International Statistical Classification of Diseases, Tenth Revision, Clinical Modification (ICD-10-CM)	The future US coding classification for institutions to report procedural information.	Developed by 3M Health Information Services under contract with the Centers for Medicare and Medicaid Services	www.cms.hhs.gov/providers/pufdownload/icd10.asp
International Classification of Primary Care (ICPC)	A reliable classification system for primary care physicians that enables the labeling of the most prevalent conditions that exist in the community as well as symptoms and complaints.	Published by the World Organization of Family Doctors	www.globalfamilydoctor.com

Recommended Resources	Description	Sponsoring Organization	Web Site
International Classification of Diseases for Oncology (ICD-O)	The standard tool for coding diagnoses of neoplasms in tumor and cancer registrars and in pathology laboratories. ICD-O is a dual classification with coding systems for both topography and morphology. The topography code describes the site of origin of the neoplasm and uses the same three-character and four-character categories as in the neoplasm section of Chapter II, ICD-10.	World Health Organization	www.who.int/bookorders/ anglais/detart1.jsp?sesslan =1&codlan=1&codcol=15& codcch=3350
International Classification of Functioning, Disability and Health (ICF)	The ICF is a health and health-related classification system that reports body functions and structures, activities, and participation.	World Health Organization	www3.who.int/icf/icftem plate.cfm?myurl=homepage. html&mytitle=Home%20Page
Logical Observation and Identifier Codes (LOINC)	The LOINC coding system electronically exchanges laboratory and clinical information.	The Regenstrief Institute maintains the LOINC database and its supporting documentation.	www.loinc.org
MEDCIN	MEDCIN is a terminology and presentation engine. It includes more than 250,000 clinical data elements encompassing symptoms, history, physical examination, tests, diagnoses, and therapy.	Medicomp Systems, Inc.	www.medicomp.com
Medical Dictionary for Regulatory Activities (MedDRA)	MedDRA is a global standard medical terminology and expected to supersede or replace terminologies currently in use with the medical product development process.	Maintenance and Support Services Organization	www.meddramsso.com/ NewWeb2003/medra_over view/index.htm
National Drug File Reference Terminology (NDF-RT)	The NDF-RT is being developed for the Veterans Administration as a reference standard for medications to support a variety of clinical, administrative, and analytical purposes.	Department of Veterans Affairs	www.va.gov/vdl/Clinical. asp?appID=89
RxNorm	RxNorm is a clinical drug nomenclature that provides standard names for clinical drugs (active ingredient, strength, and dose form) and for dose forms as administered.	National Library of Medicine	www.nlm.nih.gov/ research/ umls/rxnorm _main.html
North American Nursing Diagnosis Association (NANDA) International	Organization of the NANDA-International nursing diagnoses has evolved from an alphabetical listing in the mid-1980s to a conceptual system that guides the classification of nursing diagnoses in a taxonomy.	North American Nursing Diagnosis Association	www.nanda.org/html/ taxonomy.html
Nursing Intervention Classification (NIC)	NIC is a comprehensive, research-based, standardized classification of interventions that nurses perform.	University of Iowa College of Nursing	www.nursing.uiowa.edu/ centers/cncce/nic
Nursing Outcomes Classification (NOC)	NOC is a comprehensive, standardized classification of patient/client outcomes developed to evaluate the effects of nursing interventions.	University of Iowa College of Nursing	www.nursing.uiowa.edu/ centers/cncce/noc
Omaha System	The Omaha System is a research-based, comprehensive taxonomy designed to generate meaningful data following usual or routine documentation of client care.	Omaha System Advisory Committee	www.omahasystem.org

Recommended Resources	Description	Sponsoring Organization	Web Site
Systematized Nomenclature of Dentistry (SNODENT)	SNODENT is a systematized nomenclature of dentistry containing dental diagnoses, signs, symptoms, and complaints.	American Dental Association	www.ada.org
Systematized Nomenclature of Medicine Clinical Terms (SNOMED CT)	SNOMED CT is a comprehensive clinical terminology and infrastructure that enables a consistent way of capturing, sharing, and aggregating health data across specialties and sites of care.	SNOMED International, a division of the College of American Pathologists and the United Kingdom's National Health Service	www.snomed.org
Universal Medical Device Nomenclature System (UMDNS)	UMDNS is a standard international nomenclature and coding system used to facilitate identifying, processing, filing, storing, retrieving, transferring, and communicating data about medical devices.	ECRI (formerly the Emergency Care Research Institute)	www.ecri.org
Health, Research, and Comparative Data			
Unified Medical Language System (UMLS)	A program initiated by the National Library of Medicine to build an intelligent, automated system that can understand biomedical concepts, words, and expressions and their interrelationships.	National Library of Medicine	www.nlm.nih.gov/ research/ umls
Medical Literature, Analysis, and Retrieval System Online (MEDLINE)	MEDLINE is an online database that offers access to millions of clinical articles. The topic areas include medicine, dentistry, nursing, pharmacy, allied health, and veterinary medicine.	National Library of Medicine	http://medlineplus.gov
Agency for Healthcare Research and Quality (AHRQ)	AHRQ supports research and provides information on the quality of healthcare, patient safety issues, and healthcare costs.	Department of Health and Human Services	www.ahrq.gov
Medicare Provider Analysis and Review (MEDPAR)	The MEDPAR database is used for administrative purposes to collect information on Medicare claims and consists of data such as DRGs, ICD-9-CM codes, Medicare coverage information, and patient demographics.	Centers for Medicare and Medicaid Services	www.cms.hhs.gov/ statistics/ medpar/default.asp
American Hospital Directory (AHD)	The AHD provides an inpatient and outpatient Medicare claims database for more than 6,000 hospitals.	American Hospital Directory	www.ahd.com
Medstat	Medstat is a healthcare information company that provides market intelligence and benchmark databases, decision support solutions, and research services for managing the cost and quality of healthcare.	Thomson Corporation	www.medstat.com
Statistics			
National Committee on Vital Healthcare and Statistics (NCVHS)	NCVHS serves as a national advisory board to the public on health data, statistics, and information systems.	Department of Health and Human Services	www.ncvhs.hhs.gov

Recommended Resources	Description	Sponsoring Organization	Web Site
National Center for Health Statistics (NCHS)	NCHS is a public health statistics agency charged with collecting statistical information critical for improving public health in the US.	Department of Health and Human Services	www.cdc.gov/nchs
Centers for Disease Control and Prevention (CDC)	CDC includes federal agencies that oversee health promotion and disease control and prevention activities in the US.	Department of Health and Human Services	www.cdc.gov
National Center for Vital Statistics (NCVS)	NCVS provides statistical information compiled at the state level. Statistics include births, deaths, and fetal deaths.	Department of Health and Human Services	www.cdc.gov/nchs/nvss.htm
Clinical Resources			
National Institutes of Health (NIH)	NIH consists of 18 separate health institutes, the National Center for Complementary and Alternative Medicine, and the National Library of Medicine.	Department of Health and Human Services	www.nih.gov
National Library of Medicine (NLM)	NLM is the national online library for biomedicine and health science information.	National Institutes of Health	www.nlm.nih.gov
The Visible Human Project	NLM's development of anatomically detailed and three-dimensional representations of normal human bodies.	National Institutes of Health	www.nlm.nih.gov/research/ visible/visible_human.html
Virtual Hospital	Virtual Hospital is a digital health sciences library for healthcare providers and patients. It contains thousands of textbooks and booklets.	University of Iowa Health Care	www.vh.org
Compliance Resources			
Department of Health and Human Services (HHS) Office of Inspector General (OIG)	OIG protects the integrity of HHS programs, as well as the health and welfare of the beneficiaries of those programs.	Department of Health and Human Services	www.oig.hhs.gov
Fiscal Year OIG Work Plan	The focused CMS Work Plan assists OIG with the prevention of healthcare fraud, waste, and abuse.	Department of Health and Human Services	http://oig.hhs.gov/publications. html
Fraud Prevention and Detection	Resources including compliance programs, corporate integrity agreements, and exclusion programs.	Department of Health and Human Services	http://oig.hhs.gov/fraud.html
Fighting Fraud and Abuse	Resources to assist with the integrity of the Medicare program.	Centers for Medicare and Medicaid Services	www.cms.hhs.gov/providers/ fraud/default.asp
Health Care Compliance Association	The Health Care Compliance Association is a professional association providing its members with compliance news, information, and a variety of related services.	Health Care Compliance Association	www.hcca-info.org
Medicare Reimbursement Resources			
Federal Register	The daily publication of the US Government Printing Office for proposed rules, rules, and notices of federal agencies and organizations, as well as executive orders and other presidential documents.	US Government	www.gpoaccess.gov/fr and www.access.gpo.gov/su_docs/ fedreg/frcont04.html

Recommended Resources	Description	Sponsoring Organization	Web Site
Conditions of Participation and Conditions for Coverage	CMS develops Conditions of Participation (CoPs) and Conditions for Coverage (CfCs) that healthcare organizations must meet to participate in the Medicare and Medicaid programs.	Centers for Medicare and Medicaid Services	www.cms.hhs.gov/cop
Documentation Guidelines Evaluation and Management Services	Documentation guidelines developed to supplement the CPT Evaluation and Management service code definitions used for physician reporting.	Centers for Medicare and Medicaid Services	www.cms.hhs.gov/medlearn/emdoc.asp
Electronic Code of Federal Regulations (e-CFR)	E-CFR is a sample model of a currently updated version of the Code of Federal Regulations (CFR). The CFR is the official compilation of federal rules and requirements.	National Archives and Records Administration's Office of the Federal Register and the Government Printing Office	www.gpoaccess.gov/ecfr
Intermediary-Carrier Contacts	A private company directory that contracts with CMS to pay Medicare Part A (Intermediary) and Part B (Carrier) claims.	Centers for Medicare and Medicaid Services	www.cms.hhs.gov/contacts/incardir.asp
Internet Only Manuals (IOMs)	IOMs provide technical and professional information about the Medicare and Medicaid programs.	Centers for Medicare and Medicaid Services	www.cms.hhs.gov/manuals
Medicare Coverage Home Page	CMS develops coverage policies to indicate whether and under what circumstances certain services are covered under the Medicare program. The Medicare coverage home page provides access to coverage updates, coverage policies, and a Medicare coverage database.	Centers for Medicare and Medicaid Services	www.cms.hhs.gov/coverage
Medicare Learning Network (Medlearn)	The Medlearn site provides access to a variety of education products to assist providers and beneficiaries and their advocates in understanding the Medicare program.	Centers for Medicare and Medicaid Services	www.cms.hhs.gov/medlearn
Medlearn Matters	Medlearn Matters includes informational articles designed to help providers understand new or changed Medicare policy.	Centers for Medicare and Medicaid Services	www.cms.hhs.gov/medlearn/matters
Medicare Payment Systems	This site provides valuable links to pages containing informational materials on Medicare payment systems and coding files.	Centers for Medicare and Medicaid Services	www.cms.hhs.gov/payment systems
Medicare Payment System Files	This site provides files for download for Medicare payment systems.	Centers for Medicare and Medicaid Services	www.cms.hhs.gov/providers/pufdownload
Medicare Providers	This provider-specific home page is a one-stop resource focused on the informational needs and interests of Medicare providers, including physicians and other practitioners.	Centers for Medicare and Medicaid Services	www.cms.hhs.gov/providers
Paper Forms and Instructions	This link provides information on the CMS-1500, UB-92, CMS 1491, CMS 1490S, and EDI enrollment form.	Centers for Medicare and Medicaid Services	www.cms.hhs.gov/providers/edi/edi5.asp

Recommended Resources	Description	Sponsoring Organization	Web Site
Medicare Preventive Services	Coding and reporting guidance for preventive services covered under the Medicare program.	Centers for Medicare and Medicaid Services	www.cms.hhs.gov/ preventiveservices
Health Information	This site provides Medicare beneficiaries with information about Medicare benefits, publications, and valuable Web sites.	Centers for Medicare and Medicaid Services	www.medicare.gov/Health/ Overview.asp
Quality Improvement Organizations (QIOs)	QIOs contract with CMS to ensure that Medicare beneficiaries receive high-quality healthcare that is medically necessary and appropriate and meets professionally recognized standards of care.	Centers for Medicare and Medicaid Services	www.cms.hhs.gov/qio
CMS Quarterly Provider Update	The update communicates current provider information on regulations, policies, and revisions made to the manual instructions.	Centers for Medicare and Medicaid Services	www.cms.hhs.gov/provider update
Governmental Data Sets			
Data Elements for Emergency Department Systems (DEEDS)	Developed to create uniform specifications for data entered in emergency department patient records.	National Center for Injury Prevention and Control	www.cdc.gov/ncipc/pub-res/ deedspage.htm
Minimum Data Set for Long-Term Care (MDS 2.0)	A patient-centered assessment instrument that Medicare- and Medicaid-certified nursing facilities must use to conduct a comprehensive, accurate, standardized, reproducible assessment of each resident's functional capacity.	Centers for Medicare and Medicaid Services	www.cms.hhs.gov/medicaid/ mds20
Minimum Data Set for Post Acute Care (MDS-PAC)	A patient-centered assessment instrument that must be completed for every Medicare patient and emphasizes a patient's care needs instead of provider characteristics.	Centers for Medicare and Medicaid Services	www.cms.hhs.gov/review/ 03spring/default.asp
Nursing Minimum Data Set (NMDS)	This data set covers nursing diagnosis; nursing intervention; nursing outcome; intensity of nursing care; unique identifier of principal nurse provider; patient demographics; and service items from the uniform hospital data set.	NMDS Consortium	www.nursing.uiowa.edu/NI/ collabs_files/Synopsis%20 NMDS%20Nov%202003.pdf
Outcomes and Assessment Information Set (OASIS)	A standard core assessment data tool developed to measure the outcomes of adult patients receiving home health services under the Medicare and Medicaid programs.	Centers for Medicare and Medicaid Services	www.cms.hhs.gov/oasis/ oasisdat.asp
Uniform Hospital Discharge Data Set (UHDDS)	A core set of data elements adopted by the US Department of Health, Education, and Welfare in 1974 that are collected by hospitals on all discharges and all discharge abstract systems. The UHDDS definitions are used by acute care short-term hospitals to report inpatient data elements in a standardized manner.	Developed through NCVHS, required by HHS departmental policy	www.cms.hhs.gov/manuals/ 45_smm/sm_11_11375.asp
Uniform Ambulatory Care Data Set (UACDS)	A data set developed by the National Committee on Vital and Health Statistics consisting of a minimum set of patient/client-specific data elements to be collected in ambulatory care settings.	Recommended by NCVHS	www.ncvhs.hhs.gov/ncvhsr1. htm

Recommended Resources	Description	Sponsoring Organization	Web Site
Nongovernmental Data Sets			
Health Plan Employer Data and Information Set (HEDIS)	A set of performance measures designed to provide purchasers and consumers of healthcare with the information they need to compare the performance of managed care plans.	National Committee for Quality Assurance	www.ncqa.org/communi cations/publications/ hedispub. htm
ORYX	ORYX integrates outcomes and other performance measurement data into the accreditation process. Joint Commission–accredited hospitals collect data on standardized—or core—performance measures.	Joint Commission on Accreditation of Healthcare Organizations	www.jcaho.org/accredited +organizations/hospitals/ oryx/ oryx+facts.htm
AHIMA Member Resources			
Communities of Practice (CoP)	The CoP is an online member interaction tool providing up-to-date industry news, links to helpful resources, and, most importantly, solutions and ideas from peers. The monthly *CodeWrite* newsletters are contained in the Coding CoP.	AHIMA	https://www.ahimanet.org /COP
FORE Library: HIM Body of Knowledge	The FORE Library: HIM Body of Knowledge offers AHIMA-owned content and links to public material that encompass the theory and practice of health information management.	AHIMA	www.ahima.org, click on "Body of Knowledge"
HIM Productivity Standards	This site provides resources to locate productivity standards for health information management functions in an acute care facility	AHIMA	www.ahima.org, click on "Body of Knowledge"
HIM Resources: Coding	The AHIMA coding home page includes information on coding events, coding education, coding roundtables, and more.	AHIMA	www.ahima.org/coding
"Managing and Improving Data Quality"	This practice brief offers guidelines and recommendations for adhering to coding data quality mandates.	AHIMA	www.ahima.org, click on "Body of Knowledge"
Standards of Ethical Coding	The standard of professional ethics for health information coding professionals.	AHIMA	www.ahima.org/infocenter/ guidelines/standards.cfm
"Where to Find Answers to Your Coding Questions"	This article will help you find solutions to your toughest coding questions by using available guidelines and by leveraging the networking and resource-sharing capabilities of AHIMA's CoP.	AHIMA	www.ahima.org, click on "Body of Knowledge"
"Developing a Physician Query Process"	This practice brief provides information on developing a query to improve physician documentation and coding professionals' understanding of the unique clinical situation.	AHIMA	www.ahima.org, click on "Body of Knowledge"
"Regulatory Journey to Destination 10: Understanding the Process for Adoption of ICD-10-CM and ICD-10-PCS"	This article provides an understanding of the regulatory process for the adoption and implementation of ICD-10.	AHIMA	www.ahima.org, click on "Body of Knowledge"

Prepared by

AHIMA Coding Practice Team

Kathy Giannangelo, RHIA, CCS
Susan Hull, MPH, RHIA, CCS
Karen Kostick, RHIT, CCS, CCS-P
Rita Scichilone, MHSA, RHIA, CCS, CCS-P
Mary Stanfill, RHIA, CCS, CCS-P
Sarah Wills-Dubose, MA, MEd, RHIA
Ann Zeisset, RHIT, CCS, CCS-P

Can You Manage Managed Care?

by Sue Willner, RHIA

You just received an enticing offer from a nationally known managed care organization (MCO) to interview for a newly created position to "manage their data." The money is great and the location intriguing. But you have never worked in managed care, and you don't know how well your skills translate. In fact, you are not even clear what managed care is. Are you naïve to think that you can consider this job?

No, not at all. Not only are you qualified to consider this job, but in fact, you have skills, vision, and expertise that are valuable to helping MCOs achieve their goals.

In recent years, healthcare has become so complicated that the lines between managed care and the rest of the industry have blurred in unexpected and surprising ways. The mergers, buy-outs, restructuring, and integrations of the last 10 years have affected both managed and "non-managed" care so comprehensively that there are more similarities than differences in the aspects of the business regarding data and information management.

So before insecurities undermine you, consider performing an objective pre-interview assessment to determine if this is a worthwhile opportunity for you. What do you know, what don't you know, and how difficult will it be to converse knowledgeably and confidently about data, databases, and data-related needs in the managed care setting? This article will help you find out.

What Is Managed Care?

With all the recent negative publicity surrounding managed care, it is easy to forget that managed care is merely a generic term for a system or process designed to manage costs, quality, and access to healthcare services for a select population of enrolled members. The MCO could be a health maintenance organization (HMO), a preferred provider organization (PPO), a point-of-service plan (POS), or more likely a hybrid, because most of the original models have metamorphosed into a mélange of MCOs with varied characteristics. Furthermore, if the MCO is an HMO, it could be a staff, group, or network model, an independent practice association (IPA), or a mix of different models.

All MCOs, despite their diverse structures, are facing an information maelstrom. Now, more than ever, their ability to deliver information to the right place at the right time is a strategy for survival. MCOs are scrambling, not unlike their colleagues in the nonmanaged care world, to translate their voluminous data into accurate, complete, and timely information that serves the needs of their primary stakeholders.

An HIM professional preparing for a job in managed care must therefore understand the incentives of each of the major players and be able to answer the question "How can I, through my knowledge, experience, and vision of information management, support these stakeholders so that this organization can attain its short- and long-term goals?"

Stakeholders: Who Is Bearing the Risk?

First, it's important to understand that the concept of risk is at the heart of managed care. Historically, managing care meant that healthcare providers were "at risk" by accepting the same payment per plan member, regardless of the actual cost of treatment. Those fixed prepaid fees, known as capitation, are the bedrock upon which managed care was based.

But like everything else in the healthcare industry today, things have gotten complicated. Capitation is disappearing as a basis for risk payments and is being replaced by more sophisticated risk-adjustment systems. Everyone involved with managed care has a stake in the competing demands of patient care and economic viability, and therefore risk is now shared by many.

For HIM professionals, this means that the various stakeholders need accurate information and efficient information systems to help them play their respective roles in balancing the goals of trying to provide quality healthcare while maintaining financial health.

HIM professionals are already familiar with the healthcare industry's four primary stakeholders: patients, providers/ practitioners, payers/insurers, and the government (as regulator). But as you consider entering managed care, you must also appreciate the role of employer groups and health plans, two players who add considerable complexity to an already crowded field of data needs.

The Primary Stakeholders

Employer Groups

As a managed care novice, you may be surprised by the influence, power, and impact of employer groups. But it makes sense once you realize that employers are the largest purchasers of healthcare, with huge incentives to reduce overall healthcare costs by keeping employees healthy. In a recent article describing General Motors' internal disease management program, the authors note that "the challenge for GM and hundreds of other health plan sponsors is to invest healthcare dollars in prevention and treatment that provide return on investment (ROI)."[1]

Employer groups therefore apply major pressures and significant data demands on MCOs, which means much work for HIM professionals. The Health Plan Employer Data and Information Set (HEDIS), for example, provides employer groups and healthcare consumers with the data needed to compare health plan performance.

A continuously evolving set of performance measures, HEDIS requires tremendous health plan resources to collect, submit, and ensure the quality of data. You, as the MCO's health information professional, would be intimately familiar with the HEDIS set of quality, access, and cost indicators, the source databases, and the process from data collection to submission to audit.

Many large companies and employer groups require MCO accreditation to demonstrate that they deliver high-quality healthcare that is accessible and responsive to member needs. As a key member of any accreditation survey preparation team, you would ensure that your MCO's data could meet the rigorous standards set by the accrediting organizations.

The National Committee for Quality Assurance (NCQA), for example, requires an MCO to show baseline data on why a particular problem or area was chosen for quality improvement, where they started, where they are now, where they expect to go, and how they will know when they improve. Furthermore, the data must be properly sampled, presented, and interpreted to the satisfaction of sophisticated surveyors. An HIM professional specializing in data management would be a central player in using data to demonstrate quality or identify areas for quality improvement.

More recently, employer groups are again leading the way as the healthcare industry is faced with the challenge of increasing efforts to protect patient safety and reduce medical errors. The damaging 1999 Institute of Medicine (IOM) Report, with its stunning announcement of patient mortality due to medical errors, was followed by a second report in February 2001 that criticized a healthcare delivery system "plagued by a serious quality gap."[2] Your contribution will likely be to help select and implement systems designed to minimize medical errors and provide members with data that demonstrate meaningful improvements in patient safety.

Health Plans and Their Members

In a recent article in Health Data Management, Ralph Korpman, president and CEO of e-health company HealthTrio, Inc., observed that health plan members, another managed care stakeholder, have two basic needs: gaining information on their own health and knowing how much money they owe to whom.[3] These needs may sound simple, but the information demands of plan members are a comprehensive challenge for data experts in any organization. Now, with the new privacy and security requirements of the Health Insurance Portability and Accountability Act (HIPAA), this task becomes even more daunting.

In the volatile and threatened managed care market, where member retention is of considerable concern, health plans must increase their membership by enhancing relationships between members and providers and between members and the plan itself. To accomplish this, innovative MCOs are planning to invest in building one-on-one relationships with their members through the Internet. They want to communicate with their members about everything that a member cares about, including enrollment, benefits, referral information, health assessments, claims status reports, online prescription ordering, accreditation results, quality report cards, and preventive health.

However, HIM professionals know that patient data are often far from accurate and complete. Data and databases abound but MCOs, like the nonmanaged care world, still lack the ability to provide the right information at the right place and time. With so many different databases, healthcare analyst Cynthia Burghard of the Gartner Group commented recently that "you spend 50 percent to 80 percent of your time reconciling differences in data rather than actually doing something with it."[4]

Furthermore, the quality of the data that are acceptable to MCOs for making business decisions is different than the quality required of personal data that will be scrutinized by members. This point is key to why MCOs need the services of skilled HIM professionals who are adept at managing data.

Inside the organization, poor data quality is a problem. But it could be downright disastrous if a member viewed her own health information online and found that her MCO had incorrect or missing data in her record.

This is where MCOs need your expertise to help design IT systems that efficiently deliver online information to their members. As their HIM professional, you know the data, you know the databases, and you understand the users' needs; this makes you a vital consultant when it comes time to design the new generation of healthcare information delivery systems.

Health Plans and Providers

MCO physicians, like physicians in any healthcare organization, are key stakeholders who want to devote more of their time and energy to treating patients and therefore seek to reduce the time and cost of administrative tasks. Their wish list often includes less intrusion by MCOs into treatment decisions, less onerous medical record documentation, reduction of conflicting and confusing third-party payer regulations and billing rules, and more administrative support.

Recent actions on the national scene have intensified physician concerns with these same issues. The IOM's reports identifying patient safety problems, the Office of the Inspector General's (OIG) work plans and compliance programs, and the Healthcare Financing Administration's (HCFA) ongoing onslaught of changing Medicare regulations and reimbursement systems will continue to increase physician concerns regarding the support they need.

Physicians look to their MCO to solve their perceived problems. They want information systems that eliminate or greatly reduce their administrative work. HIM professionals, with their expertise in data and data systems and their understanding of physicians' needs, can provide expert consultation in designing systems of value to physicians. When it comes to order entry, the electronic patient record, integrated documentation, billing and claims systems, and other clinical support systems, you can provide crucial input and guidance to improve patient data while supporting the needs of physicians and, ultimately, of the MCO.

The Health Plan and Its Information Needs

Of all the managed care stakeholders, the health plan itself has the broadest and most diverse set of information needs, encompassing all realms of the business of healthcare. The MCO has numerous databases due to its administrative, financial, and clinical responsibilities. Many are similar to those in the nonmanaged care world and others are unique. Databases of enrollees, authorized outside referrals, and claims for referred services to plan members are common in MCOs, while utilization and claims data are found inside and outside managed care.

Even when the databases might be familiar to both settings, the interpretation and understanding of the data might differ. To succeed as an HIM professional in an MCO, for example, you must understand the different incentives involved in utilization management.

Unlike in the nonmanaged care setting, the financial incentive for MCOs is to reduce utilization of healthcare resources so that the risk payment they receive for a member exceeds the money they expend on care. But the government and employer groups who want to ensure that members are getting the health services they require and who are primary payers for that care vigilantly watch for evidence that managed care organizations (MCOs) withhold necessary and appropriate care to save money. So while the nonmanaged care world is constantly audited for overutilization of healthcare services, MCOs are under scrutiny for underutilization.

The HIM professional's role in this MCO challenge is to optimize accurate, complete, and timely data at the points of care so that correct utilization decisions can be made at the appropriate times in the appropriate places. While MCOs require data that reflects the full range of health services provided to avoid the suspicion of limiting care to protect profits, they also require quality utilization data for numerous other reasons, including forecasting rates and premiums, identification of medical outcomes and best clinical practices, analysis of provider practice patterns, and of course, accurate third-party reimbursement.

In recent years, MCOs have recognized that they need to keep members healthy so that they don't require expensive health services. The turnaround has resulted in a renewed appreciation of maintaining members' health through preventive screenings and services and recognizing the importance of managing member illnesses now instead of responding with more expensive treatment later.

To accomplish this, MCOs must identify their high-risk and high-cost member populations, initiate and record actions, and track outcomes. From the need for these activities have grown entirely new clinical and administrative functions—e.g, case management, care management, disease management—all of which have significant data and systems needs. Very recently, predictive modeling, which uses a self-evaluation survey of non-disease-based factors to predict those individuals at risk for developing serious health problems, is drawing the attention of MCOs investigating innovative ways to increase quality of care and decrease costs.

At the same time, HCFA and the federal Agency for Healthcare Research and Quality are researching ways to better align payment methods with quality improvement goals. In the next years, MCOs will receive financial incentives to demonstrate compliance with HCFA's specific clinical guidelines. Beginning with treatment of congestive heart failure, payment for healthcare services will be tied to quality of patient care as defined by pre-defined clinical criteria. MCOs will therefore have additional motivations to collect and submit complete and accurate clinical and administrative data. The success of all these efforts will depend on new data, databases, and user-friendly data systems, which of course will require the expertise of HIM professionals.

Reimbursement Mechanisms: What You Should Know

When it comes to reimbursement, the good news is that the HIM professional's knowledge of HCFA's prospective payment systems (DRGs, APCs, RUGs, new PPS for inpatient rehabilitation and home health care) and the coding systems upon which they are based (ICD-9-CM, HCPCS, CPT) will be as vitally important in managed care as in your current job. Furthermore, familiarity with OASIS for home health, the Minimum Data Set for long term care, and any of the upcoming prospective payment systems will be applicable in this new world as well.

However, you also have some learning to do to understand the complexities of billing in managed care. While you are probably all too familiar with the confusing mix of funding mechanisms used in today's healthcare delivery system, billing and payment in the managed care world is even more complicated.

Issues like health plan members versus nonmembers, types and nature of coverage, capitation versus cost-based payments, out-of-network versus in-plan, out-of-area versus in-area, negotiated contracts or fee-for-service, and more, must be considered in addition to those we know from the nonmanaged care world.

In addition, HCFA is currently implementing an entirely new payment program for Medicare beneficiaries who choose managed care. The reimbursement mechanism for these Medicare+Choice beneficiaries is a risk adjustment classification system that requires MCOs to provide diagnosis and service data for virtually all patient encounters. The system bases payments for healthcare services on the identification of certain chronic conditions that predict subsequent healthcare service costs. Collection, aggregation, and external submission of this comprehensive data set is relatively new to the managed care industry and presents serious challenges to most MCOs.

To be phased in within the next three years, this payment mechanism is having a significant impact on MCOs from a data and cost perspective. The databases and systems that MCOs must design and maintain in order to submit full UB 92 and HCFA 1500 data sets for Medicare reimbursement of all members for all care provided across the continuum are extensive and expensive and require comprehensive data management skills.

As an HIM professional for an MCO, you will have to understand this new payment system and appreciate the difference in the data requirements and incentives. While the correct principal diagnosis and complication and comorbidities (CCs) are crucial to DRGs and the accurate coding of procedures and services is key to APCs, the coding of chronic conditions is now of utmost importance to the managed care world. Your knowledge of coding and reimbursement systems, understanding of the basic principles of data quality management, including the importance of standardized data definitions, and experience with minimizing organizational risk by compliance with regulatory requirements will be important to your MCO.

Furthermore, bearing in mind the four key functions serving as the basis for an HIM process in a MCO—data process and records management, informatics, decision support/ analytics, and quality improvement—can help to understand the big picture. (See part one of this series, "How HIM Adds Value to Managed Care," in the June 2001 issue.)

Looking Ahead

The last few years have been especially difficult for managed care. The hope that it would magically ensure accessible and affordable quality healthcare for all Americans has faded. MCOs face serious challenges and barriers.

A recent report by the President's Information Technology Advisory Committee criticized the healthcare industry for not using information technology as a strategic resource to improve access to care, to more effectively prevent medical errors, and to accelerate medical research. It blames the industry for not having vital information because its data is spread across multiple information systems and organizations with differing systems.[5] The reluctance of industry leaders to invest in information technology to standardize data and systems has placed healthcare behind every other American industry in its use of new technologies. Recognizing the same problem, the IOM has proposed a $1 million innovation fund to upgrade healthcare delivery systems in the US.

So, as always, data is everywhere, but usable information is disturbingly limited due to its lack of standardization, integration, and interconnectivity. Despite the preponderance of data and databases, MCOs either do not have the information necessary to impact decisions or "have not yet learned how to effectively use information to change or make decisions."[6] The initial excitement over the potential of data warehousing to provide standardized data to the desktop for easy manipulation into information has waned as the reality of the resources and commitments required set in. The industry has been exceptionally slow to embrace standardized data definitions and formats and in fact is only beginning to do so as HIPAA implementation looms on the horizon.

You, as the HIM professional, can help the organization manage the conflicting data priorities of its stakeholders and help integrate and connect data and systems with each other and with its audiences. You have the skills, experience, and vision, and with managed care, you have the arena. This is a challenging and exciting time for HIM professionals to contribute all you know to a multidisciplinary effort to make a difference to the many layered challenges and opportunities in healthcare. Don't let the organizational structure fool you; you have much to give to managed care. And they will succeed with your help.

Keep Up to Date on Managed Care

The Journal of AHIMA is publishing a series of articles on managed care and HIM professionals. The first installment, "How HIM Adds Value to Managed Care," appeared in the June 2001 issue. Look for more on managed care in upcoming issues of the Journal.

Notes

1. Cubbin, James, and Doug Shaw. "GM and DM—A Winning Team." *Health Management Technology* 22, no. 4 (2001): 31.

2. IOM Committee on Quality of Health Care in America. "Crossing the Quality Chasm: A New Health System for the 21st Century." Washington, DC: National Academy Press, 2001. Available online at www.nap.edu.

3. Korpman, Ralph. "Managed Care and e-Health." *Health Management Technology* 22, no. 2 (2001): 13.

4. Chidley, Elise. "Data—Still an Untapped Asset." *For the Record* 13, no. 5 (2001): 25.

5. Tieman, Jeff. "Wasted Opportunities." Modern Healthcare 31, no. 9 (2001): 12. Read the President's Information Technology Advisory Committee report online at www.itrd.gov/pubs.

6. Chidley, Elise.

References

Abdelhak, Mervat et al. *Health Information: Management of a Strategic Resource.* Philadelphia: W.B. Saunders, 1996.

Barber, Michael. "Fight Illness with Information." *Health Management Technology* 22, no. 4 (2001): 32.

Benko, Laura. "Shake, Rattle and Disenroll." *Modern Healthcare* 31, no. 6 (2001): 94–96.

Berry, Gretchen. "HIM PROs & MCOs: Quid Pro Quo." *Advance for Health Information Professionals* 11, no. 5 (2001): 22–24.

Gillespie, Greg. "Online Managed Care Transactions Gain Some Ground." *Health Data Management* 9, no. 3 (2001): 43–54.

Kelly, Beckie. "Stacking the Shelves with Data." *Health Data Management* 9, no. 2 (2001): 122–126.

Lovern, Ed. "IOM Strikes Again." *Modern Healthcare* 31, no. 10 (2001): 4–6.

McCue, Michael. "Knocking Down Walls." *Managed Healthcare Executive* 11, no. 2 (2001): 14–24.

Seeley, Rich. "Data Warehousing Lets Its Hair Down." *Application Development Trends* 8, no. 4 (2001): 19.

Slaughter, James. Presentation to Kaiser Permanente Northern California Region. March 2001.

Willner, Sue, and Martha Feinberg. "Are You Ready for Ambulatory Accreditation?" 1999 AHIMA National Convention Proceedings. Chicago, 1999: pp. 337–342.

Sue Willner (suewillner@triannaconsulting.com) is a healthcare consultant at Trianna, Inc., in Oakland, CA. She has spent more than half her career in managed care.

The Care and Maintenance of Charge Masters

Background

The various supplies and services listed on the charge master for the average facility drives reimbursement for approximately 73 percent of the UB-92 claims for outpatient services alone. The charge master—often called the master charge list or charge description list—is simply a computer file of charges for each item that may be used to treat the patient, as well as a select group of services.

A current and accurate charge master is vital to any healthcare provider seeking proper reimbursement. Without it, the facility would not receive proper reimbursement. Among the negative impacts that may result from an inaccurate charge master are:

- Overpayment
- Underpayment
- Undercharging for services
- Claims rejections
- Fines
- Penalties

Because a charge master is an automated process that results in billing numerous services for high volumes of patients—often without human intervention—there is a high risk that a single coding or mapping error could spawn error after error before it is identified and corrected.

Key Elements of a Charge Master List

The content and layout of a healthcare provider's charge master may vary from one organization to the next. However, one can expect to see the following data elements in the typical charge master file.

- Procedure description: This title describes the procedure to be performed. There is no set format or vocabulary for this description. Each description should be unique to your facility, yet comprehensible to all staff members who need to identify the procedure. Furthermore, each description should be separately identifiable. For example, no two line items should have the exact same description. Grouped under the heading of procedure might be surgery, laboratory, radiology, etc.

- Service description: This title describes the service to be performed. There is no set format or vocabulary for this description. As with procedure description, each service description should be unique to your facility, yet comprehensible to all staff members who need to identify the service. Again, each service description should be separately identifiable—no two line items should have the exact same description. Grouped under the heading of service might be evaluation and management, observation, emergency room visits, and clinical visits.

- CPT/HCPCS code: The corresponding CPT or HCPCS code that identifies the specific service or procedure. It is important to note that not all services and procedures listed on the charge master will have a corresponding code. Since all supplies and services may not require a code assignment and the use of unlisted or nonspecific codes is not desirable to the organization, it may be better to just leave this field blank in these instances.

- Revenue code: A three-digit code number representing a specific accommodation, ancillary service, or billing calculation required for Medicare billing. National and state uniform billing committees and HCFA update the list of acceptable revenue codes on an ongoing basis.

- Charge dollar amount: The specific amount charged by the facility for each procedure or service. This is not the actual amount that the facility will be reimbursed by a third-party payer. Instead, the charge dollar amount represents the standard charge for that item. The facility may want to compare the charge amount listed to the Medicare fee schedule to ensure that the charge amount is equal to or higher than the Medicare fee. Some facilities maintain unique charge dollar amount listings by payer.

- Department code number: A unique number assigned to each ancillary department by the facility.

- Charge description number: An internally assigned unique number that identifies each specific procedure or service listed on the charge master.

The Charge Master Committee

Ideally, charge master maintenance should not be the responsibility of one individual. Rather, it should be overseen by a committee composed of key facility representatives that will contribute to the accuracy and quality of both the document database and charge master review process. Proper charge master maintenance requires expertise in coding, billing regulations, clinical procedures, and health record documentation.

The charge master committee should include representation from:

- Health information management
- Ancillary departments
- The financial services/business office
- Information systems

Responsibilities of the charge master committee include:

- Develop policies and procedures for the charge master review process
- Perform an annual charge master review when new CPT/HCPCS codes are available
- Key elements of the annual charge master review, including:
  —Review all CPT codes for accuracy, validity, and relationship to charge description number
  —Review all procedure and service descriptions for accuracy and clinical appropriateness
  —Review all revenue codes for accuracy and linkage to charge description numbers
  —Ensure that the usage of all HCPCS, CPT, and revenue codes are in compliance with Medicare guidelines or other existing payer contracts
  —Review all charge dollar amounts for appropriateness by payer
  —Review all charge description numbers for uniqueness and validity
  —Review all department code numbers for uniqueness and validity
- Perform ongoing charge master maintenance as the facility adds or deletes new procedures, updates technology, or changes services provided
- Establish a procedure to allow clinical department directors to submit charge master change requests for new, deleted, or revised procedures or services
- Make sure there is no duplication of code assignment by coders and charge master assigned codes in any department (e.g., GI endoscopy lab or cardiology cath lab)
- Review all charge ticket and order entry screens for accuracy against the charge master and appropriate mapping to CPT/HCPCS codes when required
- Review and comply with directives in Medicare bulletins, transmittals, Medicare manual updates, and official coding guidelines
- Comply with guidelines in the National Correct Coding Initiative or other known coding or bundling edits

- Carefully consider any application that involves one charge description number "exploding" into more than one CPT/HCPCS code to prevent inadvertent unbundling and unearned reimbursement for services

- Review and take action on all remittance advice denials involving HCPCS/CPT coding or HCFA coding guidelines

Charge Master Resources

- CPT-4 codes and guidelines: Contact the American Medical Association, 515 N. State St., Chicago, IL 60610, (312) 464-5000, http://www.ama-assn.org

- HCPCS codes and guidelines: Contact the US Government Printing Office, Superintendent of Documents, Washington, DC 20402, (202) 783-3232. For training and guidance, contact your regional Medicare fiscal intermediary

- National Correct Coding Initiative: Contact the National Technical Information Service (NTIS), Technology Administration, US Department of Commerce, 5285 Port Royal Rd., Springfield, VA 22161, (703) 605-6000, http://www.ntis.gov

Prepared by
Harry Rhodes, MBA, RHIA, CHPS, Director of Practice Leadership

Acknowledgments
Assistance from the following individuals is gratefully acknowledged:

Rita Scichilone, MHSA, RRA, CCS, CCS-P
Dianne Willard, MBA, RRA, CCS-P

References
Abdelhak, Mervat. *Health Information: Management of a Strategic Resource.* Philadelphia, PA: W. B. Saunders Company, 1996.

"Expert Advice on Preparing for the APCs." *Medical Record Briefing* 14, no. 4 (1999): 3.

Falconer, Carol. *St. Anthony's UB-92 Editor: A Guide to Medicare Billing.* Reston, VA: St. Anthony Publishing, 1994.

Prophet, Sue. *Health Information Management Compliance: A Model Program for Healthcare Compliance.* Chicago, IL: AHIMA, 1998.

Richard, Tricia. *The Hospital Chargemaster Guide.* Reston, VA: St. Anthony Publishing, 1999.

Coding Connections in Revenue Cycle Management

Ruth Cummins, RHIA, CCS, and Julie Waddell

Recently, there has been a significant amount of talk in the healthcare industry about revenue cycle improvement. So what is all of the excitement about? It is about the bottom line. Specifically, how we can improve our bottom line through more effective and efficient revenue cycle management. For hospitals to maintain financial viability under the pressures of the current healthcare environment, the revenue cycle must be a significant focal point, and HIM and coding professionals should play major roles in the process. This article will highlight many of the coding connections for the key revenue cycle processes within patient access, HIM, and patient financial services.

The Coding Connection in Patient Access Services

Critical revenue cycle processes that occur in the patient access department include initial data collection (e.g., name, date of birth, insurance information, reason for admission, patient type); medical record number (MRN) assignment; and medical necessity determination. Coding connects (or needs to connect) with patient access services in the following areas: MRN, patient type, source documentation, and medical necessity.

The MRN is vital in connecting the patient documentation to the services provided to the patient. If an inaccurate MRN is used, complete and historical clinical information may not be available, resulting in potentially incomplete or inaccurate code assignment. Regular communication and collaboration between HIM and patient access to maintain accurate MRN assignment is imperative.

The patient access department, in many facilities, is responsible for assigning the patient type (e.g., inpatient versus observation patient). It is very frustrating for the coding staff to have to alter a patient type post-service due to inappropriate assignment. This correction process slows down the revenue cycle. The coding staff should collaborate with patient access in identifying ways to resolve inaccurate patient type assignments.

During the scheduling and patient registration process, test order documentation, including reason for the test, should be presented. Source documentation is critical for the final code assignment. Coding professionals should be involved in educating front-line personnel (i.e., those registering patients) regarding appropriate test order requirements.

The coding staff should also have access to the source documentation when coding to ensure complete, accurate, and consistent coding.

Hospitals and healthcare providers must determine if services will be covered based on the reason for the test prior to services being rendered. In most healthcare organizations, this is left to the front-line staff in patient access. Often, these individuals are in entry-level positions with little or no healthcare background. Connecting the patient access department with coding professionals is critical in complying with medical necessity requirements and reducing the risk of denials on the back end.

Although it is not always feasible to employ a coding professional in patient access, healthcare providers should consider creating a coding liaison position to assist patient access in determining medical necessity and following up with physicians on proper test orders. Coding orientation courses should be provided as a requisite for patient access staff as well. The revenue cycle can be dramatically affected by connecting coding to the patient access process.

Documentation, HIM, Coding, and Chargemaster Services

Key focal points in documentation, HIM, coding, and chargemaster services that affect revenue cycle performance include who assigns the codes; source documentation; coding quality and productivity; and revenue integrity.

Healthcare providers must determine where CPT and HCPCS codes will originate, or "who codes for what." Information system requirements should be considered when determining whether a code will be generated with a charge (i.e., hard-coded in the chargemaster) or whether the code will be assigned by coding staff based on source documentation.

Typically, routine diagnostic services such as lab and radiology are hard-coded in the chargemaster while surgical interventions are normally assigned by a coder. Lack of coordination between coding and chargemaster staff can cause conflicts, duplicative coding, and billing errors.

When determining whether a code belongs in the chargemaster or if it should be coded by a coder, ask yourself the following questions: "Is the code always the same for the procedure or service provided?" If yes, then the code likely belongs in the chargemaster. "Is coding assignment variable, contingent upon site, method, or complication?" If yes, then the code should be assigned by a coder. "Are there variables inherent in the documentation that would modify the code?" If yes, then the code should be assigned by a coder.

Equally important as who codes for what is the source documentation a coder uses to assign the appropriate ICD-9-CM and CPT or HCPCS code. As we all know, if it was not documented, it was not done. Whether the code is hard-coded in the chargemaster or is assigned by a coder, the source documentation must paint a clear picture of the clinical condition of the patient and the services provided. Often clinicians will witness services being provided; however, final dictation or documentation may omit specifics, which allow additional codes or charges to be added. Coding plays a critical role in validating source documentation for coding and billing purposes.

Concurrent clinical documentation management programs and query processes should be implemented to ensure physician documentation appropriately reflects the clinical picture of the patient and the services provided so that accurate and complete coding and billing can be accomplished.

HIM departments should establish coding quality and productivity standards. Ongoing internal and external quality audits are essential to ensure both compliance with coding rules and regulations, and appropriate payment for services. Coders need to keep current on coding and payment guidelines through continuing education and regulatory alerts and updates. To improve the efficiency of the revenue cycle (specifically, to reduce the discharged not final billed cases), coding productivity standards should be in place with a tool to effectively monitor daily progress.

Revenue integrity is the process of validating documentation, charges, and codes to ensure complete, compliant, and accurate billing and coding processes. A good revenue integrity team, which includes coding professionals, identifies lost charges and coding issues along with providing education and the development of processes to improve this component of the revenue cycle.

The Coding Connection and Patient Financial Services

Of the many activities that occur in patient financial services (PFS), two key revenue cycle components are billing and denial management. Data collected from patient access, information from the chargemaster, and HIM coding all come together in the form of a bill. Sophisticated bill edit systems have the ability to apply Medicare medical necessity, Outpatient Code Edits (OCE), and Correct Coding Initiative (CCI) edits to the claim prior to submission. Once these edits are applied, someone knowledgeable in coding and clinical protocols must resolve the edits to try to avoid claim delays and denials.

Coding connects (or needs to connect) with PFS in the following areas: discharged not final billed (DNFB) monitoring; medical necessity; OCE and CCI edits; and payment verification.

Every HIM department should have an effective DNFB reporting tool. HIM staff should be able to quickly identify high-dollar cases and the oldest cases. A process should be in place to quickly address the cases identified. Goals should also be set (e.g., one day over the bill hold days), and aggressive monitoring should be done on a daily basis. Significant communication and collaboration among the entire revenue cycle team is required to maintain the DNFB at industry best-practice standards.

Medical necessity does not take place only in the patient access area. Most billing systems allow providers to check for medical necessity one last time prior to claim submission. Connecting the billing process to coding is critical in reducing the number of medical necessity denials. Coding professionals are key players in querying the physician a final time for additional documentation to support services ordered and performed.

Coders are also critical in resolving OCE and CCI edits. Edit conflicts may be caused by a number of reasons, including lack of knowledge by the clinician entering charges and codes coming from both the chargemaster and the coding process. Coders should be involved in the daily bill edit process in order to avoid delays in final billing and claim rejections. Coders can resolve difficult edits by removing an inappropriate charge, recommending a chargemaster change, or evaluating source documentation to ensure complete and accurate coding. Some bill edit systems allow specific edits to be driven or assigned to certain individuals or departments. Edits such as comprehensive, component, and mutually exclusive should be assigned to a coder for resolution.

Finally, a verification process should be in place to ensure expected payments are received on both the outpatient (APC) and inpatient (DRG) assignment.

For healthcare providers to survive under the surmounting financial and operational pressures in an ever-changing environment, the coding process must be connected to the key services within the revenue cycle. Ongoing teamwork between coding and the areas of patient access, chargemaster maintenance, and PFS creates an exciting opportunity for HIM and coding professionals to spotlight their leadership skills. Make sure you are connected!

Key Points of the UB-04

In February 2005 the National Uniform Billing Committee (NUBC) approved the UB-04 paper claim and data set as the replacement to the existing UB-92 paper form.[1] After May 27, 2007, all paper claims must be submitted using the UB-04.

It is important to stress that the change applies only to claims submitted on paper, which are now in the minority. According to NUBC, "Today, more than 98 percent of hospital claims are submitted electronically to the Medicare program. Overall, more than 80 percent of all institutional claims are being submitted electronically."[2] This rate will continue to increase.

The preparation for the UB-04 conversion going on right now has limited impact on the provider community, since it allows for either a specific location on the paper claim for items that are already being collected or provides a placeholder for items that may be required for billing purposes in the future (for example, ICD-10). The current version of the electronic institutional claim, the ANSI X12N 837, will be upgraded and conform to the data elements that will now be required on the paper UB-04.

This practice brief addresses what this latest update means for HIM professionals. It also discusses the two UB-04 data elements that will have the greatest impact on HIM.

What Is the UB-04?

NUBC maintains the billing data set known as the Uniform Bill (UB) designed for institutional healthcare providers. A uniform hospital bill, currently the UB-92, is the required billing mechanism that contains data elements identified as necessary for claims processing in the paper environment. In most cases, data elements are assigned designated spaces on the paper claim form. The designated spaces are referred to as form locators (FLs), and each has a unique number.

The UB-92 form was reviewed and upgraded to the approved UB-04 version. Clearinghouses and health plans must be ready to accept the paper UB-04 format on March 1, 2007. Providers will be able to submit claims via UB-92 or UB-04 from March 1 to May 27, 2007. However, after May 27, 2007, all paper claims must be submitted using the UB-04 format.

Note: It is important to note that this article discusses the *upcoming* implementation of the revision to the UB-92 form or the UB-04. The UB-04 was in fact implemented by CMS in May 2007.

All rebilling of paper claims must also use the UB-04 from that date forward, even though earlier submissions may have been on the UB-92.

The UB-04 contains a number of improvements and enhancements that resulted from nearly four years of research, including better alignment with the electronic HIPAA ASC X12N 837-Institutional transaction standard. This change addresses items that are collected today and submitted in the electronic format that the UB-92 paper version does not adequately identify. For example, the paper UB-92 limits the number of diagnoses included on the claim tied to a specific form locator (overflow diagnosis codes may be listed in the remark section), but the current electronic transaction is already accepting an increased number of diagnosis codes. The UB-92 was reviewed and upgraded to the UB-04 in part because of the discrepancy between the required elements for the electronic transaction standard today and the paper format.

The UB-04 is expected to last 10 years. In order to be proactive, some new data elements are included on the paper UB-04 claim that are not yet supported in the electronic standard. There is no definitive timeline of the current electronic transaction to be upgraded to the next version. It is anticipated that the implementation date of the updated electronic transaction standard will not occur before 2009.

Changes to the UB-04 Claim Form

Changes to the UB-04 claim form include:

- New field for diagnosis present at time of admission
- Expansion of the diagnosis and procedure field sizes to accommodate the ICD-10-CM and ICD-10-PCS codes
- New field to denote version of ICD classification used
- Expansion of the number of fields for secondary diagnoses
- Addition of distinct fields for patient's reason for visit
- Distinct fields for E-code reporting
- Field to identify national provider identifier (NPI)

The table [below] compares the current and anticipated inclusion of HIM-related data elements. Two changes are expected to have the greatest impact on HIM professionals: the addition of distinct fields for patient's reason for visit and the new field for diagnosis present at time of admission.

Patient's Reason for Visit

FL76 on the UB-92 is currently a dual-purpose field depending on whether the bill is for inpatient or outpatient services. On outpatient bills, FL76 is used to report the ICD-9-CM diagnosis code for the patient's reason for visit. In the UB-04, the reason for visit will have its own designated form locator (FL 70A–C) and will be expanded to capture up to three reason for visit codes for certain outpatient encounters.

According to the UB-92 manual, FL76 is used on outpatient claims to report the ICD-9-CM diagnosis code describing the patient's stated reason for seeking care (or as stated by the patient's representative). This may be a condition representing patient distress, an injury, a poisoning, or a reason or condition (not an illness or injury) such as follow-up or pregnancy in labor. In addition, the UB-92 manual specifies a revenue code requirement that "the patient's reason for visit information should be reported for all unscheduled outpatient visits when revenue codes 45X [emergency room], 516 [urgent care clinic], 526 [free-standing urgent care clinic], or 762 [observation] are present."

The expanded reason for visit requirement will alleviate payment delays that occur when the outpatient claim is suspended because of the need for additional information regarding the circumstances of the encounter or visit. Payers use ICD-9-CM diagnosis codes to adjudicate claims and to determine whether the services provided meet medical necessity. Coders should be aware that they can now report up to three reason for visit codes for certain outpatient claims. To review the history and the coding advice related to reason for visit, consult the fourth quarter 1999 and second quarter 2000 issues of the American Hospital Association's *Coding Clinic for ICD-9-CM.*

Present on Admission Indicator

Among the new UB-04 data elements is the present on admission (POA) indicator. Its purpose is to differentiate between conditions present at admission and conditions that develop during an inpatient admission.

The definition of "present on admission" poses challenges. It is defined as present at the time the order for inpatient admission occurs. Conditions that develop during an outpatient encounter such as the initial emergency department visit or during observation are considered as present on admission. The NUBC work group considered "present on admission" versus "present on arrival" and concluded variable payer requirements regarding the inclusion of outpatient services on the inpatient claim and issues with the multiple avenues that lead to an inpatient admission would cause a "present on arrival" definition difficult and inconsistent data would result.

Furthermore, the POA indicator definition is not only based on conditions known at the time of admission but also includes those conditions that were clearly present, but not diagnosed, until after the admission took place. For example, should a patient have a documented skin lesion on admission that is later diagnosed as malignant melanoma, this diagnosis would be assigned POA indicator Y (yes).

Conditions that are suspected at the time of admission and subsequently confirmed during the hospitalization also are considered to be present on admission. For example, a patient is admitted for syncope. After study this symptom is attributed to new onset of atrial fibrillation and would have the POA indicator Y assigned for atrial fibrillation.

Principal diagnosis is to be assigned a POA indicator under the UB-04 reporting requirements. In some state reporting, such as Florida, this assignment is not required. Logically the vast majority of the time the principal diagnosis would have a POA indicator of Y. However, ICD-9-CM combination codes and instances when an acute exacerbation of a chronic condition occurs during the admission warrant consideration. Without standardized reporting guidelines cases such as an obstetric patient with the principal diagnosis of

664.21, third-degree perineal laceration during delivery, could be unreliably reported. The cooperating parties are developing a set of guidelines for reporting the present on admission indicator, which will be included as a special section in the October 2006 version of the ICD-9-CM Official Guidelines for Coding and Reporting.

The goal is to assess when the condition was present. The addition of this data element is viewed by many as a method for improving the utility of administrative claims data to assess the quality of healthcare. The National Committee on Vital and Health Statistics and the Agency for Healthcare Research and Quality are among those entities that consider this information valuable in performing risk adjustment and other quality measurement activities.

With the implementation of present on admission reporting in 2007 the Florida Agency for Health Care Administration is planning to publish the rate of certain complications such as infections that occur after admission to the hospital on its Web site. MEDPAC, the federally appointed advisory committee to Medicare and Congress on Medicare, urged Medicare to adopt the POA indicator for inclusion in Medicare's pay-for-performance system. While Medicare has not formally announced its intentions, the indicator is clearly being considered.

New York and California have required hospitals to report the timing of each diagnosis as a component of the medical discharge information submitted to the state since 1993 and 1996, respectively. Diagnoses reported include a flag indicating if the condition was present on admission or not. This additional information is useful when developing risk adjustment models for hospitalized patients, because conditions present on admission (comorbidities) can be distinguished from conditions that develop during the hospital stay (complications) and are therefore potentially reflective of a service of care quality problem. Indeed, the POA indicator currently used for California and New York has been helpful in distinguishing conditions and infections that occurred during the patient's stay or prior to hospitalization.

As approved by NUBC, the POA indicator applies to the diagnosis codes for claims involving inpatient admissions to general acute care hospitals and other facilities, as required by state law or regulations for public health reporting. The indicator is to be reported for the principal and all secondary or other diagnoses using the following reporting options:

- Y: yes

- N: no

- U: no information in the record

- W: clinically undetermined

- – Unreported/Not used—exempt from POA reporting

The cooperating parties have yet to compile the list of ICD-9-CM codes that will not require a POA indicator. It is expected this list will be published in the October 2006 updated version of the ICD-9-CM Official Guidelines for Coding and Reporting. The indicator can be left unreported only for the codes on this list. Many V codes in the "Supplementary Classification of Factors Influencing Health Status and Contact with Health Services" chapter are expected to be on the exempt list.

NUBC did not exclude E codes from the POA indicator, as members of the NUBC work group that developed recommendations for the UB-04 POA reporting requirements felt that E codes should be included because of the importance of this information from a patient safety perspective. The California Office of Statewide Health Planning and Development and New York State specifically exclude E codes from the present on admission reporting for secondary diagnoses. E codes will be excluded as well in January 2007 when Florida hospitals begin using the POA indicator when reporting inpatient data to the Agency for Health Care Administration.

For POA indicator reporting consistency and accuracy further parameters are necessary. Available data and lessons learned from states that have implemented this reporting requirement are available and can be used to guide this process. This data may be used for many purposes, including adjusting for patient risk for quality outcome measures and in determining patient complexity for payment purposes. In the future, reporting a POA indicator for diagnoses will be a new and important responsibility for all hospitals when this becomes a billing requirement; however, many facilities, based upon state reporting requirements, may be affected sooner.

In preparation for the UB-04, with particular emphasis on reason for visit and present on admission data elements, organizations should consider items in the following checklist.

UB-04 Readiness Checklist

Remember that this information only applies if your facility performs paper billing with the UB, and it is not applicable for facilities using the electronic format.

Investigation Tasks

- Perform gap analysis to identify software programs that contain ICD-9-CM codes.

- Talk with all vendors that have software with ICD-9-CM codes and discuss their plans for field expansion, including number of diagnosis, E codes, and reason for visit. Also inquire as to the ability to capture POA indicators.

- Identify interfaces that will be affected by the updates related to UB-04.

- Develop a plan with vendors and IT representatives to update interfaces, if applicable.

- Even though POA is not a billing requirement at this time, investigate if other agencies are requiring this information to be collected and reported (e.g., state reporting).

Training Tasks

- Develop UB-04 (paper) education for patient financial services, compliance, HIM, and patient access staff. All departmental managers and an executive champion should also be present.

- Include UB-04 (paper) education in compliance training.

- Ensure coders are aware of the changes and implement them into their daily coding practices (e.g., begin reporting three reason for visit codes).

Policies

- Evaluate the need to update internal coding guidelines regarding the number of diagnoses, procedures, and E-codes abstracted.

- Update internal abstracting guidelines regarding reason for visit and (if applicable) present on admission.

External Tasks

- Discuss UB-04 requirements with fiscal intermediary to understand its position and preparation process. If it is necessary to process a paper UB-04 claim, when will the intermediary be ready?

- Evaluate other payers' readiness to accept paper UB-04 claims. Patient financial services should prioritize those payers that do not accept claims submitted electronically because those will be the entities most affected by this change.

- Discuss UB-04 with the state reporting agency to understand how it will utilize the data.

Areas to Involve within the Organization

- Executive

- Contracts management

- Finance

- Patient financial services

- Revenue cycle management

- Performance improvement, quality improvement

- HIM

- Risk management

- Infection control

- Case management, utilization review, disease management

- Physicians

- Compliance

Web Sites to Monitor for Updates

- National Uniform Billing Committee, www.nubc.org

- AHIMA, www.ahima.org

- Centers for Medicare and Medicaid Services, 2006 Transmittals, www.cms.hhs.gov

As an HIM professional, it is important to be aware of the changes that will affect claim submission in both the electronic and paper environments. HIM professionals are encouraged to be proactive and to be a resource within their organizations when questions arise related to the HIM data elements included within the billing process.

Comparing the Current and Anticipated HIM-related Data Elements in the Uniform Bill

HIM-related Data Element	UB-92 Paper Format	Current Electronic Transaction	Upcoming UB-04 Requirements	Need to Consider for Future Electronic Standard Update?
Expansion of the diagnosis and procedure field sizes to accommodate ICD-10-CM and ICD-10-PCS codes	Does not accommodate	Accommodates ICD-10-CM/PCS codes, but does not identify the assigned code version	Field size will be increased to allow for ICD-10-CM and ICD-10-PCS codes	Yes—even though the ICD-10 format can be accepted, the current electronic standard does not identify the version of ICD being submitted.
Expansion of the number of fields for secondary diagnoses and distinct fields for E codes	Does not accommodate	Accommodates the increased number of secondary diagnoses but limits the number of E codes	Number of secondary diagnoses will increase, and E codes will have distinct fields	Yes—the current electronic standard will need to address the current E-code limitation.
Addition of distinct fields for patient's reason for visit	Uses FL76 as a dual field	Uses FL76 as a dual field	Will separate reason for visit into a separate field and will allow reporting of up to three codes	Yes—the current electronic standard does not accommodate
New field to denote version of ICD classification used	Does not accommodate	Does not accommodate	Will have a separate field	Yes—the current electronic standard does not accommodate
Addition of national provider indicator	Does not accommodate	Does accommodate	Will include this as a field	No—the current electronic standard accommodates
New field for diagnosis present at time of admission	Does not accommodate	Does not accommodate	Will be a separate one-character field at the end of each diagnosis and E-code assigned	Yes—the current electronic standard does not accommodate

Notes

1. Established in 1975, the NUBC is the official data content body responsible for maintaining the data set for institutional healthcare providers. Representation includes provider, payer, electronic standards development organizations, public health data standards organizations, and others. NUBC is also one of six designated standard maintenance organizations responsible for the maintenance and development of HIPAA administrative simplification transaction standards. Visit www.nubc.org for more information.

2. National Uniform Billing Committee. "History." Available online at www.nubc.org/history.htm.

Acknowledgments

Jackie Miller, RHIA, CPC

Angie Comfort, RHIT, CCS

Ann Zeisset, RHIT, CCS, CCS-P

Sue Bowman, RHIA, CCS

Prepared by

AHIMA Clinical Terminology and Classification Practice Council

Gail Garrett, RHIT

Laurine Johnson, MS, RHIA

Kathy Johnson, RHIA

Charge Capture and the Physician Revenue Cycle

Susan M. Hull, MPH, RHIA, CCS, CCS-P

Poor charge capture processes are responsible for the loss of millions of dollars in revenue every year. Particularly in the area of inpatient services, loss of charges is a frequent occurrence. At Shands Healthcare in Florida, John Hajjar, MD, director of the urology practice group, found that 20 percent of all inpatient services rendered by the members of his group were not billed.[1] Among the process failures that may result in lost revenue are the following:

- Charges are not captured at all.

- Codes are incorrect or inappropriate for the patient and/or service.

- The order of codes is not optimal.

- ICD-9-CM diagnosis codes are not appropriately linked to CPT codes to assure documentation of medical necessity.

The revenue cycle in the typical physician's office setting differs from the hospital revenue cycle only in scope or size. The basic components are the same. In this presentation, we are going to primarily focus on the issue of charge capture and charge generation. I will begin with a brief overview of the entire revenue cycle and then focus on these topics.

The revenue cycle in the physician office setting has two basic components: front-end functions and back-end functions. The so-called front-end functions begin at the time of first encounter and continue through the provision of services and bill generation. The back-end functions begin with receipt of a remittance advice or equivalent and end at the time that the account is zero-balanced.

Overview of the Physician Practice Revenue Cycle

The basic elements in the physician practice revenue cycle include the following:

1. Initial contact. The initial contact may take any one of several forms. The most common are patient request for services, a request for consultation from

another practitioner, or a referral from another service provider, either a physician, or the emergency department of a hospital on whose referral staff the physician serves. Other sources of first contact may include medicolegal referrals, such as from attorneys in personal injury suits or workers compensation cases. In addition, mandated second opinions from HMOs and PPOs may be a source of referrals.

In the hospital, initial contact may come from the emergency department or the admissions office, notifying the attending physician that a patient has been admitted.

At this stage of the cycle, obtaining accurate patient information is critical. The earlier in the process that essential data can be obtained, the greater the likelihood of preventing future errors. Staff should assure that the services are appropriate and covered as soon as possible, as well as assuring that the patient is appropriate for the practice.

2. Patient registration. At the time that the patient presents to the physician office, the process of patient registration begins. This process can be begun prior to the patient physically presenting at the office, of course. Included in the processes of patient registration are insurance verification and generation of the charging instrument.

    The collection of complete and accurate demographic and insurance data at this point in the cycle is critical. Small errors made at the time of patient registration can become huge impediments later in the revenue cycle. Also at this point, the Advance Beneficiary Notice should be obtained for any services that will be rendered in the office that may not be covered by Medicare. These would include routine diagnostic assessments, screening tests (except in specific covered circumstances), questionably covered procedures, and any other services for which documentation of medical necessity is not present.

    When a patient is admitted to the hospital, the office staff may not be aware of the admission for days. Most hospital data systems, however, now generate a notification message to the attending physician's office at the time of patient admission. If the patient does not have an existing office record, one should be begun at this time.

3. Provision of services and charge capture. At the point that services are provided, the process of charge capture begins. Among the issues that must be addressed to assure appropriate charge capture are the following:

    *   Identification of the person or persons responsible for charge capture in specific circumstances and at specific points during the provision of services

    *   Assuring the presence of appropriate, legible documentation of services

    *   Assuring the timeliness of charge capture

    *   Maintenance of a charging instrument that is complete, current, accurate, and does not tend to result in over-coding or under-coding

4. Charge reconciliation process. The charge reconciliation process is one of the most important and frequently over-looked aspects of the revenue cycle. Included in the charge reconciliation process are the following functions:

- Lost charge identification and entry

- Late charge identification

- Validation of charges by comparison with the physician documentation (Were the correct procedures billed?)

- Physician query process, often highly unsophisticated in physician office setting

- Making sure that the documentation matches the charge ticket (Do the notes support what was billed?)

- Process assessment to identify reasons for late and/or missed charges and corrective action

5. Coding. During the coding process, ICD-9-CM and CPT codes are assigned to report the services performed and the reasons for these services. Accuracy of CPT code assignment directly impacts reimbursement based upon the physician fee schedule; accuracy of ICD-9-CM codes indirectly impacts reimbursement. The function of the ICD-9-CM diagnosis codes is to substantiate and validate the CPT code assignment.

Issues addressed during the coding process, in addition to substantiation of the services billed, include documentation of medical necessity for additional services ordered and observance of the requirements of the National Correct Coding Initiative.

The adequacy of the coding process is a function of staffing and resources. A knowledgeable coding staff, with quality materials available for assistance, is necessary to assure appropriate code assignment. Care must be taken that the coding resources are complete and current. If electronic coding resources are used, they must be maintained.

The assignment of modifiers is also a part of the coding process. Inappropriate use of modifiers may result in over- or under-reporting of services and consequent inappropriate reimbursement.

6. Claim generation. Once the services have been rendered and codes assigned, the claim is generated. Our goal is always a clean claim the first time, every time.

A clean claim is one that accurately and completely reflects the circumstances of the visit and passes through all payer edits without delay. The demographics, ICD-9-CM codes, and CPT codes must all correlate. If additional documentation is needed to support a code assignment (such as an operative report), it should be obtained at this time.

At this time, too, coordination of benefits should be addressed. All payers have requirements for coordination of benefits. The Medicare Web site now contains a valuable resource for explaining coordination of Medicare benefits, which can be accessed at www.cms.hhs.gov/medicare/cob/.

The timeliness of claims submission is also important. Although Medicare allows the provider until the end of the calendar year following that in which the services were provided to file an initial claim, many managed care companies have very stringent requirements for claim submission, sometimes as short a time as thirty days following services. If the claim is not submitted within the contracted period of time, the practice will have no further recourse.

7. Notification of payment. The practice is notified of payment in various ways, depending upon the payer. At the time that payment is obtained, payments and adjustments must be posted. Good business practices are important in posting of payments and adjustments.

8. Reimbursement analysis. The reimbursement is virtually never the billed amount. The practice must review all denials or significant reductions in payment to determine the cause. If appropriate, claims should be resubmitted. In addition, all denials that can be appealed should be appealed. Only if the bill was clearly erroneous should denials be written off.

Of note, the identities of those who have authority to write off claims must be clearly stated and under what circumstances they can write off claims. A sampling of written off claims should be done by the practice manager on a regular basis.

The simple act of appealing a denial will usually result in improved reimbursement. Particularly with Medicare, an appeal to the area medical director, with appropriate supporting documentation, will usually result in reversal of the denial.

If significant numbers of claims are being reimbursed at lower than expected rates, a process review should be done and corrective action taken. The new process should then be tested to assure that it is having the desired effect. If training needs are identified as a part of the process review, the education should be provided to the appropriate staff. Money spent on education is always worth it.

9. Receivables analysis. The practice should conduct a periodic review of all pending claims and follow up as appropriate.

10. Credit/Collections. This is the last step in the revenue cycle. This process ends at the time that an account is zero-balanced. Return all credits promptly. Medicare regulations require that credits be returned within 60 days of receipt.

In addition, form CMS-838 must be completed and submitted quarterly, to report any credit balances. Follow established procedures for collection. An account cannot be written off to bad debt until the established processes of attempted collection have been completed. These processes should be the same for all patients, regardless of payer.

Charge Capture

The consequences of inadequate charge capture processes include the following:

- Lost billings due to process collapse
- Denied claims due to inadequate linkage of diagnosis and procedure codes
- Extension of the reimbursement cycle. Time is money.
- Excess administrative costs and reduction in time available for patient care

As noted above, the processes that must be addressed in evaluating the charge capture process include the following:

- Identifying the person or persons responsible for charge capture in specific circumstances and at specific points during the provision of services. The physician is ultimately responsible for all charging in his or her practice and is the most qualified to assign the evaluation and management level of service codes, whereas the radiologic technician is the appropriate staff to enter charges for imaging services.

- Assuring the presence of appropriate, legible documentation of services. Electronic health records may increase the legibility of documentation, but cannot automatically guarantee that the documentation is appropriate to the presenting problem. A possible advantage of having someone other than the physician enter the evaluation and management level of service codes is that that individual will be forced to rely upon the actual documentation, rather than a combination of the documentation in the record and that in the physician's head.

- Assuring the timeliness of charge capture. Charges should be captured as soon as possible after the services are delivered.

- Maintaining a charging instrument that is complete, current, accurate, and does not tend to result in over-coding or under-coding.

The goals of a good charge capture methodology should include the following:

- As much as possible, capture data one time, preferably in an electronic environment. Repeated episodes of data capture lead to increased opportunities for errors, duplications, and missed charges.

- Decrease the number of instances where data are entered manually by either the physician or other staff (for example, laboratory personnel, radiology technologist, and nurse). Physician practice data systems are currently available that will allow laboratory data to be downloaded directly into the patient's clinical record.

- Eliminate as much as possible the need for physically moving data from one place to another.

- Place the decision making for charging with the person who is performing the work. Wherever possible, the person who actually performed the service should be entering the charges.

Charge Ticket Design

The design of the charging instrument is critical to the charge capture process. Whether electronic or paper, the form must be designed in such a way as to assure that ICD-9-CM and CPT codes can be linked, that all charges can be captured, and that all possible charges are available for capture. There are currently countless electronic charge capture programs available for physician use. Several of these are listed in the "Endnotes" section of this paper. The level of sophistication of these systems varies widely. Some are essentially electronic notepads on which the physician makes notes that are later converted into charges. Others incorporate prescription pads in the charging form and may include electronic calculation of evaluation and management level of service based upon interface with the documentation in the electronic record.

The minimum required information for inclusion on charge ticket is the following:

- Patient identification, including a secondary identifier, such as date of birth or Social Security number, to assure that the proper patient account is charged.

- Date of service

- Treating physician if a multi-physician practice

- Services or procedures rendered (for example, CPT code)

- Reason for each service (for example, ICD-9-CM diagnosis)

- Place that service or procedure was rendered if several sites

Additional data elements that might be appropriate include time of service and the name of the referring physician if this is a consultation. A few payers will reimburse additional for services rendered after-hours and on an emergency basis.

Devising an effective charge ticket for hospital services has been a challenge for practices forever. Typically, the hospital charge ticket contains room for an inadequate number of diagnoses to support varying levels of hospital visits. The most effective charging instrument for recording hospital visits, in the absence of a fully electronic, fully integrated system with capability for bedside data entry by all practitioners, is the classic 3 × 5 card. These 3 × 5 cards generally work better than 8-1/2 × 11-inch pages, as they fit into the pocket of the rounds coat and can be easily accessed without repeated folding and unfolding. The format of the card should be such that the physician can easily add all the above pieces of data. Each service code (whether evaluation and management level of service or interventional procedure) should have a matching diagnosis code box. Physicians should be encouraged to vary the levels of evaluation and management codes assigned, in accordance with the CPT guidelines. In addition, if highest-level services are being charged, there may be need for a more "intense" ICD-9-CM diagnosis code for that particular day's service. For example, a patient who enters the hospital with an acute myocardial infarction and improves steadily would be coded as a level 1 subsequent hospital visit on the days he is improving. If, however, the patient develops cardiogenic shock, for that day a higher-level evaluation and management code would be assigned; the diagnosis for that visit would not be AMI, but rather cardiogenic shock.

Some practices opt for cards that allow recording of multiple days' visits. Such a system, however, makes it more difficult to link services and diagnoses (such as in the above example) and makes it more likely that the card (and its charges) will be lost. Ideally, charges for hospital visits should be entered on a daily basis, rather than at the end of the admission.

If the office is linked to the hospital data system, the day's cards can be printed up in the morning and provided to the physician prior to rounds. At the end of the day, a reconciliation record should be maintained to assure that all cards have been returned.

Whether an electronic or paper format is used, the most important functions are the appropriate linking of ICD-9-CM and CPT codes and the availability of all possible procedure codes.

It is extremely important that the charge capture instrument offer the physician the opportunity to charge all levels of service. A University of Chicago physician practice group was found to be billing only the two highest levels of evaluation and management codes, and review of their charge ticket showed that only these levels were available for charging.[3] It is essential that all five levels of evaluation and management codes be present on the charge ticket. Inappropriate charging can result in severe penalties to the practice, including potential prosecution under Medicare for fraud and abuse and even exclusion from the Medicare program (and other programs).

The issue of whether to include ICD-9-CM diagnosis codes on the superbill has long been debated. Assigning a non-specific code when a more specific and more accurate one exists is not appropriate. Program Memorandum AB-01-144, issued September 26, 2001 (available for review at http://cms.hhs.gov/manuals/pm_trans/ab01144.pdf) defines the outpatient coding guidelines, which also apply to physicians' offices. The guidelines clearly state that the condition that was responsible for the services rendered must be reported to the highest degree of specificity possible and with the correct number of digits. Inclusion of ICD-9-CM codes on superbills requires that the number of codes be severely restricted. Even a practice that sees a well-defined patient population may need to report hundreds of ICD-9-CM codes at one time or another.

There are several options for addressing the issue of ICD-9-CM code assignment. These include:

- Include no diagnosis codes on the superbill, but have professional coding staff assign the codes based upon the physician documentation in the health record. Advantages of this option include high quality coding, assigned in accordance with the most current guidelines. Disadvantages include the need for access to the dictated (or written) visit report. Electronic records, which allow access by multiple staff members concurrently, may address this issue, but the need for very rapid transcription of dictated reports may be an issue.

- Attempt to include all possible diagnosis codes on the superbill, complete to the required fourth or fifth digits. Advantages of this option include rapid turnaround of the charges. Disadvantages include the need for an extensive document, the possibility for errors from checking the wrong box, and the need for frequent review and updating.

- Include truncated ICD-9-CM diagnosis codes and provide blanks for the entry of additional diagnostic descriptors, then have trained staff assign the most accurate code. Advantages of this option include the need for fewer diagnosis codes on the charge ticket, but disadvantages include the need for additional physician input to assure appropriate coding, which may not be easy to obtain.

Linkage of ICD-9-CM and CPT Codes

Linkage of ICD-9-CM and CPT codes is critical to reimbursement. The physician billing form (CMS-1500) contains spaces for only four diagnosis codes. Thus, the diagnoses selected must be those that are most supportive of the services performed. The first-listed diagnosis should be that which is the reason for the visit, per outpatient (physician) coding guidelines. The first-listed procedure code should be that with the highest relative weight. This may or may not be the evaluation and management visit code. Each CPT code should be linked to that ICD-9-CM diagnosis code that is most supportive of the service.

The easiest way to link diagnosis and procedure codes is to encourage physicians to number diagnoses rather than to simply check them off on a list. If a coding professional receives a diagnosis sheet with four check-marks on it, she is forced to make a clinical judgment about sequencing and linkage, a decision which she is not professionally qualified to make. Only the practitioner can link the procedures and diagnoses, as this is a part of the medical decision-making process. Many electronic charging programs require the physician to number the diagnoses and to provide the linkages.

Physician Query Process

If the charge ticket does not contain adequate documentation to assign ICD-9-CM diagnosis codes, the physician must be queried. This should be a written process, not relying upon additional information provided verbally. If the physician states that an additional diagnosis may be listed, the diagnosis should be added to the visit record by the physician and authenticated by him or her.

All diagnoses addressed during a visit should be documented in the visit record. Simply noting the diagnosis on the charge ticket is not sufficient. The charge ticket is not a part of the official visit record, and the information included in it is not part of the documentation that will be assessed if the practice is ever audited. If no diagnoses are recorded in the visit record, there is no documented basis for medical decision making, and an auditor would give no "credit" for medical decision making.

Summary

The creation of an effective charge capture mechanism requires attention to the financial needs of the practice, as well as compliance issues. A charging instrument that fulfills all important functions will allow for complete and accurate assignment of both ICD-9-CM diagnosis and CPT procedural codes, facilitate linkage between the code sets, and assure that all compliance guidelines are met. Whether a paper or an electronic format is used, the charge ticket is the most important element in the creation of an optimal charge capture system and must be tailored to the particular practice. Any expense incurred in developing the appropriate instrument will be more than equaled in reduction of lost or late charges, improvement in timeliness and appropriateness of reimbursement, and reduced exposure under Medicare compliance guidelines.

Endnotes

1. Pamela L. Moore. "Improving Charge Capture: Lost Charges Can Really Add Up," *PhysiciansPractice,* 2002. Available at www.shands.org/professional/ppd/practice/ finance/lostcharges.asp.

2. http://cms.hhs.gov/forms/cms838a.pdf

3. "Whistleblower, charge ticket, and upcoding spell trouble for U of Chicago Hospitals," hcPro Compliance Info.com.

Appendix C
Answer Key for
"Check Your Understanding" Questions

Check Your Understanding 1.1

1. B

2. 1929 in Texas, when Blue Cross first created a plan for school teachers

3. D

4. Resource-based relative value scale (RBRVS)

5. Global surgical package, including the procedure, local/topical anesthesia, preoperative visit, and postoperative care/follow-up; special-procedure package, including costs associated with a diagnostic or therapeutic procedure; ambulatory-visit package, including physicians' charges, laboratory tests, and x-rays

Check Your Understanding 2.1

1. The Health Insurance Portability and Accountability Act of 1996 (HIPAA)

2. C

3. National Center for Health Statistics (NCHS) and the Centers for Medicare and Medicaid Services (CMS), which together compose the ICD-9-CM Coordination and Maintenance Committee

4. *Coding Clinic for ICD-9-CM*

5. CPT

Check Your Understanding 2.2

1. Abuse, the submission of unintentionally inaccurate charges on a claim for reimbursement

2. C

3. Policies and procedures, education and training, and auditing and monitoring

4. False

5. Listings of diagnoses are the same but the presence or absence of complication or comorbidity diagnoses prompts assignment of cases to higher or lower DRGs.

Check Your Understanding 3.1

1. A healthcare plan offering dependent coverage includes benefits for spouses and family members of the insured individual.

2. Comprehensive policies provide coverage for most healthcare services but may have deductibles that must be met before the insurance company pays expenses, and the insured must also pay coinsurance for all covered expenses until the maximum out-of-pocket cost is reached.

3. C

4. Credited coverage

5. Prior approval is typically required for outpatient surgeries; diagnostic, interventional, and therapeutic outpatient procedures; physical, occupational, and speech therapies; mental health and dependency care; inpatient care including surgery, home health, private nurses, and nursing homes; and organ transplants.

Check Your Understanding 4.1

1. a. Inpatient hospital services

    b. Supplemental medical insurance

    c. Medicare Advantage

    d. Medicare drug benefit

2. Medigap policies offer supplemental insurance covering the cost-shared expenses such as the deductibles and 20 percent of durable medical equipment costs that patients otherwise pay.

3. Coverage differs among the states because Medicaid allows states to maintain a unique program adapted to state residents' needs and average incomes. Although state programs must meet coverage requirements for groups such as recipients of adoption assistance and foster care, other types of coverage, such as vision and dental services, are determined by the states' Medicaid agencies.

Check Your Understanding 4.2

1. a. TRICARE Extra

    b. TRICARE Standard

    c. TRICARE Prime

    d. TRICARE for Life (TFL)

2. True; CHAMPVA becomes a secondary payer when another health insurance benefit is available.

3. B

Check Your Understanding 5.1

1. To have visits to an oncologist—or any other specialist—an MCO member obtains a referral from his or her primary care provider.

2. Types are preventive, wellness-oriented, acute, and chronic.

3. Wellness programs

Check Your Understanding 5.2

1. The hospital-led IDS is the most common type of IDS and may include group practices; home health agencies; hospices; nursing homes; ambulatory surgery, outpatient care centers, and urgicenters; and ancillary providers.

2. The four types are: group practice without walls, physician-hospital organization, management service organization, and the medical foundation.

3. Group practices without walls (PWWs) or clinics without walls (CWWs) share administrative systems and have greater leverage in negotiating reimbursement with MCOs. Management service organizations (MSOs) provide management services and administrative and information systems to multiple group practices or small hospitals, thereby distributing overhead costs.

Check Your Understanding 6.1

1. Yale University in the late 1960s and early 1970s

2. Ignored

3. Is a CC present? Is a major complication or complex diagnosis present? Is the patient's age greater or less than seventeen years? What is the patient's sex? What is the patient's discharge disposition? For neonates, what is the birth weight of the baby?

4. The base-year payment rate is updated using an update factor established by Congress to account for inflation. Also, the labor-related share is adjusted by the wage index for the hospital's geographic area.

5. The market basket index, which is based on the mix of goods and services included in the PPS

Check Your Understanding 6.2

1. An inpatient deductible must be paid for the ninety-day benefit period, plus a daily coinsurance payment applies for the sixty-first through ninetieth day.

2. True

3. Standard federal rate

4. Inpatient rehabilitation facility patient assessment instrument (IRF PAI)

5. False; staff members do not enter RICs; the pricer (grouper) calculates the appropriate categories from the impairment group codes (IGC) entered on the PAI.

Check Your Understanding 7.1

1. CPT codes

2. Physician work (WORK), physician practice expenses (PE), and malpractice (MP)

3. Levels are dependent on the complexity of service performed (basic versus specialty care), the EMT's level of training required to perform the service, and the type of transport involved (land vehicle versus helicopter).

4. False; Medicare-certified ASCs must maintain their own administrative functions, record keeping, and financial and accounting systems

5. The ASC list

Check Your Understanding 7.2

1. The ambulatory payment group (APG) system developed by 3M HIS

2. Fee schedules and a PPS

3. True

4. The low-utilization payment adjustment (LUPA) is applied when an agency provides four or fewer visits in an episode; reimbursement in this case is made for each visit rather than for the sixty-day episode.

5. Clinical severity, functional status, and service utilization

Check Your Understanding 8.1

1. Preclaims submission activities such as collecting responsible parties' information, educating patients about their ultimate financial responsibility for services rendered, collecting appropriate waivers, and verifying data about procedures before they are performed and their charges submitted.

2. Electronic order entry systems help to capture charges at their point of service delivery. If facilities lack electronic systems, staff collect paper-based charges on charge tickets, superbills, or encounter forms to be entered by billing staff into the patient accounting system.

3. Scrubbers edit claims to locate and flag for correction any data that may contain errors, such as dates of service that are incompatible, inaccurate diagnosis and procedure codes, no substantiation of medical necessity, and inaccurate assignment of revenue codes.

Check Your Understanding 8.2

1. Can be measured to gauge performance improvement

2. The Medicare Outpatient Code Editor (OCE)

3. The CDM stored several incorrect codes and retained a previous code after it was updated; training in updated codes was not conducted for everyone who used them; and the chart flow process bypassed the staff who would have coded and reported use of supplies on claims.

Check Your Understanding 9.1

1. *Crossing the Quality Chasm*, the Committee on Quality of Health Care in America of the Institute of Medicine

2. Performance and incentives

3. False

4. False

5. Reward-based models and penalty-based models

6. Most significant problems in terms of quality or cost, proportion of population covered by the service or provider, and availability of valid and reliable performance measures

Check Your Understanding 9.2

1. 2% reduction in the annual payment update

2. False

3. High cost or high volume or both; results in the assignment of a higher weighted/paying MS-DRG; reasonably preventable through application of evidence-based guidelines

4. Catheter-associated UTI; pressure ulcers; serious preventable event—object left in surgery; serious preventable event—air embolism; serious preventable event – blood incompatibility; vascular catheter-associated infection; mediastinitis after coronary artery bypass graft; fall, fracture, dislocation, intracranial injury, crushing injury, and burns

5. Deficit Reduction Act (DRA)

6. Premier, Inc.; over 260 hospitals

Appendix D
CMS 1500 Claim Form

$\boxed{1500}$

HEALTH INSURANCE CLAIM FORM

APPROVED BY NATIONAL UNIFORM CLAIM COMMITTEE 08/05

PICA		PICA

1. MEDICARE ☐ (Medicare #) MEDICAID ☐ (Medicaid #) TRICARE CHAMPUS ☐ (Sponsor's SSN) CHAMPVA ☐ (Member ID#) GROUP HEALTH PLAN ☐ (SSN or ID) FECA BLK LUNG ☐ (SSN) OTHER ☐ (ID) **1a.** INSURED'S I.D. NUMBER (For Program in Item 1)

2. PATIENT'S NAME (Last Name, First Name, Middle Initial)

3. PATIENT'S BIRTH DATE MM DD YY   SEX M ☐ F ☐

4. INSURED'S NAME (Last Name, First Name, Middle Initial)

5. PATIENT'S ADDRESS (No., Street)

6. PATIENT RELATIONSHIP TO INSURED   Self ☐ Spouse ☐ Child ☐ Other ☐

7. INSURED'S ADDRESS (No., Street)

CITY   STATE

8. PATIENT STATUS   Single ☐ Married ☐ Other ☐   Employed ☐ Full-Time Student ☐ Part-Time Student ☐

CITY   STATE

ZIP CODE   TELEPHONE (Include Area Code) (   )

ZIP CODE   TELEPHONE (Include Area Code) (   )

9. OTHER INSURED'S NAME (Last Name, First Name, Middle Initial)

10. IS PATIENT'S CONDITION RELATED TO:

11. INSURED'S POLICY GROUP OR FECA NUMBER

a. OTHER INSURED'S POLICY OR GROUP NUMBER

a. EMPLOYMENT? (Current or Previous) YES ☐ NO ☐

a. INSURED'S DATE OF BIRTH MM DD YY   SEX M ☐ F ☐

b. OTHER INSURED'S DATE OF BIRTH MM DD YY   SEX M ☐ F ☐

b. AUTO ACCIDENT? YES ☐ NO ☐ PLACE (State)

b. EMPLOYER'S NAME OR SCHOOL NAME

c. EMPLOYER'S NAME OR SCHOOL NAME

c. OTHER ACCIDENT? YES ☐ NO ☐

c. INSURANCE PLAN NAME OR PROGRAM NAME

d. INSURANCE PLAN NAME OR PROGRAM NAME

10d. RESERVED FOR LOCAL USE

d. IS THERE ANOTHER HEALTH BENEFIT PLAN? YES ☐ NO ☐ If yes, return to and complete item 9 a-d.

READ BACK OF FORM BEFORE COMPLETING & SIGNING THIS FORM.

12. PATIENT'S OR AUTHORIZED PERSON'S SIGNATURE I authorize the release of any medical or other information necessary to process this claim. I also request payment of government benefits either to myself or to the party who accepts assignment below.   SIGNED _____ DATE _____

13. INSURED'S OR AUTHORIZED PERSON'S SIGNATURE I authorize payment of medical benefits to the undersigned physician or supplier for services described below.   SIGNED _____

14. DATE OF CURRENT: MM DD YY ILLNESS (First symptom) OR INJURY (Accident) OR PREGNANCY(LMP)

15. IF PATIENT HAS HAD SAME OR SIMILAR ILLNESS. GIVE FIRST DATE MM DD YY

16. DATES PATIENT UNABLE TO WORK IN CURRENT OCCUPATION FROM MM DD YY TO MM DD YY

17. NAME OF REFERRING PROVIDER OR OTHER SOURCE   17a.   17b. NPI

18. HOSPITALIZATION DATES RELATED TO CURRENT SERVICES FROM MM DD YY TO MM DD YY

19. RESERVED FOR LOCAL USE

20. OUTSIDE LAB? YES ☐ NO ☐ $ CHARGES

21. DIAGNOSIS OR NATURE OF ILLNESS OR INJURY (Relate Items 1, 2, 3 or 4 to Item 24E by Line)
1. _____ 3. _____
2. _____ 4. _____

22. MEDICAID RESUBMISSION CODE   ORIGINAL REF. NO.

23. PRIOR AUTHORIZATION NUMBER

24. A. DATE(S) OF SERVICE From MM DD YY To MM DD YY	B. PLACE OF SERVICE	C. EMG	D. PROCEDURES, SERVICES, OR SUPPLIES (Explain Unusual Circumstances) CPT/HCPCS MODIFIER	E. DIAGNOSIS POINTER	F. $ CHARGES	G. DAYS OR UNITS	H. EPSDT Family Plan	I. ID. QUAL.	J. RENDERING PROVIDER ID. #
1								NPI	
2								NPI	
3								NPI	
4								NPI	
5								NPI	
6								NPI	

25. FEDERAL TAX I.D. NUMBER SSN ☐ EIN ☐

26. PATIENT'S ACCOUNT NO.

27. ACCEPT ASSIGNMENT? (For govt. claims, see back) YES ☐ NO ☐

28. TOTAL CHARGE $

29. AMOUNT PAID $

30. BALANCE DUE $

31. SIGNATURE OF PHYSICIAN OR SUPPLIER INCLUDING DEGREES OR CREDENTIALS (I certify that the statements on the reverse apply to this bill and are made a part thereof.)   SIGNED _____ DATE _____

32. SERVICE FACILITY LOCATION INFORMATION   a. NPI   b.

33. BILLING PROVIDER INFO & PH # (   )   a. NPI   b.

NUCC Instruction Manual available at: www.nucc.org   APPROVED OMB-0938-0999 FORM CMS-1500 (08/05)

CARRIER · PATIENT AND INSURED INFORMATION · PHYSICIAN OR SUPPLIER INFORMATION

BECAUSE THIS FORM IS USED BY VARIOUS GOVERNMENT AND PRIVATE HEALTH PROGRAMS, SEE SEPARATE INSTRUCTIONS ISSUED BY APPLICABLE PROGRAMS.

NOTICE: Any person who knowingly files a statement of claim containing any misrepresentation or any false, incomplete or misleading information may be guilty of a criminal act punishable under law and may be subject to civil penalties.

REFERS TO GOVERNMENT PROGRAMS ONLY

MEDICARE AND CHAMPUS PAYMENTS: A patient's signature requests that payment be made and authorizes release of any information necessary to process the claim and certifies that the information provided in Blocks 1 through 12 is true, accurate and complete. In the case of a Medicare claim, the patient's signature authorizes any entity to release to Medicare medical and nonmedical information, including employment status, and whether the person has employer group health insurance, liability, no-fault, worker's compensation or other insurance which is responsible to pay for the services for which the Medicare claim is made. See 42 CFR 411.24(a). If item 9 is completed, the patient's signature authorizes release of the information to the health plan or agency shown. In Medicare assigned or CHAMPUS participation cases, the physician agrees to accept the charge determination of the Medicare carrier or CHAMPUS fiscal intermediary as the full charge, and the patient is responsible only for the deductible, coinsurance and noncovered services. Coinsurance and the deductible are based upon the charge determination of the Medicare carrier or CHAMPUS fiscal intermediary if this is less than the charge submitted. CHAMPUS is not a health insurance program but makes payment for health benefits provided through certain affiliations with the Uniformed Services. Information on the patient's sponsor should be provided in those items captioned in "Insured"; i.e., items 1a, 4, 6, 7, 9, and 11.

BLACK LUNG AND FECA CLAIMS

The provider agrees to accept the amount paid by the Government as payment in full. See Black Lung and FECA instructions regarding required procedure and diagnosis coding systems.

SIGNATURE OF PHYSICIAN OR SUPPLIER (MEDICARE, CHAMPUS, FECA AND BLACK LUNG)

I certify that the services shown on this form were medically indicated and necessary for the health of the patient and were personally furnished by me or were furnished incident to my professional service by my employee under my immediate personal supervision, except as otherwise expressly permitted by Medicare or CHAMPUS regulations.

For services to be considered as "incident" to a physician's professional service, 1) they must be rendered under the physician's immediate personal supervision by his/her employee, 2) they must be an integral, although incidental part of a covered physician's service, 3) they must be of kinds commonly furnished in physician's offices, and 4) the services of nonphysicians must be included on the physician's bills.

For CHAMPUS claims, I further certify that I (or any employee) who rendered services am not an active duty member of the Uniformed Services or a civilian employee of the United States Government or a contract employee of the United States Government, either civilian or military (refer to 5 USC 5536). For Black-Lung claims, I further certify that the services performed were for a Black Lung-related disorder.

No Part B Medicare benefits may be paid unless this form is received as required by existing law and regulations (42 CFR 424.32).

NOTICE: Any one who misrepresents or falsifies essential information to receive payment from Federal funds requested by this form may upon conviction be subject to fine and imprisonment under applicable Federal laws.

NOTICE TO PATIENT ABOUT THE COLLECTION AND USE OF MEDICARE, CHAMPUS, FECA, AND BLACK LUNG INFORMATION
(PRIVACY ACT STATEMENT)

We are authorized by CMS, CHAMPUS and OWCP to ask you for information needed in the administration of the Medicare, CHAMPUS, FECA, and Black Lung programs. Authority to collect information is in section 205(a), 1862, 1872 and 1874 of the Social Security Act as amended, 42 CFR 411.24(a) and 424.5(a) (6), and 44 USC 3101;41 CFR 101 et seq and 10 USC 1079 and 1086; 5 USC 8101 et seq; and 30 USC 901 et seq; 38 USC 613; E.O. 9397.

The information we obtain to complete claims under these programs is used to identify you and to determine your eligibility. It is also used to decide if the services and supplies you received are covered by these programs and to insure that proper payment is made.

The information may also be given to other providers of services, carriers, intermediaries, medical review boards, health plans, and other organizations or Federal agencies, for the effective administration of Federal provisions that require other third parties payers to pay primary to Federal program, and as otherwise necessary to administer these programs. For example, it may be necessary to disclose information about the benefits you have used to a hospital or doctor. Additional disclosures are made through routine uses for information contained in systems of records.

FOR MEDICARE CLAIMS: See the notice modifying system No. 09-70-0501, titled, 'Carrier Medicare Claims Record,' published in the Federal Register, Vol. 55 No. 177, page 37549, Wed. Sept. 12, 1990, or as updated and republished.

FOR OWCP CLAIMS: Department of Labor, Privacy Act of 1974, "Republication of Notice of Systems of Records," Federal Register Vol. 55 No. 40, Wed Feb. 28, 1990, See ESA-5, ESA-6, ESA-12, ESA-13, ESA-30, or as updated and republished.

FOR CHAMPUS CLAIMS: PRINCIPLE PURPOSE(S): To evaluate eligibility for medical care provided by civilian sources and to issue payment upon establishment of eligibility and determination that the services/supplies received are authorized by law.

ROUTINE USE(S): Information from claims and related documents may be given to the Dept. of Veterans Affairs, the Dept. of Health and Human Services and/or the Dept. of Transportation consistent with their statutory administrative responsibilities under CHAMPUS/CHAMPVA; to the Dept. of Justice for representation of the Secretary of Defense in civil actions; to the Internal Revenue Service, private collection agencies, and consumer reporting agencies in connection with recoupment claims; and to Congressional Offices in response to inquiries made at the request of the person to whom a record pertains. Appropriate disclosures may be made to other federal, state, local, foreign government agencies, private business entities, and individual providers of care, on matters relating to entitlement, claims adjudication, fraud, program abuse, utilization review, quality assurance, peer review, program integrity, third-party liability, coordination of benefits, and civil and criminal litigation related to the operation of CHAMPUS.

DISCLOSURES: Voluntary; however, failure to provide information will result in delay in payment or may result in denial of claim. With the one exception discussed below, there are no penalties under these programs for refusing to supply information. However, failure to furnish information regarding the medical services rendered or the amount charged would prevent payment of claims under these programs. Failure to furnish any other information, such as name or claim number, would delay payment of the claim. Failure to provide medical information under FECA could be deemed an obstruction.

It is mandatory that you tell us if you know that another party is responsible for paying for your treatment. Section 1128B of the Social Security Act and 31 USC 3801-3812 provide penalties for withholding this information.

You should be aware that P.L. 100-503, the "Computer Matching and Privacy Protection Act of 1988", permits the government to verify information by way of computer matches.

MEDICAID PAYMENTS (PROVIDER CERTIFICATION)

I hereby agree to keep such records as are necessary to disclose fully the extent of services provided to individuals under the State's Title XIX plan and to furnish information regarding any payments claimed for providing such services as the State Agency or Dept. of Health and Human Services may request.

I further agree to accept, as payment in full, the amount paid by the Medicaid program for those claims submitted for payment under that program, with the exception of authorized deductible, coinsurance, co-payment or similar cost-sharing charge.

SIGNATURE OF PHYSICIAN (OR SUPPLIER): I certify that the services listed above were medically indicated and necessary to the health of this patient and were personally furnished by me or my employee under my personal direction.

NOTICE: This is to certify that the foregoing information is true, accurate and complete. I understand that payment and satisfaction of this claim will be from Federal and State funds, and that any false claims, statements, or documents, or concealment of a material fact, may be prosecuted under applicable Federal or State laws.

Appendix E
UB-04 Form

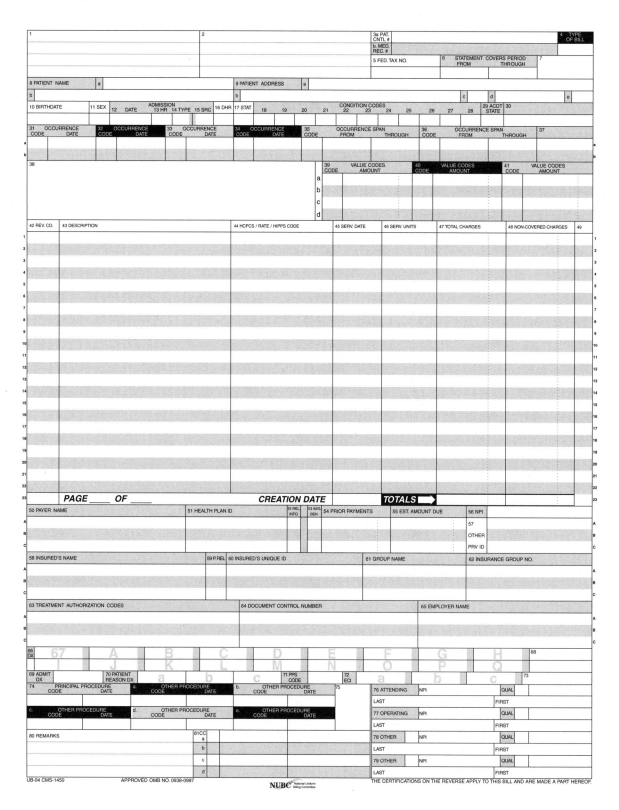

Submission of this claim constitutes certification that the billing information as shown on the face hereof is true, accurate and complete. That the submitter did not knowingly or recklessly disregard or misrepresent or conceal material facts. The following certifications or verifications apply where pertinent to this Bill:

1. If third party benefits are indicated, the appropriate assignments by the insured /beneficiary and signature of the patient or parent or a legal guardian covering authorization to release information are on file. Determinations as to the release of medical and financial information should be guided by the patient or the patient's legal representative.

2. If patient occupied a private room or required private nursing for medical necessity, any required certifications are on file.

3. Physician's certifications and re-certifications, if required by contract or Federal regulations, are on file.

4. For Religious Non-Medical facilities, verifications and if necessary re-certifications of the patient's need for services are on file.

5. Signature of patient or his representative on certifications, authorization to release information, and payment request, as required by Federal Law and Regulations (42 USC 1935f, 42 CFR 424.36, 10 USC 1071 through 1086, 32 CFR 199) and any other applicable contract regulations, is on file.

6. The provider of care submitter acknowledges that the bill is in conformance with the Civil Rights Act of 1964 as amended. Records adequately describing services will be maintained and necessary information will be furnished to such governmental agencies as required by applicable law.

7. For Medicare Purposes: If the patient has indicated that other health insurance or a state medical assistance agency will pay part of his/her medical expenses and he/she wants information about his/her claim released to them upon request, necessary authorization is on file. The patient's signature on the provider's request to bill Medicare medical and non-medical information, including employment status, and whether the person has employer group health insurance which is responsible to pay for the services for which this Medicare claim is made.

8. For Medicaid purposes: The submitter understands that because payment and satisfaction of this claim will be from Federal and State funds, any false statements, documents, or concealment of a material fact are subject to prosecution under applicable Federal or State Laws.

9. For TRICARE Purposes:

    (a) The information on the face of this claim is true, accurate and complete to the best of the submitter's knowledge and belief, and services were medically necessary and appropriate for the health of the patient;

(b) The patient has represented that by a reported residential address outside a military medical treatment facility catchment area he or she does not live within the catchment area of a U.S. military medical treatment facility, or if the patient resides within a catchment area of such a facility, a copy of a Non-Availability Statement (DD Form 1251) is on file, or the physician has certified to a medical emergency in any instance where a copy of a Non-Availability Statement is not on file;

(c) The patient or the patient's parent or guardian has responded directly to the provider's request to identify all health insurance coverage, and that all such coverage is identified on the face of the claim except that coverage which is exclusively supplemental payments to TRICARE-determined benefits;

(d) The amount billed to TRICARE has been billed after all such coverage have been billed and paid excluding Medicaid, and the amount billed to TRICARE is that remaining claimed against TRICARE benefits;

(e) The beneficiary's cost share has not been waived by consent or failure to exercise generally accepted billing and collection efforts; and,

(f) Any hospital-based physician under contract, the cost of whose services are allocated in the charges listed in this bill, is not an employee or member of the Uniformed Services. For purposes of this certification, an employee of the Uniformed Services is an employee, appointed in civil service (refer to 5 USC 2105), including part-time or intermittent employees, but excluding contract surgeons or other personal service contracts. Similarly, member of the Uniformed Services does not apply to reserve members of the Uniformed Services not on active duty.

(g) Based on 42 United States Code 1395cc(a)(1)(j) all providers participating in Medicare must also participate in TRICARE for inpatient hospital services provided pursuant to admissions to hospitals occurring on or after January 1, 1987; and

(h) If TRICARE benefits are to be paid in a participating status, the submitter of this claim agrees to submit this claim to the appropriate TRICARE claims processor. The provider of care submitter also agrees to accept the TRICARE determined reasonable charge as the total charge for the medical services or supplies listed on the claim form. The provider of care will accept the TRICARE-determined reasonable charge even if it is less than the billed amount, and also agrees to accept the amount paid by TRICARE combined with the cost-share amount and deductible amount, if any, paid by or on behalf of the patient as full payment for the listed medical services or supplies. The provider of care submitter will not attempt to collect from the patient (or his or her parent or guardian) amounts over the TRICARE determined reasonable charge. TRICARE will make any benefits payable directly to the provider of care, if the provider of care is a participating provider.

SEE http://www.nubc.org/ FOR MORE INFORMATION ON UB-04 DATA ELEMENT AND PRINTING SPECIFICATIONS

Index

(continued)

Look for These **Quality AHIMA Publications** at **Bookstores, Libraries,** and **Online**

- *Analyzing the Financial Impact of MS-DRGs*
- *Basic CPT/HCPCS Coding*
- *Basic CPT/HCPCS Coding Exercises*
- *Basic ICD-9-CM Coding*
- *Basic ICD-9-CM Coding Exercises*
- *Benchmarking to Improve Coding Accuracy and Productivity*
- *The Best of In Confidence*
- *Calculating and Reporting Healthcare Statistics*
- *Clinical Coding Workout: Practice Exercises for Skill Development*
- *Coding and Reimbursement for Hospital Inpatient Services*
- *Coding and Reimbursement for Hospital Outpatient Services*
- *CPT/HCPCS Coding and Reimbursement for Physician Services*
- *Documentation for Ambulatory Care*
- *Documentation for Medical Records*
- *Documentation and Reimbursement for Behavioral Healthcare Services*
- *Documentation and Reimbursement for Long-Term Care* (Book and CD)
- *Documentation and Reimbursement for Home Care and Hospice Programs*
- *Effective Management of Coding Services*
- *Electronic Health Record*
- *Essentials of Healthcare Finance* (Workbook)
- *Fundamentals of Law for Health Informatics and Health Information Management*
- *Healthcare Code Sets, Clinical Terminologies, and Classification Systems*

- *Health Informatics Research Methods: Principles and Practice*
- *Health Information Management*
- *Health Information Management Technology*
- *Health Information Management Compliance* (Book and CD)
- *HIPAA by Example*
- *HIPAA in Practice*
- *How to Evaluate Electronic Health Record (EHR) Systems*
- *ICD-9-CM Diagnostic Coding and Reimbursement for Physician Services*
- *ICD-9-CM Diagnostic Coding and Reimbursement for Physician Services Exercises*
- *ICD-9-CM Diagnostic Coding for Long-Term Care and Home Care* (Book and CD)
- *ICD-10-CM and ICD-10-PCS Preview* (Book and CD)
- *The Legal Health Record*
- *Medical Coding for Non-Coders*
- *Medical Identity Theft* (Book and CD)
- *Medical Records Disaster Planning: A Health Information Manager's Survival Guide*
- *Pocket Glossary of Health Information Management and Technology*
- *Present on Admission*
- *Principles of Healthcare Reimbursement*
- *Quality and Performance Improvement in Healthcare*
- *Severity DRGS and Reimbursement: An MS-DRG Primer*

More Information: For details and easy ordering, visit **www.ahima.org/publishing**. For textbook content questions, contact **publications@ahima.org or (800) 335-5535.**

AHIMA
American Health Information
Management Association®